365 CROSSWORD PUZZLES

Published by Hinkler Pty Ltd
45–55 Fairchild Street
Heatherton Victoria 3202 Australia
www.hinkler.com

Cover design: Sam Grimmer

ISBN: 978 1 4889 1746 2

Printed and bound in China

INSTRUCTIONS

If you're not familiar with crossword puzzles, here are some tips for how to solve them.

The goal is to solve the clues and write in the answers, letter by letter, into the blank squares in the grid. The numbered clues will direct you to fill in the answers both across and down the grid. Fill in the obvious answers first and then look again at the puzzle clues, there may be an easy answer you didn't notice or one that's easier now because some letters have been filled in.

Numbers in parentheses after each clue reveal the number of letters in each answer, matching the number of spaces in the grid. Multiple numbers separated with a comma indicate multiple words; numbers separated with a hyphen indicate hyphenated words.

Clues ending in "(abbrev.)" indicate that the solution is an abbreviation; clues ending in "(anag.)" indicate that the solution is an anagram; if there is "(pl.)" after the clue it means the answer is a plural, while clues ending in "(inits.)" indicate that the solution is a set of initials.

Some handy tricks are checking if an "s" in the last position works for standard plural-words clues and "ed" for past-tense clues. Keep working through the list of clues and, if you're stumped, try again later! Sometimes you just need a break for your brain to retrieve the answer.

CROSSWORD 1

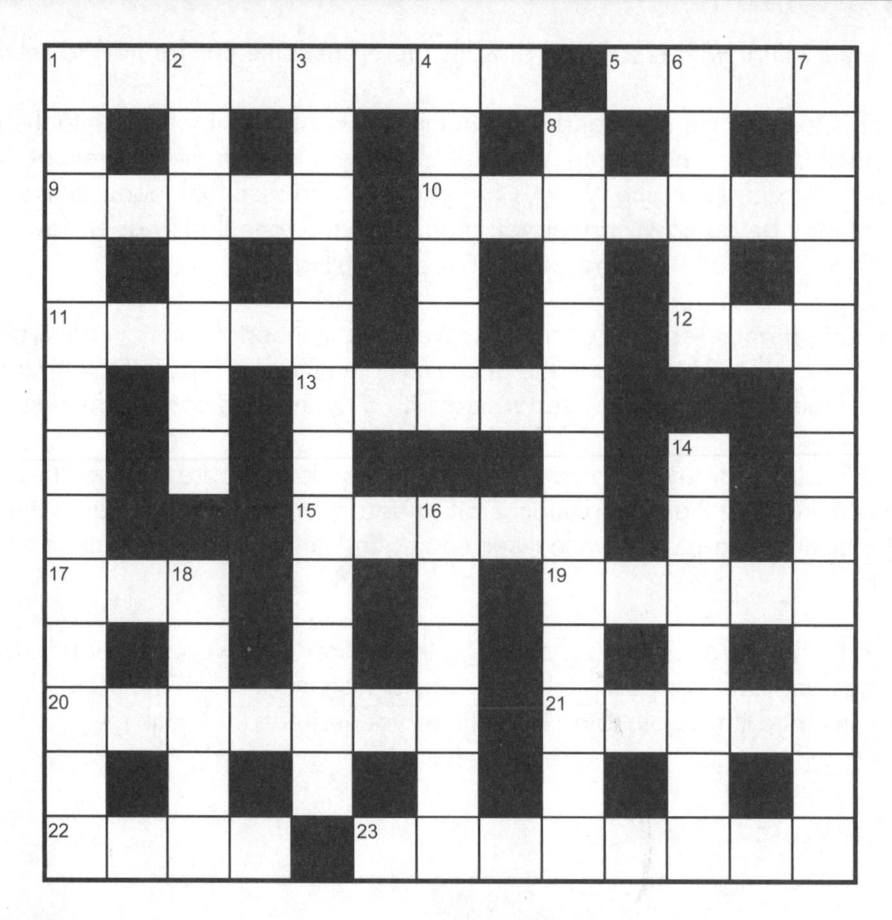

ACROSS

1. Slight hints (8)
5. Chopped; cancelled (4)
9. Loose scrums (rugby) (5)
10. Curbs (7)
11. Parody (5)
12. Spoil (3)
13. Japanese mattress (5)
15. Wash in water to remove soap or dirt (5)
17. Total (3)
19. Precipice (5)
20. Fighter (7)
21. Coral reef (5)
22. Near (anag.) (4)
23. Shiny; sparkly (8)

DOWN

1. Untrustworthy (13)
2. Start (4,3)
3. Intolerable (12)
4. Cup (6)
6. Vascular tissue in plants (5)
7. Suspiciously (13)
8. Germicide (12)
14. Horizontal underground stem (7)
16. Pertaining to a nerve (6)
18. Thing that imparts motion (5)

CROSSWORD 2

ACROSS

1. Always in a similar role (of an actor) (8)
5. Puns (anag.) (4)
9. Wild dog of Australia (5)
10. Trailer (7)
11. Nationally (12)
14. Chemical element (3)
15. Great sorrow (5)
16. Excellent serve (3)
17. Therapeutic use of plant extracts (12)
20. People of noble birth (7)
22. Arose from slumber (5)
23. Relax and do little (4)
24. Rigorous appraisal (4,4)

DOWN

1. Clean up (4)
2. Flat-bottomed boat (7)
3. Art of planning a dance (12)
4. Tree liquid (3)
6. Bottle (5)
7. Recently married person (5-3)
8. From this time on (12)
12. Upper part of the leg (5)
13. Aggressor (8)
16. Sanction (7)
18. Leaves out (5)
19. Hit hard (4)
21. Dry (of wine) (3)

CROSSWORD 3

ACROSS

1. Noticeably different (11)
9. Waterlogged ground (5)
10. Chewy substance (3)
11. Uncertainty (5)
12. Used up; exhausted (5)
13. Having a pleasing scent (8)
16. Supervisor (8)
18. Floating timber platforms (5)
21. Ethos (anag.) (5)
22. Annoy continuously (3)
23. Animal noise (5)
24. Letter of recommendation (11)

DOWN

2. Brutal; cruel (7)
3. Food samplers (7)
4. Make tidier (6)
5. Records (5)
6. Not clearly stated (5)
7. Unconcerned (11)
8. Small pieces (11)
14. Set down on paper (7)
15. Plant with bright flowers (7)
17. Space devoid of matter (6)
19. Contrapuntal composition (5)
20. Sense of seeing (5)

CROSSWORD 4

ACROSS

1. Shouts orders (5)
4. Admit (7)
7. Fun activities (5)
8. Bed covers (8)
9. Joint (5)
11. Slapdash (8)
15. Gather together in one place (8)
17. Sudden surprise (5)
19. Strong inclination (8)
20. Signals a taxi (5)
21. Large flightless bird (7)
22. Pillars (5)

DOWN

1. Cooks food outdoors (9)
2. Competition (7)
3. Moodily (7)
4. Boxes (6)
5. Leads a discussion (6)
6. Eating plans (5)
10. Menaces (9)
12. Tomato sauce (7)
13. Acquires (7)
14. Having only magnitude (6)
16. Stink (6)
18. Perceives audibly (5)

CROSSWORD 5

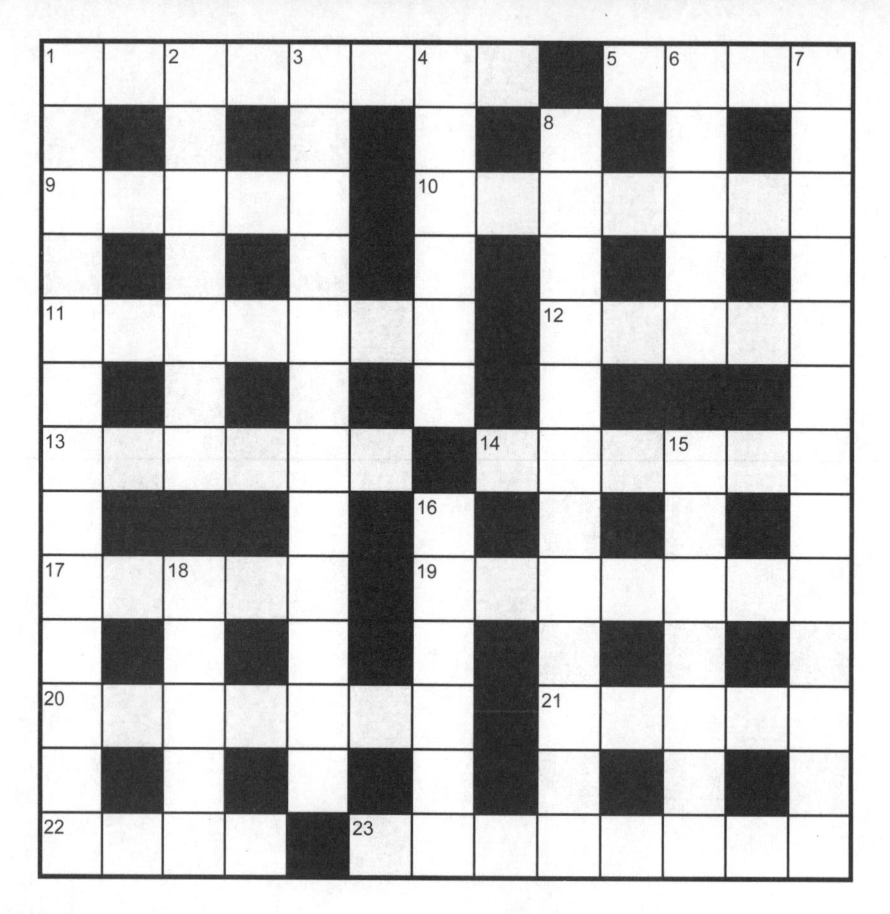

ACROSS

1. Central American monkey (8)
5. Mark or blemish (4)
9. Slender woman or girl (5)
10. River in Africa (7)
11. Witty saying (7)
12. Faithful (5)
13. Isolated inlet of the sea (6)
14. Share out food sparingly (6)
17. Pertaining to birth (5)
19. Something showing a general rule (7)
20. Prophets (7)
21. Lazy person (5)
22. Japanese beverage (4)
23. Majesty (8)

DOWN

1. Of mixed character (13)
2. Turning over and over (7)
3. Dreamy; odd and unfamiliar (12)
4. Biochemical catalyst (6)
6. Reverence for God (5)
7. Problem-solving method (5,3,5)
8. Process of combining (12)
15. Sudden inclination to act (7)
16. Device that detects a physical property (6)
18. Express gratitude (5)

CROSSWORD 6

ACROSS

1. Place of education (6)
4. Performing on stage (6)
9. Large area of land (7)
10. Responses (7)
11. Workers (5)
12. Spin (5)
14. Entrance hall (5)
17. E.g. molar or incisor (5)
19. Neatens (5)
21. Caring for (7)
23. Extreme enthusiast (7)
24. Impresses a pattern on (6)
25. Entertained (6)

DOWN

1. Remorse (6)
2. Dagger handle (4)
3. Taken as a whole (7)
5. Cloaked (5)
6. An indirect and sometimes snide implication (8)
7. Metamorphic rock (6)
8. Likeness (11)
13. Distinguishing mark (8)
15. Chemical element (7)
16. Pushes filling inside (6)
18. Cuddled (6)
20. Scheme intended to deceive (3-2)
22. Public houses (4)

CROSSWORD 7

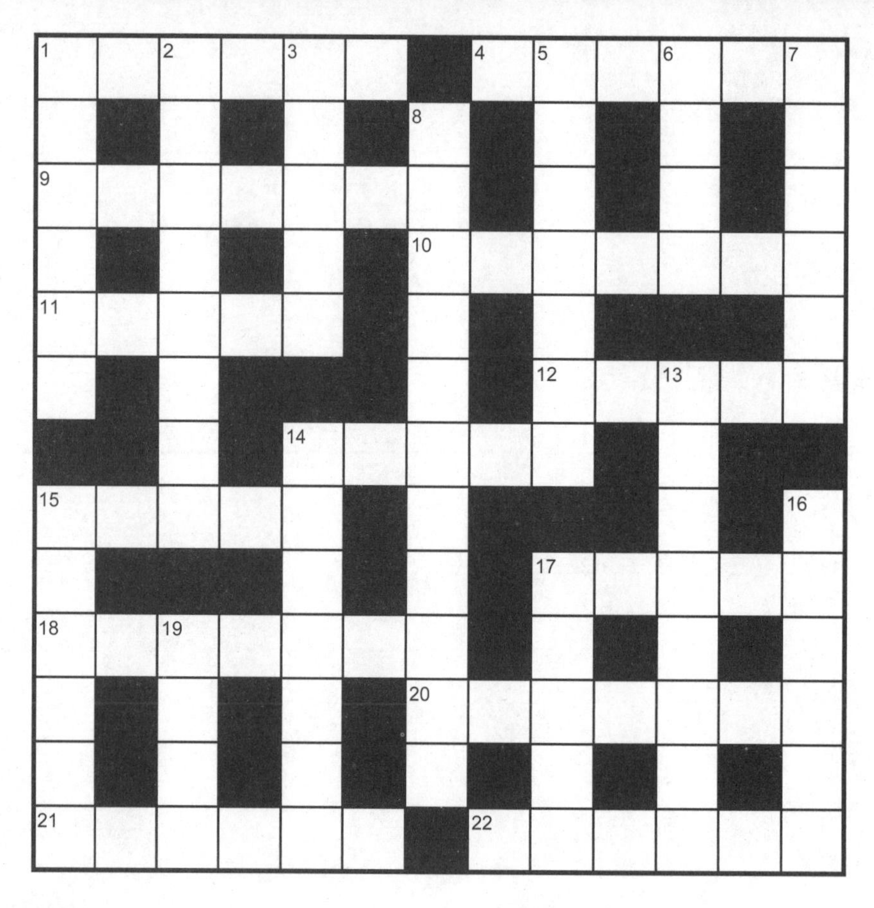

ACROSS

1. Motor vehicle storage building (6)
4. Increases in size (6)
9. Deciphering machine (7)
10. Alternative forms of genes (7)
11. People not ordained (5)
12. Harsh and grating in sound (5)
14. Wished (5)
15. Strength (5)
17. Therefore (5)
18. Clique (7)
20. Biting sharply (7)
21. Expression of praise (6)
22. Young swan (6)

DOWN

1. Annoying person (6)
2. Easy chair (8)
3. Dizzy (5)
5. Military commander (7)
6. Hang loosely (4)
7. Sloppy (6)
8. Diaphanous (11)
13. Metrical analysis of verse (8)
14. North Atlantic food fish (7)
15. Casually changeable (6)
16. Altitude (6)
17. Content (5)
19. Ring a bell (4)

CROSSWORD 8

ACROSS

1. Pristine (5-3)
5. Antelopes (4)
8. Act slowly (5)
9. Large island of Indonesia (7)
10. Demanded (7)
12. Subdues (7)
14. Incredible (7)
16. Laid open to view (7)
18. Kitchen appliance (7)
19. Recycle (5)
20. Ladder step (4)
21. Fugitives (8)

DOWN

1. Remain or stay somewhere (4)
2. In flower (6)
3. Reveries (9)
4. Follows (6)
6. Write a music score (6)
7. Burning (8)
11. Ridge of the Himalayas (9)
12. E.g. Baz Luhrmann (8)
13. Wrench an ankle (6)
14. Makes more attractive (6)
15. Bring forth (6)
17. Implements used to unlock doors (4)

CROSSWORD 9

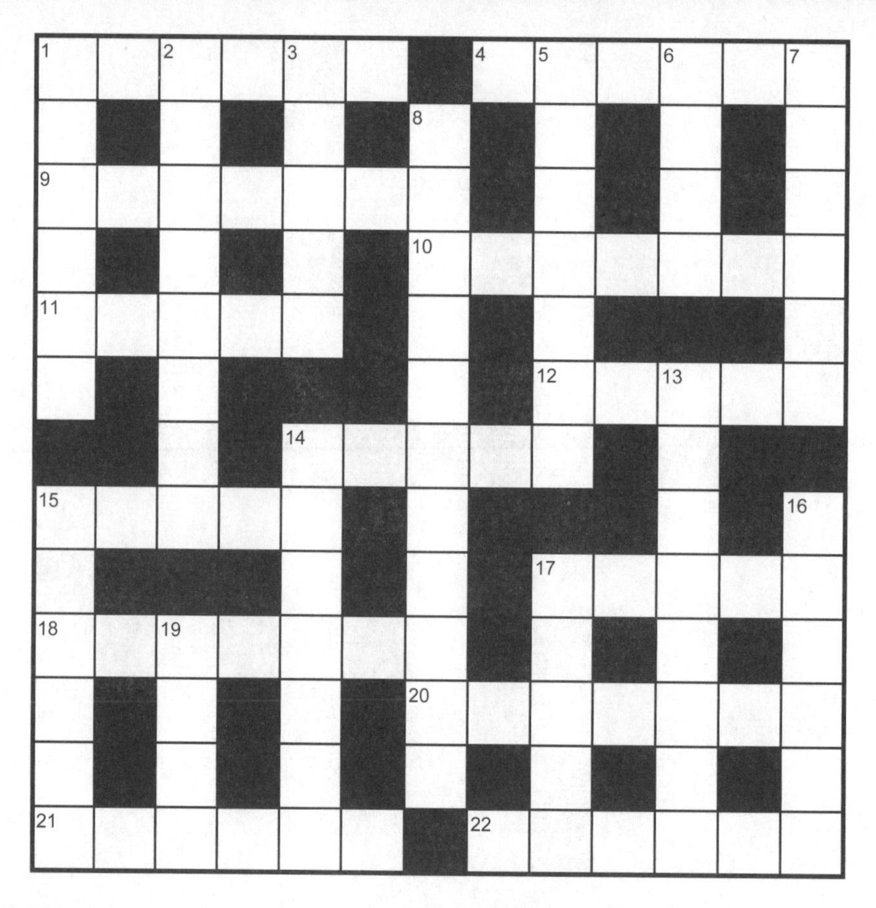

ACROSS

1. Common volcanic rock (6)
4. Lightweight garment (1-5)
9. Throw into disorder (7)
10. Garden flower (7)
11. Card game (5)
12. Answer (5)
14. Electrical cables (5)
15. Picture border (5)
17. Remove hair (5)
18. Box of useful equipment (7)
20. Fully occupy (7)
21. Indicate (6)
22. Get away from (6)

DOWN

1. Indistinct (6)
2. Representations or descriptions of data (8)
3. Tall and thin (5)
5. Rosters (anag.) (7)
6. Metallic element (4)
7. Written agreement (6)
8. Sent back to one's own country (11)
13. Baseless distrust of others (8)
14. Most feeble (7)
15. Made to fill a space precisely (6)
16. Person to whom a lease is granted (6)
17. Emits a breath of relief (5)
19. Cooking appliance (4)

CROSSWORD 10

ACROSS

1. Innovative or pioneering (7,4)
9. Wounded by a wasp (5)
10. Hit forcibly (3)
11. Fortune-telling card (5)
12. Noble gas (5)
13. Evoke memories (8)
16. Functioned (8)
18. Giraffes have long ones (5)
21. Horse sound (5)
22. Bitumen (3)
23. Lazed (5)
24. Basically (11)

DOWN

2. Remove garments (7)
3. Challenging (7)
4. Type of confectionery (6)
5. Keen (5)
6. Stared into space (5)
7. Having definite limits (11)
8. Straightforward (4-3-4)
14. Father of a parent (7)
15. Uncomplaining (7)
17. Small projectile (6)
19. Complains continually (5)
20. Connected series of rooms (5)

CROSSWORD 11

ACROSS

1. Maximum number a stadium can hold (8)
5. Leave out (4)
9. Hand protector (5)
10. Relating to heat (7)
11. Effects or results (12)
14. Mist (3)
15. Sweeping implement (5)
16. By way of (3)
17. Amusing (12)
20. Feeling of indignation (7)
22. Ring-shaped roll (5)
23. Light beams (4)
24. Became visible (8)

DOWN

1. Animal enclosure (4)
2. Increase the duration of (7)
3. Fast food item (12)
4. Very small child (3)
6. Impersonator (5)
7. Charm (8)
8. Resolvable (12)
12. Allotted quantity (5)
13. Criminal (8)
16. Impure acetic acid (7)
18. This date (5)
19. Scarpered (4)
21. Short sleep (3)

CROSSWORD 12

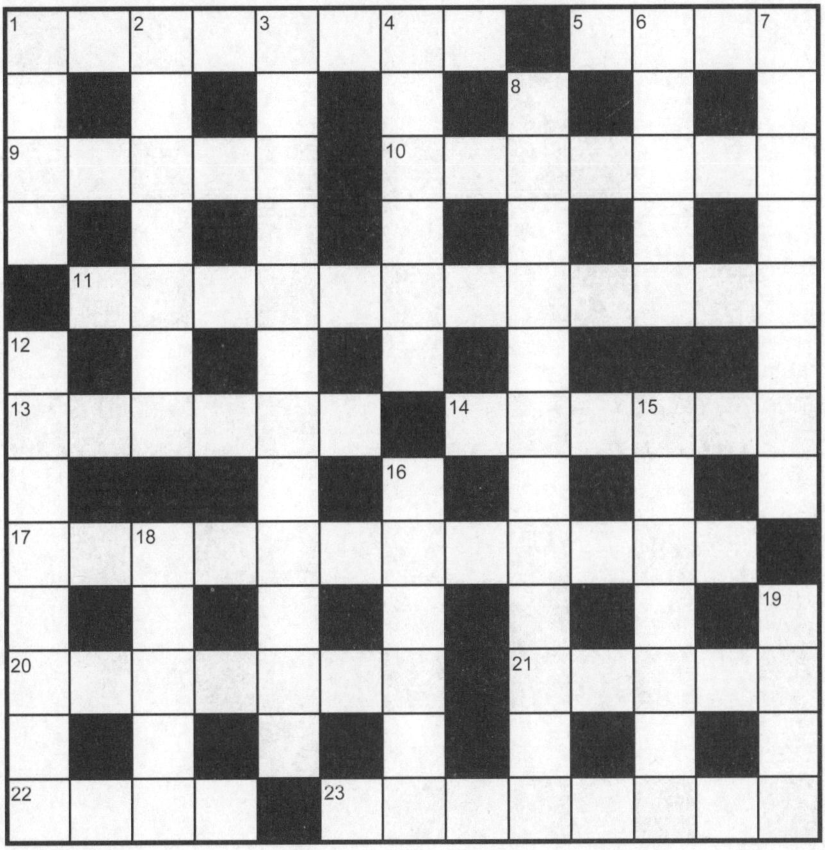

ACROSS

1. Affecting only the appearance (8)
5. Song for a solo voice (4)
9. Foreign language (informal) (5)
10. Scowls (7)
11. Irrelevant (12)
13. Peak (6)
14. Leg bone (6)
17. The proprietor of an eating establishment (12)
20. Small rounded lumps (7)
21. Put out a fire (5)
22. Seek (anag.) (4)
23. Surprised (8)

DOWN

1. Select from a large amount (4)
2. Word having a similar meaning (7)
3. Thriftily (12)
4. Take into the body (of food) (6)
6. Pass a rope through (5)
7. German shepherd dog (8)
8. Spanish adventurer (12)
12. Keep at a distance (8)
15. Uncommon (7)
16. Adjust in advance of its use (6)
18. Move sideways (5)
19. First position (4)

CROSSWORD 13

ACROSS

1. Added together (6)
7. Rare (8)
8. Annoy (3)
9. Be imminent (6)
10. Lubricates (4)
11. E.g. oxygen and nitrogen (5)
13. Engraving (7)
15. Leave quickly and in secret (7)
17. Sudden movements (5)
21. Brave person; idol (4)
22. Superhero in Gotham City (6)
23. Depression (3)
24. Item of additional book matter (8)
25. Frightens (6)

DOWN

1. Rescuing (6)
2. Sayings (6)
3. Fists (5)
4. Sourness (7)
5. Thick drink (8)
6. Mischievous creature (6)
12. Surrounds on all sides (8)
14. A person in general (7)
16. Beards (anag.) (6)
18. Cause to become (6)
19. Wading birds (6)
20. Plant stalks (5)

CROSSWORD 14

ACROSS

1. Country in central Africa (6)
4. Sounds off at length (6)
9. Late (7)
10. Alfresco (4-3)
11. Weary (5)
12. Musical toy (5)
14. Produce a literary work (5)
17. Contest (5)
19. Parts of the cerebrum (5)
21. Weaves; clothing (7)
23. Layer of earth (7)
24. Extracts a metal from its ore (6)
25. Solemn promise (6)

DOWN

1. Sat an exam again (6)
2. Apex (4)
3. Deny any responsibility for (7)
5. Tailored fold (5)
6. Sell at a lower price (8)
7. Exhausts (6)
8. Every two weeks (11)
13. Where one finds Harare (8)
15. Involve in conflict (7)
16. Shuts (6)
18. Jostle (6)
20. Member of the weasel family (5)
22. Imitated (4)

CROSSWORD 15

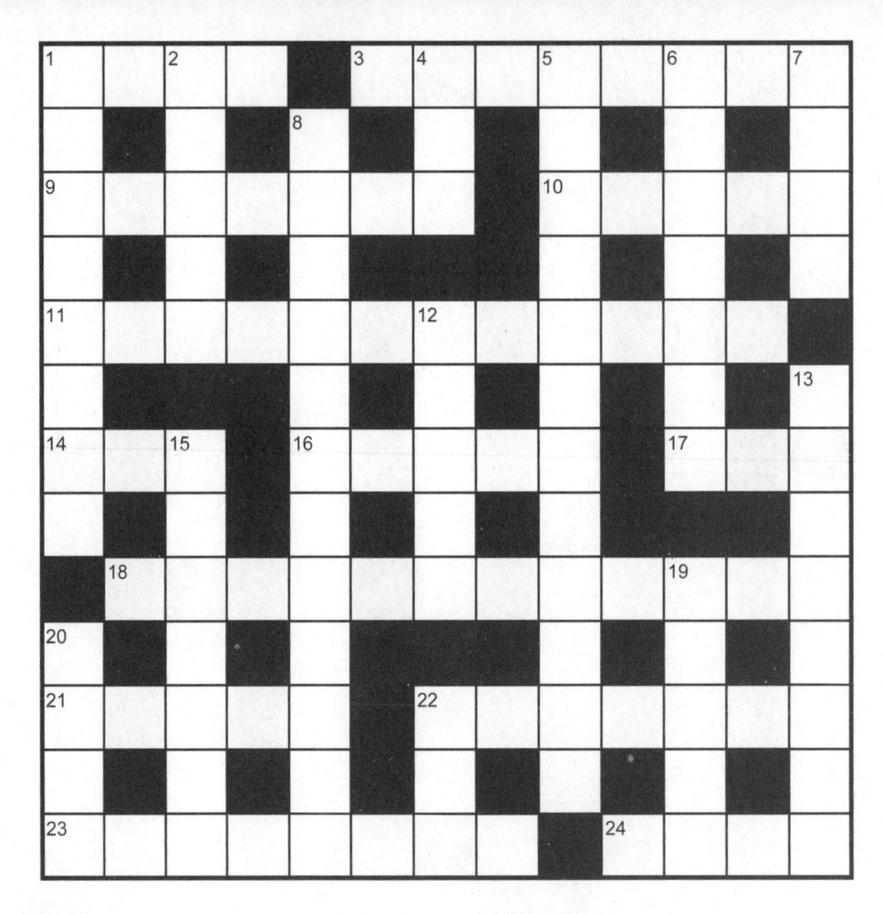

ACROSS

1. School test (4)
3. Opened a wine bottle (8)
9. Panacea (4-3)
10. Grave and serious (5)
11. Excessively forward (12)
14. Male aristocrat (3)
16. Capital of Ghana (5)
17. Place where one sees animals (3)
18. Clarity (12)
21. Willow twig (5)
22. Notwithstanding (7)
23. Statuette (8)
24. Endure; large animal (4)

DOWN

1. Daydreamer (8)
2. Consent to (5)
4. Zero (3)
5. Obfuscation (12)
6. Communal settlement in Israel (7)
7. Opposite of light (4)
8. Maker (12)
12. Brown nut (5)
13. Renounce (8)
15. Incrementing; elevating (7)
19. Select group of people (5)
20. Game played by Tiger Woods (4)
22. University teacher (3)

CROSSWORD 16

ACROSS

4. Tiny bag (6)
7. A magical quality (8)
8. Came across (3)
9. Nocturnal birds of prey (4)
10. Capital of Austria (6)
11. Postpone (7)
12. Remove wool from sheep (5)
15. Silly (5)
17. Hiding underground (7)
20. Speaks publicly (6)
21. Military force (4)
22. Pledge (3)
23. Blushed (8)
24. Where one finds Oslo (6)

DOWN

1. Packed carefully and neatly (6)
2. Disdainful rejection (5-3)
3. Overthrow covertly (7)
4. Spread by scattering (5)
5. Showing compassion (6)
6. Unsteady gait (6)
13. Forceful blow (8)
14. Alfresco (7)
15. Highly motivated (6)
16. Bloom (6)
18. Quantity (6)
19. Work of fiction (5)

CROSSWORD 17

ACROSS

1. Vehicles (4)
3. No longer in fashion (8)
9. Admirers (7)
10. Wedge placed against a wheel (5)
11. Coat with a metal (12)
13. Silver (literary) (6)
15. Visit informally (4,2)
17. Contradictory (12)
20. Pains (5)
21. Idealistic (7)
22. Putting into practice (8)
23. Quartz-like gem (4)

DOWN

1. Relating to deep feelings (8)
2. Foolishly credulous (5)
4. Eventual outcome (6)
5. Act of slowing down (12)
6. Type of dance (3-4)
7. Nobleman (4)
8. Endlessly (12)
12. Occurring within (8)
14. Armed helicopter (7)
16. Dispute the truth of (6)
18. Small airship (5)
19. Island of Indonesia (4)

CROSSWORD 18

ACROSS

4. Diminished in size (6)
7. Explode (8)
8. Bashful; reluctant to give details (3)
9. Status (4)
10. Spring suddenly (6)
11. Keeps hold of (7)
12. Beads (anag.) (5)
15. Lies back lazily in the sun (5)
17. Retorted (7)
20. Expenditure (6)
21. Part of a candle (4)
22. Knot with a double loop (3)
23. Tidiness (8)
24. Finish (6)

DOWN

1. Recount (6)
2. Item used to remember the page you're on (8)
3. Widespread; pandemic (7)
4. Capital of South Korea (5)
5. Right to enter (6)
6. Data input device (6)
13. Permitting (8)
14. This starts on 1st January (3,4)
15. Pocket of air in a sphere of liquid (6)
16. Displayed (6)
18. More than is necessary (6)
19. Throw forcefully (5)

CROSSWORD 19

ACROSS

1. Opposite of a victory (6)
7. Purple quartz (8)
8. Flexible container (3)
9. Male relatives (6)
10. Noble gas (4)
11. Brushed clean (5)
13. Breathed in sharply (7)
15. Pertaining to the stars (7)
17. Sailing boat (5)
21. Gentle accent (4)
22. Small metal projectile (6)
23. Scientific workplace (abbrev.) (3)
24. Signal that danger is over (3-5)
25. Strikes firmly (6)

DOWN

1. First appearances (6)
2. Body shape (6)
3. Follows closely (5)
4. Anapest (anag.) (7)
5. Grateful (8)
6. On land (6)
12. The activities of government (8)
14. Placed a bet (7)
16. Tremulous sounds (6)
18. Vent (6)
19. Looks into thoroughly (6)
20. Smudges (5)

CROSSWORD 20

ACROSS

4. Wreckage washed ashore (6)
7. Form of musical articulation (8)
8. Degenerate (3)
9. Desert in northern China (4)
10. Wall painting; mural (6)
11. Old Spanish currency (pl.) (7)
12. Enclosed (of animals) (5)
15. Maw (5)
17. Falsehood (7)
20. Worshipper (6)
21. Change (4)
22. Lie (3)
23. Extremely delicate (8)
24. Flattened out (6)

DOWN

1. Minion (6)
2. Mishap (8)
3. Midpoint (7)
4. Comedian (5)
5. Powerful (6)
6. Technique (6)
13. Large burrowing African mammal (8)
14. State of lawlessness (7)
15. Make a sound quieter (6)
16. Nebula (anag.) (6)
18. Imminent danger (6)
19. Removed water (5)

CROSSWORD 21

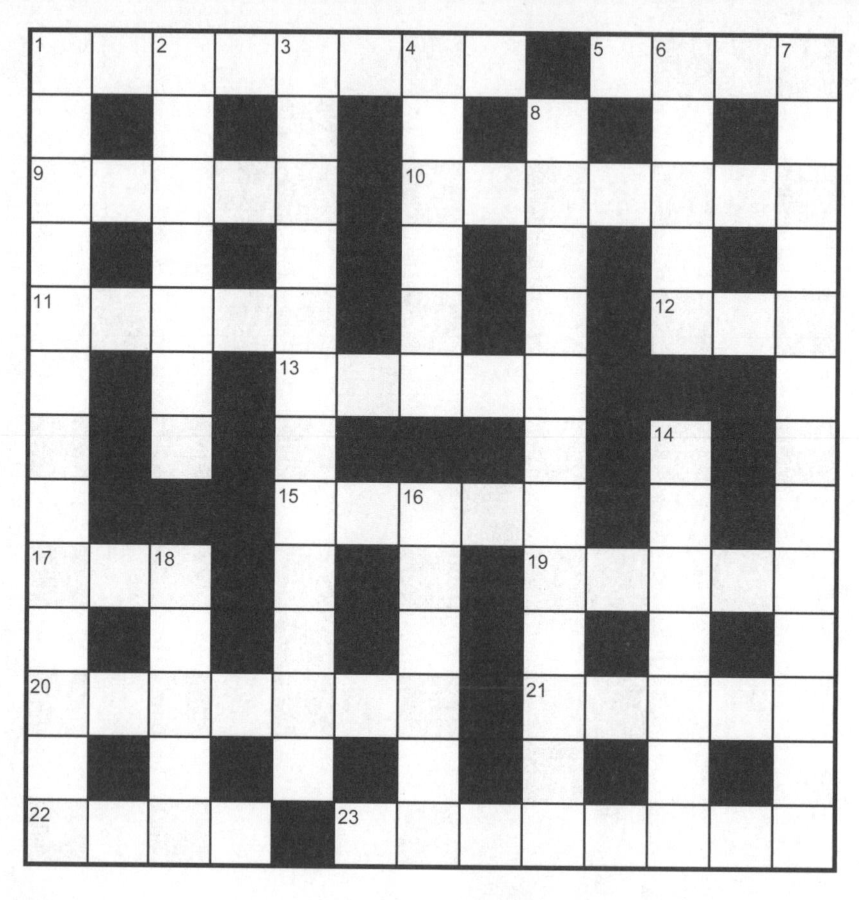

ACROSS

1. Unfit for consumption (of food) (8)
5. Young cow (4)
9. These keep your feet warm (5)
10. Shaped like a ring (7)
11. Feign (5)
12. Foot extremity (3)
13. Ultimate (5)
15. Ringing sound (5)
17. At this moment (3)
19. Period of keeping awake to pray (5)
20. Ardent (7)
21. Brought forth (5)
22. Lie in ambush (4)
23. Opposites (8)

DOWN

1. Flimsy (13)
2. Coat; decorate lavishly (7)
3. Inadequate (12)
4. Heavy (6)
6. Dole out (5)
7. Absent-mindedness (13)
8. Hard to fathom (12)
14. Diagrams or pictures (7)
16. Confine as a prisoner (6)
18. Liquid essential for life (5)

CROSSWORD 22

ACROSS

1. Scarce (4)
3. Escape from prison (8)
9. Trimmed (anag.) (7)
10. Ask for earnestly (5)
11. By chance (12)
14. Pull at (3)
16. Strong thick rope (5)
17. Make a mistake (3)
18. Airing a TV program (12)
21. Bits of meat of low value (5)
22. Make public (7)
23. Domains (8)
24. Courts (4)

DOWN

1. Gets back on a horse (8)
2. Natural elevation (5)
4. Edge of a cup (3)
5. Uneasy (12)
6. Position on top of (7)
7. Periodic movement of the sea (4)
8. Wearing glasses (12)
12. Having three dimensions (5)
13. Sets off (8)
15. Tall quadruped (7)
19. Snow house (5)
20. Building covering (4)
22. Water barrier (3)

CROSSWORD 23

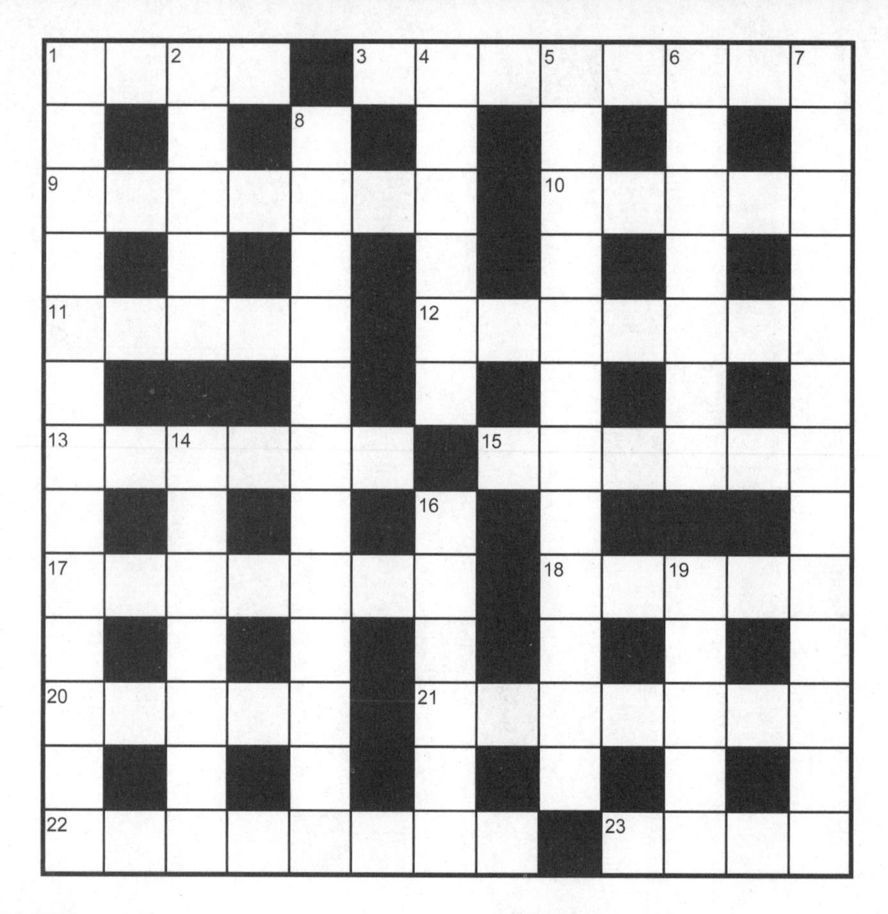

ACROSS

1. Annoy (4)
3. Decorated with a raised design (8)
9. Film starring Jim Carrey (3,4)
10. Wrinkles in the skin (5)
11. Armature of a generator (5)
12. Spoke (7)
13. Join or fasten (6)
15. Printed mistakes (6)
17. Form of an element (7)
18. Impair (5)
20. Things to be done (5)
21. Smoothing clothes (7)
22. Transporting by hand (8)
23. Stiff paper (4)

DOWN

1. Desiring worldly possessions (13)
2. Collection of ships (5)
4. Cosmetics (4-2)
5. Destruction (12)
6. Spanish beverage (7)
7. Deprived (13)
8. Unpredictably (12)
14. Routers (anag.) (7)
16. Vast number of people (6)
19. Balearic island (5)

CROSSWORD 24

ACROSS

1. Mean sect (anag.) (8)
5. Cook slowly in liquid (4)
9. Barely sufficient (5)
10. Straight line between two places (7)
11. Determined (6-6)
14. Female chicken (3)
15. Circle a planet (5)
16. Our star (3)
17. Blasphemous (12)
20. Statement of commemoration (7)
22. Beneath (5)
23. Wise man (4)
24. Stretched out (8)

DOWN

1. Apex or peak (4)
2. Neaten (7)
3. Based on legend (12)
4. Take or steal something (3)
6. Tremulous sound (5)
7. Holding and using (a weapon) (8)
8. Reallocate (12)
12. Triangular wall part (5)
13. Speaks very quietly (8)
16. Sped along; skimmed (7)
18. Remain very close to (5)
19. Network of lines (4)
21. Magic spell (3)

CROSSWORD 25

ACROSS

1. An unwelcome person; invader (8)
5. Individual article or unit (4)
9. Public square (5)
10. Looking for (7)
11. Lives (anag.) (5)
12. Untruth (3)
13. Tree of the birch family (5)
15. Sudden forward thrust (5)
17. Blade for rowing a boat (3)
19. Criminal (5)
20. Delightful (7)
21. Pertaining to the moon (5)
22. Beast of burden (4)
23. Person of varied learning (8)

DOWN

1. Style of painting (13)
2. Ripping (7)
3. Impregnable (12)
4. Followed (6)
6. Fabric with parallel ribs (5)
7. Direction to which a compass points (8,5)
8. Regretfully (12)
14. Cornmeal (7)
16. Papal representative (6)
18. Regal (5)

CROSSWORD 26

ACROSS

1. Imperial unit (4)
3. Walked about (8)
9. Act of buying or selling shares (7)
10. Eat quickly (5)
11. Retrieve (5)
12. Aseptic (7)
13. Themes (6)
15. Solitary; not married (6)
17. Kind of breakfast cereal (7)
18. Personal attendant (5)
20. Voting compartment (5)
21. Musical composition (7)
22. Passing (of time) (8)
23. Protective foot covering (4)

DOWN

1. Untiring (13)
2. Seashore (5)
4. Month (6)
5. Doubting the truth of (12)
6. Rampaging (7)
7. Distinguish between (13)
8. Garments worn in bed (12)
14. Mechanical keyboard (7)
16. High-kicking dance (6)
19. Animal restraint (5)

CROSSWORD 27

ACROSS

1. Clamber (8)
5. Partly open (4)
9. Become ready to eat (of fruit) (5)
10. A percussion instrument (7)
11. Blends; mixtures (12)
13. Safe place (6)
14. Moved at an easy pace (6)
17. Difficulty (12)
20. Pertaining to plants (7)
21. Bend or curl (5)
22. Throw a coin in the air (4)
23. Small window (8)

DOWN

1. Forefather (4)
2. Expression of blame (7)
3. Startling (4-8)
4. Yellow citrus fruits (6)
6. Very large (5)
7. Strip of land by a highway (8)
8. Relating to numeric calculations (12)
12. Highly critical remark (8)
15. Circling around (7)
16. Spiny tree or shrub (6)
18. Legendary stories (5)
19. Petty quarrel (4)

CROSSWORD 28

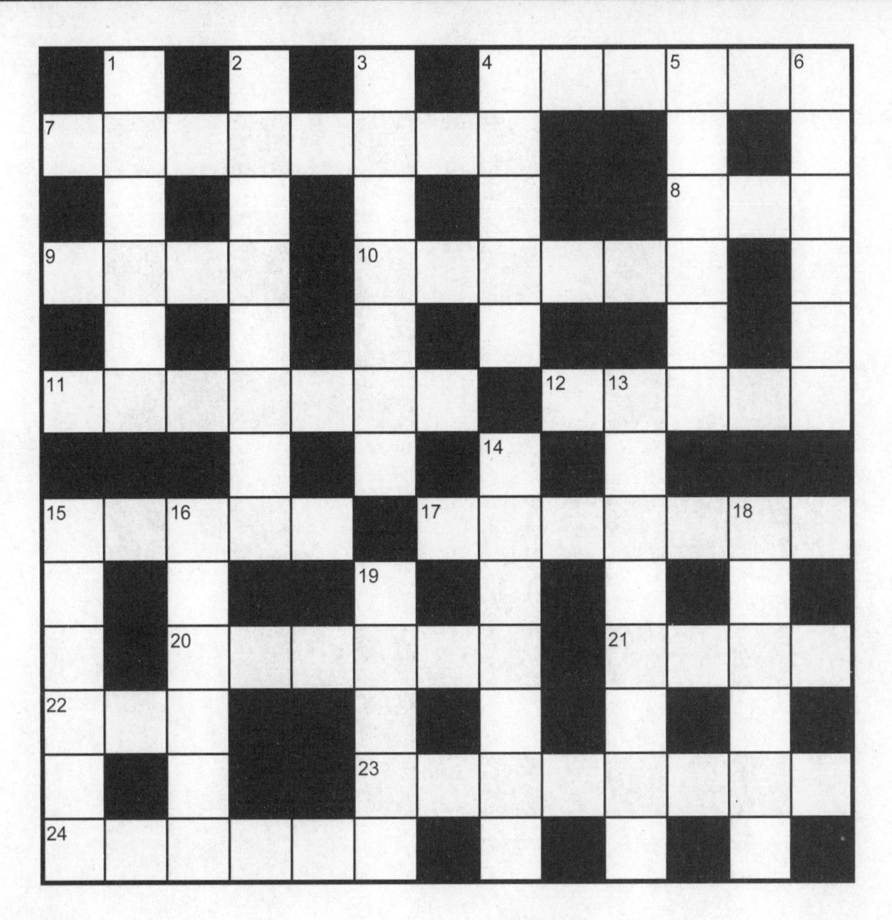

ACROSS

4. Tropical fruit (6)
7. Put into long-term storage (8)
8. Be nosy (3)
9. Not knowing where one is (4)
10. Complex problem (6)
11. Teller (7)
12. State of disgrace (5)
15. Moneys owed (5)
17. Daft (7)
20. Nudges out of the way (6)
21. E.g. beef or pork (4)
22. Lay seed in the ground (3)
23. Many (8)
24. Boldness (6)

DOWN

1. Gaseous envelope of the sun (6)
2. Gossip (4-4)
3. Ripple on water (7)
4. Length of interlaced hair (5)
5. Domesticated llama (6)
6. A person in general (6)
13. Distinctive feature (8)
14. Ingest (7)
15. Extinguished (6)
16. One who makes beer (6)
18. Relative social standing (6)
19. Opposite of old (5)

CROSSWORD 29

ACROSS

1. Impoliteness (8)
5. Spots (4)
9. Clergyman (5)
10. Farewell remark (7)
11. Redecorate (7)
12. Very informal phrases (5)
13. First born (6)
14. Season of the Church year (6)
17. Female relatives (5)
19. Type of respiration (7)
20. Slope (7)
21. Precious stone (5)
22. Negative votes (4)
23. Meddlesome person (8)

DOWN

1. Resonance (13)
2. E.g. shrimp or crab (7)
3. Vain (12)
4. Landmarks; spectacles (6)
6. Venomous snake (5)
7. Vigorously (13)
8. Significantly (12)
15. Import barrier (7)
16. Rich cake (6)
18. Mother-of-pearl (5)

CROSSWORD 30

ACROSS

1. Soft drink (US) (4)
3. Brilliant performers (8)
9. Surround entirely (7)
10. Urge into action (5)
11. Stomach (3)
12. Baking appliances (5)
13. Clear and apparent (5)
15. Deep fissure (5)
17. Hurled (5)
18. Auction item (3)
19. Warning sound (5)
20. Cyclone (7)
21. Kitchen sideboards (8)
22. Small vipers (4)

DOWN

1. Legerdemain (7,2,4)
2. Clod of turf (5)
4. Leaping antelope (6)
5. Mathematics of triangles (12)
6. Weigh down (7)
7. Pictures (13)
8. International multi-sport event (7,5)
14. Teach (7)
16. Graphical representation of a person (6)
18. Exposes secret information (5)

CROSSWORD 31

ACROSS

1. Act of operating marionettes (8)
5. Underwater ridge of rock (4)
9. Sudden fear (5)
10. Educational establishment (7)
11. Feeling let down (12)
13. Leave the nest (6)
14. Shining (6)
17. Untimely (12)
20. Nominal (7)
21. Small woodland (5)
22. Rough or harsh sound (4)
23. Closeness (8)

DOWN

1. Bursts (4)
2. Wistfully thoughtful (7)
3. Capable of being traded (12)
4. List of ingredients for a dish (6)
6. Turn inside out (5)
7. Liberties (8)
8. UFO (6,6)
12. Agitated (8)
15. Surpass (7)
16. Husky (6)
18. Locates or places (5)
19. Streams of liquid or gas (4)

CROSSWORD 32

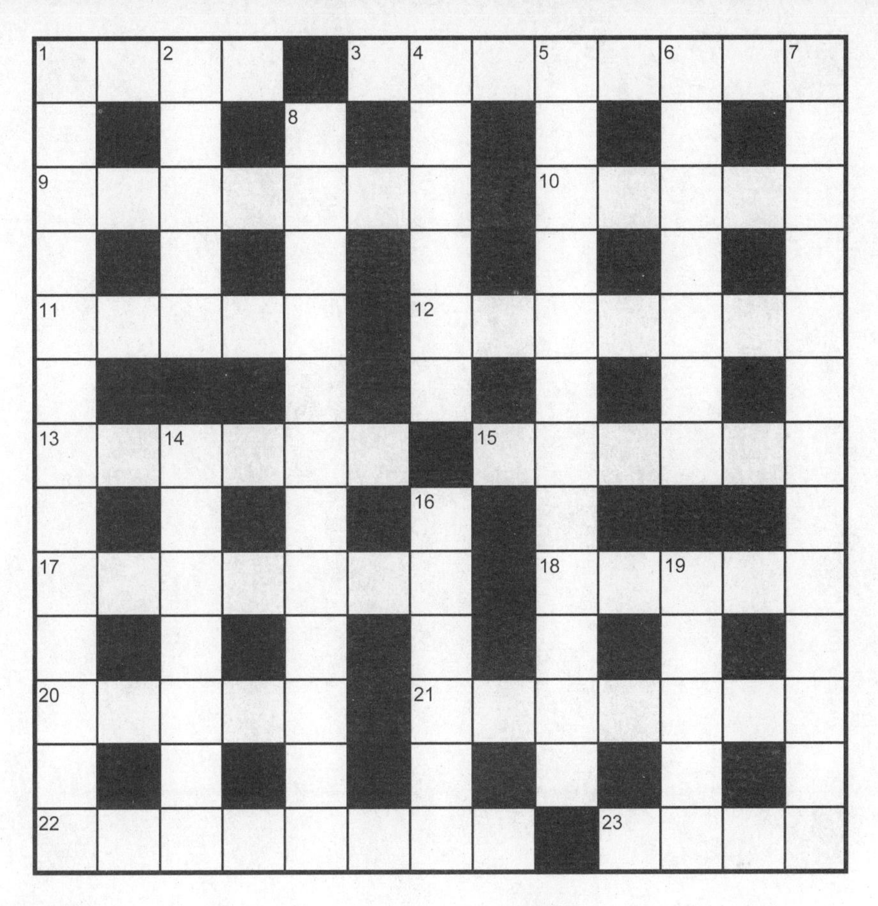

ACROSS

1. Gear wheels (4)
3. Dispute (8)
9. Plunderers (7)
10. Carer (anag.) (5)
11. Strong desires (5)
12. Kitchen implement (7)
13. Legendary tales (6)
15. Stick to (6)
17. Meals (7)
18. Country once ruled by Papa Doc (5)
20. Sound of any kind (5)
21. Eternal (7)
22. Hostilities (8)
23. Dairy product (4)

DOWN

1. Line that bounds a circle (13)
2. Departing (5)
4. Be preoccupied with a topic (6)
5. Pungent gas used as a preservative (12)
6. Have as a part (7)
7. Menacingly (13)
8. Re-evaluation (12)
14. Religious sacrament (7)
16. Guarantee (6)
19. Nationality of Oscar Wilde (5)

CROSSWORD 33

ACROSS

1. Discontented (11)
9. Broadcast again (5)
10. Belgian town (3)
11. Collection of songs (5)
12. Strain (5)
13. Most jolly (8)
16. Predict the future (8)
18. Ring-shaped object (5)
21. Expect; think that (5)
22. Fishing pole (3)
23. Very untypical (5)
24. Founded (11)

DOWN

2. Lines of equal pressure on maps (7)
3. Long distance postal service (7)
4. Compels to do something (6)
5. Ice cream is often served in these (5)
6. Follow on from (5)
7. Consisting of incomplete parts (11)
8. Fictional (4-7)
14. Officially cancels (7)
15. Accept to be true (7)
17. Trying experience (6)
19. Travels by bicycle (5)
20. Capital of Bulgaria (5)

CROSSWORD 34

ACROSS

1. Act of explaining in detail (11)
9. Increase the running speed of an engine (3)
10. Nairobi is the capital here (5)
11. Surface upon which one walks (5)
12. Birds lay their eggs in these (5)
13. Disease (8)
16. Defeat (8)
18. Student (5)
20. Join together (5)
21. Wall painting (5)
22. Label (3)
23. Reliable (11)

DOWN

2. Resides (5)
3. Cooks in the oven (5)
4. Meaner (anag.) (6)
5. Movement of vehicles en masse (7)
6. Argues against (7)
7. Changed completely (11)
8. Phraseology (11)
14. More jolly (7)
15. Plans (7)
17. The next day (6)
18. Directly opposite in character (5)
19. Piece of land (5)

CROSSWORD 35

ACROSS

1. Becomes subject to (6)
4. Decorated with feathers (6)
9. Forgives for a fault (7)
10. Philosophical theory (7)
11. Slant (5)
12. Fire a weapon (5)
14. Cruel or severe (5)
17. Assumed name (5)
19. Shire (anag.) (5)
21. Unfamiliar (7)
23. Commercial form of zinc (7)
24. Abandon (6)
25. Distorts (6)

DOWN

1. Accustoms to something (6)
2. Closing section of a piece of music (4)
3. Renaissance (7)
5. Position or point (5)
6. Midwestern US state (8)
7. Removed dirt from (6)
8. Measure of heat (11)
13. Policemen or women (8)
15. Item used to cut metal (7)
16. Done in stages (6)
18. Detects; feels (6)
20. Indian lute (5)
22. Exclamation on making a mistake (4)

CROSSWORD 36

ACROSS

1. Form of carbon (8)
5. Protective crust (4)
9. Musical note (5)
10. Sign of the zodiac (7)
11. Cancel (5)
12. Regret with sadness (3)
13. Venomous snake (5)
15. Dismiss from office (5)
17. Opposite of in (3)
19. Shadow (5)
20. Used to one's advantage (7)
21. Mature human (5)
22. Large deer (pl.) (4)
23. Climbed (8)

DOWN

1. Sympathetic and merciful (13)
2. Canvas shelters (7)
3. In a self-satisfied manner (12)
4. Utterly senseless (6)
6. Escapade (5)
7. Overwhelmed with sorrow (6-7)
8. Pay tribute to another (12)
14. Ricochet (7)
16. Exit; Bible book (6)
18. Trail (5)

CROSSWORD 37

ACROSS

1. A single time (4)
3. Partially hidden (8)
9. Helps to happen (7)
10. Titled (5)
11. Lawfully (12)
14. Cause friction (3)
16. Number after seven (5)
17. Small amount of something (3)
18. Dispirited (12)
21. Earlier (5)
22. Flog; whip (7)
23. Disregards (8)
24. Thaw (anag.) (4)

DOWN

1. Ruler (8)
2. Loud resonant noise (5)
4. Form of public transport (3)
5. Person's physical state (12)
6. Made deep sounds (7)
7. Fathers (4)
8. Framework for washed garments (12)
12. Hot fluid rock (5)
13. Complying with orders (8)
15. Capital of China (7)
19. Compass point (5)
20. On top of (4)
22. Become firm (3)

CROSSWORD 38

ACROSS

1. Elephant tooth (4)
3. Separate and distinct (8)
9. Arrived at a destination (7)
10. Extreme (5)
11. Advantageous; superior (12)
13. Generic term for a martial art (4,2)
15. Small cave (6)
17. Developmental (12)
20. Lentil or chickpea (5)
21. Country in Africa (7)
22. Re-evaluate (8)
23. Spiciness (4)

DOWN

1. Old toll road (8)
2. Move on ice (5)
4. In truth; really (6)
5. Compensate for (12)
6. Competitor (7)
7. Energy and enthusiasm (4)
8. Optimism (12)
12. Speaking many languages (8)
14. Short story (7)
16. Stagnation or inactivity (6)
18. Debate in a heated manner (5)
19. Goad on (4)

CROSSWORD 39

ACROSS

1. Sharp cry of a dog (4)
3. Excessively emotional (6,2)
9. Agitate; bother (7)
10. Looks slyly (5)
11. Overwhelmingly compelling (12)
14. Hearing organ (3)
16. Adult insect stage (5)
17. 17th Greek letter (3)
18. Grandeur (12)
21. Additional (5)
22. Having great wisdom (7)
23. Close associate (8)
24. Sight organs (4)

DOWN

1. Sheets and pillowcases (8)
2. Vertical part of a step (5)
4. Sphere or globe (3)
5. Children's toy (12)
6. Inhabitant (7)
7. Elapse (of time) (4)
8. The ? symbol (8,4)
12. Neck warmer (5)
13. Flower-shaped competition awards (8)
15. Cooked meat in the oven (7)
19. Destitute (5)
20. Pollinating insects (4)
22. Pouch; enclosed space (3)

CROSSWORD 40

ACROSS

1. A change for the better (11)
9. Purchase (3)
10. More ashen in appearance (5)
11. Elector (5)
12. Walk (5)
13. Introductory speech (8)
16. Lack of warmth (8)
18. Company emblems (5)
20. Attach to (5)
21. Exposed (5)
22. Enemy (3)
23. Fragility (11)

DOWN

2. Perhaps (5)
3. Swift (5)
4. Person who estimates the worth of something (6)
5. Astonishing things (7)
6. Savings for the future (4,3)
7. Painting genre (8,3)
8. Witches (11)
14. Pillage (7)
15. Imprecise (7)
17. Helix (6)
18. Heavily loaded (5)
19. Presents (5)

CROSSWORD 41

ACROSS

1. Starts (6)
7. Propose a candidate for office (8)
8. Hit high into the air (3)
9. Wicked (6)
10. Defer action (4)
11. Rotates (5)
13. Made available for sale (7)
15. Planned one's actions (7)
17. Precious stone (5)
21. Head covering (4)
22. Treatises (6)
23. Key on a computer keyboard (3)
24. Relating to speech sounds (8)
25. More difficult (6)

DOWN

1. Container (6)
2. Hot spring (6)
3. Breathe in audibly (5)
4. Enlarge; increase in size (7)
5. Not in a specific location (8)
6. Walk with long steps (6)
12. Annoying with continual criticism (8)
14. Say again (7)
16. Type of nursery (6)
18. Squandered (6)
19. Move slowly and awkwardly (6)
20. Area of sand (5)

CROSSWORD 42

ACROSS

1. Support (6)
4. Throws carelessly (6)
9. Excessive bureaucracy (3,4)
10. Marmoset (7)
11. Work tables (5)
12. Converses casually (5)
14. Deliberate; cogitate (5)
15. Raucous (5)
17. Flash of light (5)
18. Former Greek monetary unit (7)
20. Divide into three parts (7)
21. Gainly (anag.) (6)
22. Clasp (6)

DOWN

1. Wear away (6)
2. Small stall at an exhibition (8)
3. Examines quickly (5)
5. Knoll (7)
6. US pop star who sang "I Got You Babe" (4)
7. Causes a sharp pain (6)
8. Become worse (11)
13. Obvious (8)
14. Tropical cyclone (7)
15. Arranged like rays (6)
16. Rough drawing (6)
17. Tumble from a horse (5)
19. Associate (4)

CROSSWORD 43

ACROSS

1. Weapons (4)
3. Occasional (8)
9. Rider (7)
10. Sacred song (5)
11. Pair of people (3)
12. Country in the Middle East (5)
13. Basins (5)
15. Exposes to danger (5)
17. Paved courtyard (5)
18. Expected at a certain time (3)
19. Rock group (5)
20. Early Christian teacher (7)
21. Commonplace (8)
22. Reasons; explanations (4)

DOWN

1. Liable to get injured (8-5)
2. Extremely small (prefix) (5)
4. Financier (6)
5. Act of reclamation (12)
6. Schematic (7)
7. Militant aggressiveness (13)
8. Ruinously (12)
14. A dancer or singer (7)
16. Huge desert in northern Africa (6)
18. Pertaining to the Netherlands (5)

CROSSWORD 44

ACROSS

4. Feels uncertain about (6)
7. Game of chance (8)
8. Wetland (3)
9. Opposite of thick (4)
10. What a spider makes (6)
11. Grazed (7)
12. Yearned for (5)
15. Discovered (5)
17. Soften the effect of (7)
20. Capital of Canada (6)
21. Brood (4)
22. Part of a coat (3)
23. Calmness under pressure (8)
24. Annually (6)

DOWN

1. Style of architecture (6)
2. Starchy banana-like fruit (8)
3. Adhesive label (7)
4. Local sporting match (5)
5. Cylinder holding thread (6)
6. Autographed something for a fan (6)
13. Cruel (8)
14. Museum keeper (7)
15. Tightly curled (of hair) (6)
16. System of social perfection (6)
18. Argue against (6)
19. Whim or caprice (5)

CROSSWORD 45

1		2		■	3	4		5		6		7
	■		■	8	■		■		■		■	
9							■	10				
	■		■		■	■	■		■		■	
11						12						■
	■	■	■		■		■		■		■	13
14		15	■	16					■	17		
	■		■		■		■		■	■	■	
■	18									19		
20	■		■		■	■	■		■		■	
21					■	22						
	■		■		■		■		■		■	
23								■	24			

ACROSS

1. Religious act (4)
3. Thought curiously (8)
9. Hide (7)
10. Unpleasant facial expression (5)
11. Teach to accept a belief uncritically (12)
14. Recede (3)
16. Angry (5)
17. Hip (anag.) (3)
18. Despicable (12)
21. Ballroom dance (5)
22. Unit of sound in a language (7)
23. Urgent (8)
24. Church song (4)

DOWN

1. Part of a telephone apparatus (8)
2. Shaped up (5)
4. Lubricate (3)
5. Destruction of bacteria (12)
6. Highest vantage point of a building (7)
7. Girl's toy (4)
8. Detailed reports (12)
12. Supply with new weapons (5)
13. Final teenage year (8)
15. Chocolate chewy cake (7)
19. Muscular (5)
20. Halt (4)
22. Joke (3)

CROSSWORD 46

ACROSS

1. Sweat (8)
5. Small body of water (4)
8. Intimate companion (5)
9. Stinging plants (7)
10. Squirm (7)
12. Excavating machines (7)
14. Abrupt in manner (7)
16. Clothing (7)
18. Cigar (7)
19. Direct competitor (5)
20. Fat used to make puddings (4)
21. Progeny (8)

DOWN

1. Inner surface of the hand (4)
2. Wandering (6)
3. Outer boundary (9)
4. Rejuvenates (6)
6. Constrain or compel (6)
7. Distribute (8)
11. Initial (9)
12. Capital of Syria (8)
13. Ball-shaped object (6)
14. Mark on the skin (6)
15. Tremble; musical note (6)
17. Large family (4)

CROSSWORD 47

ACROSS

4. Plaster for coating walls (6)
7. Very large (8)
8. Young bear (3)
9. Narrow bed (4)
10. Shrub with glossy leaves (6)
11. Caressed (7)
12. Long pointed teeth (5)
15. Mild and pleasant (5)
17. Writing implements (7)
20. Assert without proof (6)
21. Flirtatious girl (4)
22. Level golf score (3)
23. Came up with a new product (8)
24. Wish for (6)

DOWN

1. French dance (6)
2. Where photographs are developed (8)
3. Soothed (7)
4. Make a search (5)
5. Rides a bike (6)
6. Paths of electrons around nuclei (6)
13. About to take place (8)
14. Merit (7)
15. Knocked into (6)
16. Acquires a new skill (6)
18. Hang around (6)
19. Give a false notion of (5)

CROSSWORD 48

ACROSS

1. Fraudulently (11)
9. Smooth cream of vegetables (5)
10. Writing instrument (3)
11. Inexpensive (5)
12. Sharp blade (5)
13. Amaze (8)
16. Imaginative (8)
18. Slopes (5)
21. Utter repetitively (5)
22. Legal ruling (3)
23. Giggle (5)
24. The military (5,6)

DOWN

2. Puts money into a venture (7)
3. Occurs (7)
4. Hospital carers (6)
5. Guide a vehicle (5)
6. Administrative capital of Bolivia (2,3)
7. Type of music (4,3,4)
8. Increasing gradually by degrees (11)
14. Charmer (anag.) (7)
15. Extraordinary occurrence (7)
17. Turn down (6)
19. Garden tool for cutting grass (5)
20. Find the solution (5)

CROSSWORD 49

ACROSS

1. Causing a blockage (11)
9. SI unit of illuminance (3)
10. Less high (5)
11. Doctor (5)
12. Linear measures of three feet (5)
13. Precious metallic element (8)
16. Huge ice masses (8)
18. Old-fashioned (5)
20. Variety of chalcedony (5)
21. Bandage that supports an arm (5)
22. Touch gently (3)
23. Devices popular before computers existed (11)

DOWN

2. Fighter (5)
3. Cash registers (5)
4. Ill (6)
5. Wood-eating insect (7)
6. Rendering invalid (7)
7. E.g. Queen of Hearts (7,4)
8. Make room for (11)
14. Unoccupied position (7)
15. Skill (7)
17. Small sword (6)
18. A finger or toe (5)
19. Come to a point (5)

CROSSWORD 50

ACROSS

1. Japanese sport (4)
3. Water (8)
9. Not in a hurry (7)
10. Sink; sag (5)
11. Allow (3)
12. Scowl (5)
13. Large marine mammal (5)
15. Conceals (5)
17. Loop with a running knot (5)
18. Great distress (3)
19. Not asleep (5)
20. Plunder (7)
21. Boating (8)
22. Resistance units (4)

DOWN

1. Additional (13)
2. Short choral composition (5)
4. Part of the eye (6)
5. Not capable of justification (12)
6. Expression of sorrow (7)
7. Ebullience (13)
8. Disregarding the rules (5,3,4)
14. Mundane (7)
16. Increase; extend (6)
18. Ire (5)

CROSSWORD 51

ACROSS

1. Recedes (4)
3. Announce publicly (8)
9. State of the USA (7)
10. Tiny arachnids (5)
11. Not found (12)
13. Line of latitude (6)
15. Bodyguard (6)
17. Made (12)
20. Start (5)
21. Lessen (7)
22. Writer of literary works (8)
23. Places containing animals (4)

DOWN

1. Empty (8)
2. Construct (5)
4. Explanation (6)
5. Reparation (12)
6. Design style of the 1920s and 1930s (3,4)
7. Church service (4)
8. Body of voters in a specified region (12)
12. School pupils (8)
14. Citrus fruits (7)
16. Hesitates (6)
18. Quantitative relation between two amounts (5)
19. Woodwind instrument (4)

CROSSWORD 52

ACROSS

1. Table linen; woven fabric (6)
4. Gardening tool (6)
9. Warning (7)
10. Give advice to (7)
11. Pulpy (5)
12. Oily organic compound (5)
14. Showered with love (5)
15. Long flower-stalk (5)
17. Follow stealthily (5)
18. Accuse of a wrong (7)
20. Plausible; defensible (7)
21. Least polite (6)
22. Oppose a plan successfully (6)

DOWN

1. Depart suddenly (6)
2. Greek dish (8)
3. Glossy (5)
5. Reconstruct (7)
6. Comedians; wist (anag.) (4)
7. Soothed (6)
8. Doubt (11)
13. Partial shadow (8)
14. Sly (7)
15. Person gliding on ice (6)
16. Thoroughfare (6)
17. Intuitive feeling (5)
19. Attack at speed (4)

CROSSWORD 53

ACROSS

1. Good fortune (11)
9. Adornment (5)
10. Tack (3)
11. Hit; steal (5)
12. Country in northeastern Africa (5)
13. Capsize (8)
16. Sharp heel (8)
18. Mallet (5)
21. Leans (5)
22. Conciliatory gift (3)
23. Short letters (5)
24. Perplexing situation (11)

DOWN

2. Stimulates; provokes (7)
3. Personal belongings (7)
4. Car operator (6)
5. Tugs (5)
6. Lukewarm (5)
7. Astronomer who studies the origin of the universe (11)
8. Without giving a name (11)
14. Floating wreckage (7)
15. Rich white cheese (7)
17. Plan; strategy (6)
19. Venomous snake (5)
20. Covered the inside of a container (5)

CROSSWORD 54

ACROSS

4. A husband or wife (6)
7. Fierce (8)
8. Domestic animal (3)
9. Luxurious car (abbrev.) (4)
10. Former female pupil (6)
11. Follow a winding course (of a river) (7)
12. Ciphers (5)
15. Puny (5)
17. Sporting contests (7)
20. Removed creases from clothes (6)
21. Route (4)
22. Blend together (3)
23. Fade away (8)
24. Strong feeling of loathing (6)

DOWN

1. System of doing things (6)
2. Famous (8)
3. Sateens (anag.) (7)
4. Corpulent (5)
5. Not yet settled (of a bill) (6)
6. Goes inside (6)
13. Dweller (8)
14. Pertaining to the heart (7)
15. Heat; affection (6)
16. Magical potion (6)
18. Tempt (6)
19. Derisive smile (5)

CROSSWORD 55

ACROSS

1. Goes to see someone (6)
4. Building devoted to worship (6)
9. Clever but false argument (7)
10. Fourth book of the Bible (7)
11. Deep chasms (5)
12. Conditions (5)
14. Folds close together (5)
15. Blowing in puffs (of wind) (5)
17. Cease being awake (5)
18. Desist from (7)
20. Type of scientist (7)
21. Layers (anag.) (6)
22. Lots of (6)

DOWN

1. Countenance (6)
2. Provides with (8)
3. Journeys (5)
5. Recluses (7)
6. Intense anger (4)
7. Equine animals (6)
8. Infinite knowledge (11)
13. Plan anew (8)
14. Cruel use of authority (7)
15. Collect or store (6)
16. Having pimples (6)
17. Tortoise carapace (5)
19. Opposite of empty (4)

CROSSWORD 56

ACROSS

1. Piece of software (11)
9. North American nation (abbrev.) (3)
10. Happen again (5)
11. Draw off liquid from (5)
12. A sure thing; easy task (5)
13. E.g. when lunch or dinner is eaten (8)
16. Not inclined to talk (8)
18. Wooden pin used to join surfaces together (5)
20. Greenish-bronze fish (5)
21. Humming (5)
22. Place (3)
23. Lack of being (11)

DOWN

2. Crustacean like a shrimp (5)
3. Stagger (5)
4. Laugh in a harsh way (6)
5. Slowly; sluggishly (7)
6. Derived from living matter (7)
7. Vulnerable to (11)
8. Think about carefully (11)
14. Fast musical composition (7)
15. Organ of digestion (7)
17. Yield or make (a profit) (6)
18. Twelve (5)
19. Totally erases (5)

CROSSWORD 57

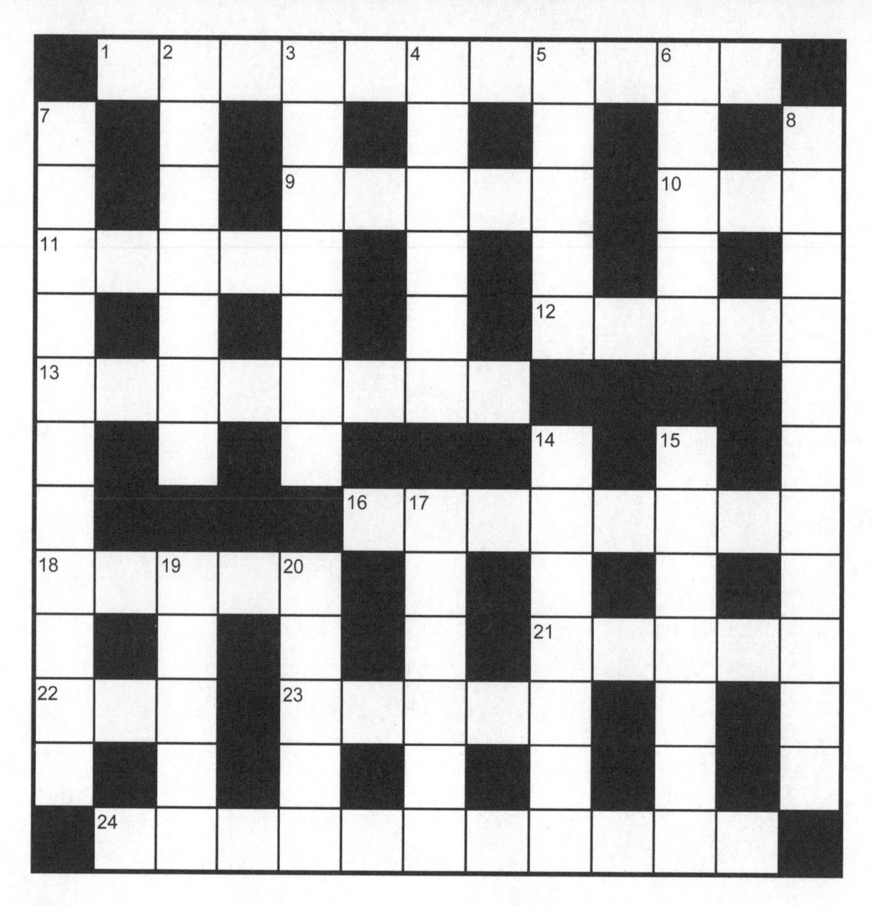

ACROSS

1. Highest peak in Africa (11)
9. Supplementary component (3-2)
10. Coniferous tree (3)
11. Growl with bare teeth (5)
12. Glasses (abbrev.) (5)
13. Happen simultaneously (8)
16. Plot outline for a play (8)
18. Municipalities (5)
21. Impress a pattern on (5)
22. Eccentric (3)
23. Join together (5)
24. Watching over one's flock (11)

DOWN

2. Live in (7)
3. Slanted letters (7)
4. Mixed up or confused (6)
5. Roman god with two faces (5)
6. Firearm (5)
7. Dehydration (11)
8. Plant-eating insect (11)
14. Eased in (anag.) (7)
15. Widen (7)
17. Selection (6)
19. Breadth (5)
20. Drink noisily (5)

CROSSWORD 58

ACROSS

1. Units of linear measure (6)
7. Changing (8)
8. Animal foot (3)
9. Person with detailed knowledge (6)
10. Persuade gently (4)
11. Hoarse (5)
13. Permitted (7)
15. Mythical female sea creature (7)
17. Coiled curve (5)
21. Arduous journey (4)
22. Hackneyed statement (6)
23. Container (3)
24. People who work with glass (8)
25. Stashes away (6)

DOWN

1. Mischievous (6)
2. Escrow (anag.) (6)
3. Rescues (5)
4. Majestic (7)
5. Fruit sugar (8)
6. Enter a country by force (6)
12. Potentially self-destructive (8)
14. Simple songs (7)
16. Weirdly (6)
18. Relating to the lower back (6)
19. Ancient Persian king (6)
20. Subdue (5)

CROSSWORD 59

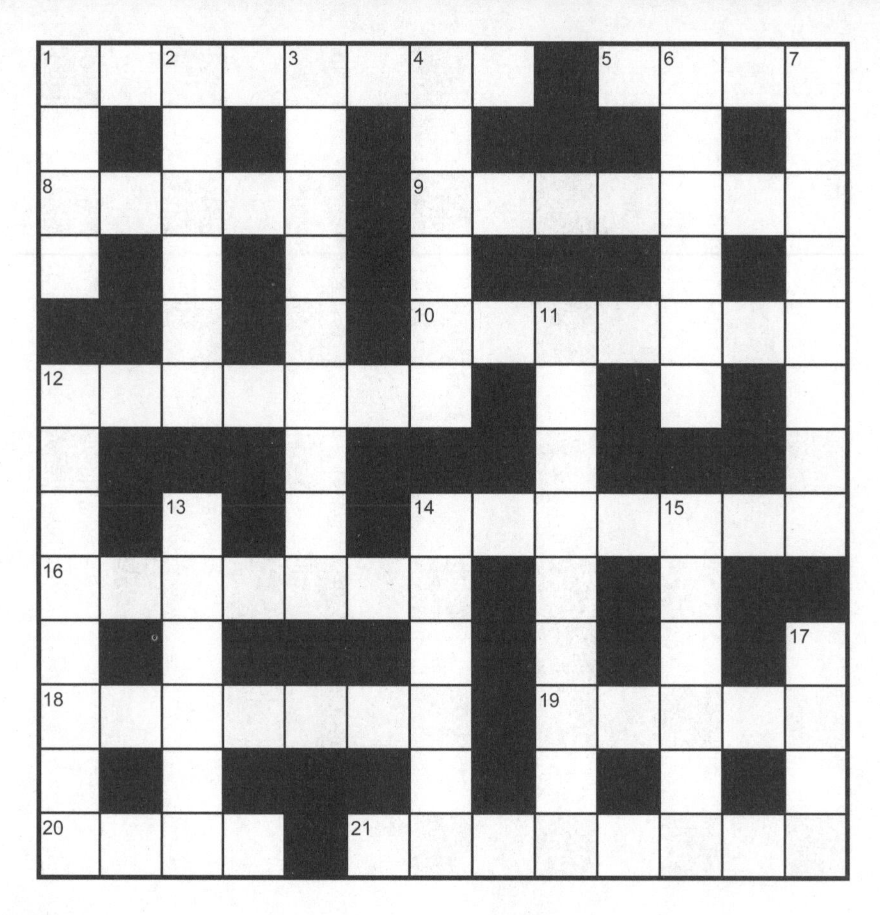

ACROSS

1. Re-emerge (8)
5. Thin strip of wood (4)
8. Fine powdery foodstuff (5)
9. Comply (with rules) (7)
10. Flight attendant (7)
12. Satisfy (7)
14. Terrestrial (7)
16. Set up (7)
18. Make right (7)
19. Ooze (5)
20. Taking a long time (4)
21. Took for granted (8)

DOWN

1. Widespread (4)
2. Apply ointment for religious reasons (6)
3. Talked into doing something (9)
4. Level a charge against (6)
6. Not written in any key (of music) (6)
7. Atmospheric moisture (8)
11. Conveys a thought in words (9)
12. Emerges from water (8)
13. A size of book page (6)
14. Newspaper boss (6)
15. Inert gaseous element (6)
17. Clutched (4)

CROSSWORD 60

1		2		■	3	4		5		6		7
	■		■	8	■		■		■		■	
9							■	10				
	■		■		■		■		■		■	
11			■		■		■	12				
	■	■	■	13					■	■	■	
	■	14	■		■	■	■		■		■	
	■		■	15		16			■	■	■	
17					■		■		■	18		
	■		■		■		■		■		■	
19					■	20						
	■		■		■		■		■		■	
21								■	22			

ACROSS

1. Doubtful (4)
3. Physical power (8)
9. Shoulder blade (7)
10. Furnish or supply (5)
11. Leg (anag.) (3)
12. Underground enlarged stem (5)
13. Detection technology (5)
15. Use to one's advantage (5)
17. Not suitable in the circumstances (5)
18. What a painter creates (3)
19. Daisy-like flower (5)
20. Stupid (7)
21. Entirety (8)
22. Effigy (4)

DOWN

1. Petty (13)
2. Threshing tool (5)
4. Exchanged goods (6)
5. Decomposition by a current (12)
6. Searched clumsily (7)
7. Excessively negative about (13)
8. Occult (12)
14. Group of four (7)
16. Afloat (6)
18. Behaved (5)

CROSSWORD 61

ACROSS

1. Roman leaders (8)
5. Still to be paid (4)
9. Ape (abbrev.) (5)
10. Stringed instruments (7)
11. Brown earth pigment (5)
12. Soft animal hair (3)
13. Dried kernel of the coconut (5)
15. Food relish (5)
17. Fantastical creature (3)
19. Mark or wear thin (5)
20. Shut in (7)
21. Evenly balanced (5)
22. Small children (4)
23. Insincere praise (8)

DOWN

1. Expression of approval (13)
2. Flexible (7)
3. Consequence of an event (12)
4. Renovate (6)
6. Brief smell (5)
7. Shamefully (13)
8. Recovering from illness (of a person) (12)
14. Design of fashionable clothes (7)
16. Imaginary (6)
18. One side of a gem (5)

CROSSWORD 62

ACROSS

1. Froth of soap and water (4)
3. Rays of natural light (8)
9. Able to read minds (7)
10. Rustic (5)
11. Pub (3)
12. Long-handled spoon (5)
13. Bamboo-eating animal (5)
15. Doglike mammal (5)
17. Major African river (5)
18. Item constructed by a spider (3)
19. Tease or pester (5)
20. Sunshade (7)
21. Discouraged from doing (8)
22. Unit of heredity (4)

DOWN

1. Refined (13)
2. Most respected person in a field (5)
4. Young child who is poorly dressed (6)
5. Electronic security device (7,5)
6. Shorten (7)
7. 25th anniversary celebration (6,7)
8. Marksman (12)
14. Confer with others (7)
16. Pass (of time) (6)
18. Use inefficiently (5)

CROSSWORD 63

ACROSS

1. Car pedal (11)
9. Surpass (3)
10. Impress on paper (5)
11. Chunk (5)
12. Reddish (5)
13. Frightening (8)
16. Imitates (8)
18. Divide by cutting (5)
20. Towering (5)
21. Puff on a cigarette (5)
22. Female sheep (3)
23. Type of artist (11)

DOWN

2. Managed to deal with something (5)
3. Not containing anything (5)
4. Fit for consumption (6)
5. Illustrated material (7)
6. Located in the fresh air (7)
7. Narrator (11)
8. Taped in advance (11)
14. Bison (7)
15. Look after an infant (7)
17. Moon of the planet Jupiter (6)
18. Charming and endearing (5)
19. Opinions (5)

CROSSWORD 64

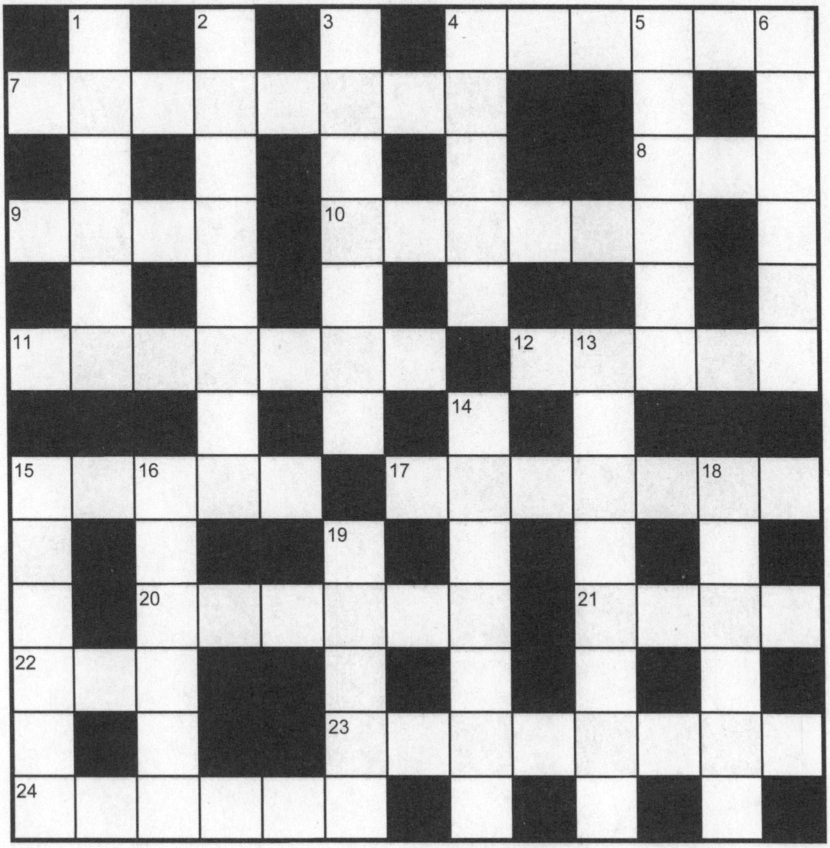

ACROSS

4. Next after seventh (6)
7. At work (2-3-3)
8. Collection of paper (3)
9. Short note or reminder (4)
10. Close tightly (6)
11. Looked up to (7)
12. Country in eastern Asia (5)
15. Plied (anag.) (5)
17. Pipe (7)
20. That is to say (6)
21. Cipher (4)
22. Facsimile (abbrev.) (3)
23. Alloy of copper and tin (8)
24. Decorative pattern (6)

DOWN

1. Straighten out (6)
2. Poisonous green gas (8)
3. Driven out (7)
4. Receded (5)
5. Type of music (3-3)
6. Concealed from view (6)
13. Physiologically dependent (8)
14. Imitating (7)
15. Breathless (6)
16. Wildcats (6)
18. E.g. from New Delhi (6)
19. Condescend (5)

CROSSWORD 65

ACROSS

1. Debatable (8)
5. Musical composition (4)
9. Surprise result (5)
10. Brass wind instrument (7)
11. Courtesy (12)
13. Hold a position or job (6)
14. Molecule that binds to another (6)
17. Productivity (12)
20. Seafarers (7)
21. Edge of a knife (5)
22. Quantity of medication (4)
23. Household cooling devices (8)

DOWN

1. Chemical salt used in dyeing (4)
2. Of the stomach (7)
3. Prediction or expectation (12)
4. Cosmetic cream (6)
6. Immature insects (5)
7. Reserved in advance (3-5)
8. Uncertain (12)
12. Muddled (8)
15. Make less intense (7)
16. One who manages finances at a college (6)
18. Individual things (5)
19. Writing instruments (4)

CROSSWORD 66

ACROSS

1. Large US feline (4)
3. Heath (8)
9. Hearing range (7)
10. Stinky (5)
11. Ability to acquire and apply knowledge (12)
13. Title of Roman emperors (6)
15. Selected (6)
17. Type of contest (12)
20. Particle that holds quarks together (5)
21. Gun holder (7)
22. Tempting (8)
23. Garden outbuilding (4)

DOWN

1. Clearly defined area (8)
2. Worthiness (5)
4. Get hold of (6)
5. Invigoratingly (12)
6. Seeks to hurt (7)
7. Extinct bird (4)
8. Devoted to music (12)
12. Made another excited about (8)
14. Wear out completely (7)
16. Inside of (6)
18. Emerge from an egg (5)
19. Look at amorously (4)

CROSSWORD 67

ACROSS

1. Dismantle (11)
9. Silk fabric (5)
10. For what purpose (3)
11. Customary practice (5)
12. Parts (anag.) (5)
13. Manner of giving a speech (8)
16. Investigate (8)
18. Fish-eating mammal (5)
21. Crucial person or point (5)
22. Metal container; is able to (3)
23. Male relation (5)
24. Pretentious display (11)

DOWN

2. To the same degree (7)
3. See (7)
4. Long-haired breed of dog (6)
5. Positions in a hierarchy (5)
6. Crouch down in fear (5)
7. Masterpiece (4,2,5)
8. Compassionate (11)
14. Admire deeply (7)
15. Stipulation (7)
17. Evoke (6)
19. Looks after (5)
20. Awake (5)

CROSSWORD 68

ACROSS

1. Negotiator (8)
5. Complain bitterly (4)
9. Plummeted (5)
10. Weakness; flaw (7)
11. First part of the Bible (3,9)
13. Give a job to (6)
14. Avoids (6)
17. Bewitchingly (12)
20. Enlarged; puffy (7)
21. With speed (5)
22. Tilt to one side (4)
23. Protector; guardian (8)

DOWN

1. Method; fashion (4)
2. Bring to maturity (7)
3. And also (12)
4. Aloof (6)
6. Stand up (5)
7. Least heavy (8)
8. Drawback (12)
12. About-face (8)
15. Foolish person (7)
16. Attitude or body position (6)
18. Annoyed (5)
19. Reel (anag.) (4)

CROSSWORD 69

ACROSS

1. Ancient objects (6)
4. Climbs (6)
9. Venetian boat (7)
10. System of interconnected things (7)
11. A fact that has been verified (5)
12. Restraining straps (5)
14. Edible fruit (5)
15. Humorous (5)
17. Business proposal (5)
18. Sends back into custody (7)
20. Listless (7)
21. Holds up (6)
22. Talkative (6)

DOWN

1. Legal entitlements (6)
2. Person skilled in languages (8)
3. Fabric (5)
5. 100 years (7)
6. Crazy (informal) (4)
7. Reptiles (6)
8. Perilously (11)
13. Teach (8)
14. Eventually (2,3,2)
15. Heated up (6)
16. Of inferior quality (6)
17. Grip tightly; steal (5)
19. Building for grinding grain (4)

CROSSWORD 70

ACROSS

1. Formal curse by a pope (8)
5. Stylish (4)
9. Assembly (5)
10. Mental strain (7)
11. Saying; slogan (5)
12. Involuntary spasm (3)
13. Tiny part of an image (5)
15. Sheet (anag.) (5)
17. Limb (3)
19. Public disturbances (5)
20. Trespass (7)
21. Brass instrument (5)
22. Makes a mistake (4)
23. Tries (8)

DOWN

1. Given to debate (13)
2. Formally approved (7)
3. Thick-skinned herbivorous animal (12)
4. Array of numbers (6)
6. Robbery (5)
7. Awareness (13)
8. Immune (12)
14. Temporary measure (7)
16. Anticipate (6)
18. A thing that measures (5)

CROSSWORD 71

ACROSS

4. Picture produced from many small pieces (6)
7. Cocktail (8)
8. Cuddle (3)
9. Extent of a surface (4)
10. Recapture (6)
11. Commander in chief of a fleet (7)
12. Geographical plan (5)
15. Strong gust of wind (5)
17. Female siblings (7)
20. Child (6)
21. Animal feet (4)
22. Young goat (3)
23. Giving off (8)
24. Uttered coarsely (6)

DOWN

1. Holy (6)
2. Sports played in water (8)
3. Active during the day (7)
4. Foggy (5)
5. Greek goddess of wisdom (6)
6. Persuasive and logical; clear (6)
13. Popular places (8)
14. Plaited lock of hair (7)
15. Street musician (6)
16. Dwells in (6)
18. Propelling a boat with oars (6)
19. Scraped at (5)

CROSSWORD 72

ACROSS

1. Sprats (anag.) (6)
4. Standards of perfection (6)
9. Opposite (7)
10. Wither (7)
11. Smug smile (5)
12. Electrician (5)
14. Utter elation (5)
17. Floral leaf (5)
19. Cook meat in the oven (5)
21. Loud sound following lightning (7)
23. Dull (7)
24. Make unhappy (6)
25. Incidental remarks (6)

DOWN

1. Playground structure (6)
2. Lion noise (4)
3. Popular saying (7)
5. Birds that are a symbol of peace (5)
6. Having no weak points (8)
7. Small spots or dots (6)
8. In a state of disrepair (11)
13. Kept hold of (8)
15. Husbands or wives (7)
16. Walks heavily and firmly (6)
18. The words of a song (6)
20. Make fun of someone (5)
22. Document of ownership (4)

CROSSWORD 73

ACROSS

1. Stole from (6)
7. Rigorous investigation (8)
8. Not many (3)
9. Eagerly (6)
10. Pulls at (4)
11. Put clothes on (5)
13. Marched (7)
15. Underwriter (7)
17. Hits with a lash (5)
21. First light (4)
22. Swimming costume (6)
23. Feline animal (3)
24. State of the USA (8)
25. Long speech (6)

DOWN

1. Pay back money (6)
2. Look out (6)
3. Fop (5)
4. People who cut wood (7)
5. Canine (3,5)
6. Mix with (6)
12. Husband of one's daughter (3-2-3)
14. Captain's record (7)
16. Silly tricks (6)
18. Frozen water spear (6)
19. Moved over ice (6)
20. Seabirds (5)

CROSSWORD 74

ACROSS

1. Sudden cry expressing surprise (11)
9. Bristle-like appendage (3)
10. Small boat (5)
11. Search rigorously for (5)
12. Military vehicles (5)
13. A desert in southwestern Africa (8)
16. Dependence (8)
18. Sweetening substance (5)
20. Periods of 60 minutes (5)
21. Adjusted the pitch of (5)
22. Sprite (3)
23. Not yet finished (11)

DOWN

2. Heavy noble gas (5)
3. Passes the tongue over (5)
4. Capital of Bahrain (6)
5. Day of the week (7)
6. Piece of furniture (7)
7. Joint business (11)
8. Instrument for recording heart activity (11)
14. Egg white (7)
15. A very skilled performer (7)
17. Arm strengthening exercise (4-2)
18. Grasslike marsh plant (5)
19. Craftiness (5)

CROSSWORD 75

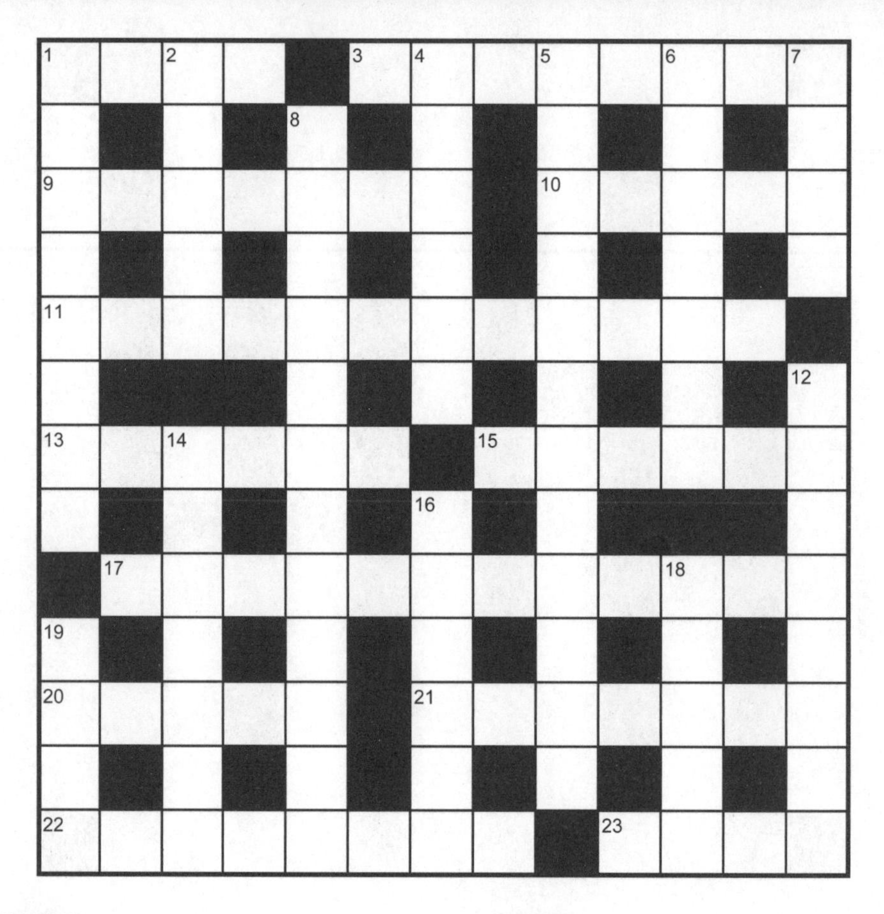

ACROSS

1. Greek god of love (4)
3. Secured with a dressing (8)
9. Giggles (7)
10. Thorax (5)
11. Formal notice (12)
13. Takes fright (6)
15. Long mountain chain (6)
17. Awkward (12)
20. One of the United Arab Emirates (5)
21. Study of animals (7)
22. Longing (8)
23. Lies (anag.) (4)

DOWN

1. Measure of the heat content of a system (8)
2. Many times (5)
4. Region of France (6)
5. Withdraw from service (12)
6. Better for the environment (7)
7. Tiny specks (4)
8. Condemnation (12)
12. Grotesquely carved figure (8)
14. African country with capital Windhoek (7)
16. Rigid; very cold (6)
18. Images of deities (5)
19. In an inactive way; with no particular purpose (4)

CROSSWORD 76

ACROSS

4. Opposite of top (6)
7. Large Spanish estate (8)
8. Breed of dog (3)
9. Capital of Norway (4)
10. Charge with a crime (6)
11. Allots (7)
12. Tearful (5)
15. Monastery church (5)
17. Duties or taxes (7)
20. Extremely fashionable; scalding (3-3)
21. Pieces of cloth (4)
22. Put down (3)
23. Float in the air (8)
24. Go back on (6)

DOWN

1. Overtakes (6)
2. Addictive tobacco drug (8)
3. Very old (7)
4. Discuss an idea casually (5)
5. Walk stealthily (6)
6. Strong (6)
13. Move to another country (8)
14. Prisoner (7)
15. Deer horn (6)
16. Subatomic particle such as a nucleon (6)
18. Engages in combat (6)
19. During (5)

CROSSWORD 77

ACROSS

1. Opposite of less (4)
3. Joins up (8)
9. Young hare (7)
10. Cowboy exhibition (5)
11. Peak (5)
12. Live together (7)
13. Fish hawk (6)
15. Punctuation mark (6)
17. Endurance (7)
18. Greeting (5)
20. Electronic message (5)
21. Realms (7)
22. How a crab moves (8)
23. Unattractive (4)

DOWN

1. Spite (13)
2. Variety show (5)
4. The science of light (6)
5. Short tale told to children (7,5)
6. Offensively discourteous (7)
7. Impulsively (13)
8. Male relation by marriage (7-2-3)
14. Poster (7)
16. Distress signal (6)
19. Not telling the truth (5)

CROSSWORD 78

ACROSS

1. Locate or place (4)
3. Very confusing (8)
9. Greatest amount possible (7)
10. Unit of weight (5)
11. Rate of increase in speed (12)
14. Fruit of a rose (3)
16. Solemn promises (5)
17. Male child (3)
18. Unfriendly (12)
21. Small antelope (5)
22. Antiquated (7)
23. Natural liking for (8)
24. Ewer (anag.) (4)

DOWN

1. Compassion (8)
2. Poisonous (5)
4. Goal (3)
5. Principal face of a building (12)
6. Having solidified from lava (of rock) (7)
7. Increased in size (4)
8. Improvement in a condition (12)
12. Imitative of the past (5)
13. Vehicle with one wheel (8)
15. The Pope (7)
19. Commerce (5)
20. Garment of ancient Rome (4)
22. Appropriate (3)

CROSSWORD 79

ACROSS

1. Sodium chloride (4)
3. Thick cotton fabric (8)
9. Provoked; encouraged (7)
10. Punctuation mark (5)
11. Hopelessly (12)
13. Coop up (6)
15. Seek out (6)
17. Scornful (12)
20. Bring into a line (5)
21. Holy place (7)
22. Support used when sitting (8)
23. Examine quickly (4)

DOWN

1. Superficial (4-4)
2. Fastens shut with a key (5)
4. Commands (6)
5. Medicine taken when blocked-up (12)
6. Walker without a fixed route (7)
7. Chinese monetary unit (4)
8. Starting here (anag.) (12)
12. E.g. rooks and knights (8)
14. Spicy Spanish sausage (7)
16. Entertains (6)
18. Relating to vision (5)
19. Abandoned person (4)

CROSSWORD 80

ACROSS

1. Occupations (4)
3. Animal that hunts (8)
9. Tranquil (7)
10. Public meeting for open discussion (5)
11. Group of shots (5)
12. Plain and clear (7)
13. Automata (6)
15. Simple; unrefined (6)
17. Express disagreement (7)
18. Instruct; teach (5)
20. Requirements (5)
21. Voter (7)
22. All people (8)
23. By word of mouth (4)

DOWN

1. Philosophy of law (13)
2. Aromatic herb of the mint family (5)
4. Long swelling wave (6)
5. Tricky elements; obstacles (12)
6. Severe mental suffering (7)
7. Device for changing TV channel (6,7)
8. Easily (12)
14. Surround with armed forces (7)
16. Scattered about untidily (6)
19. Change (5)

CROSSWORD 81

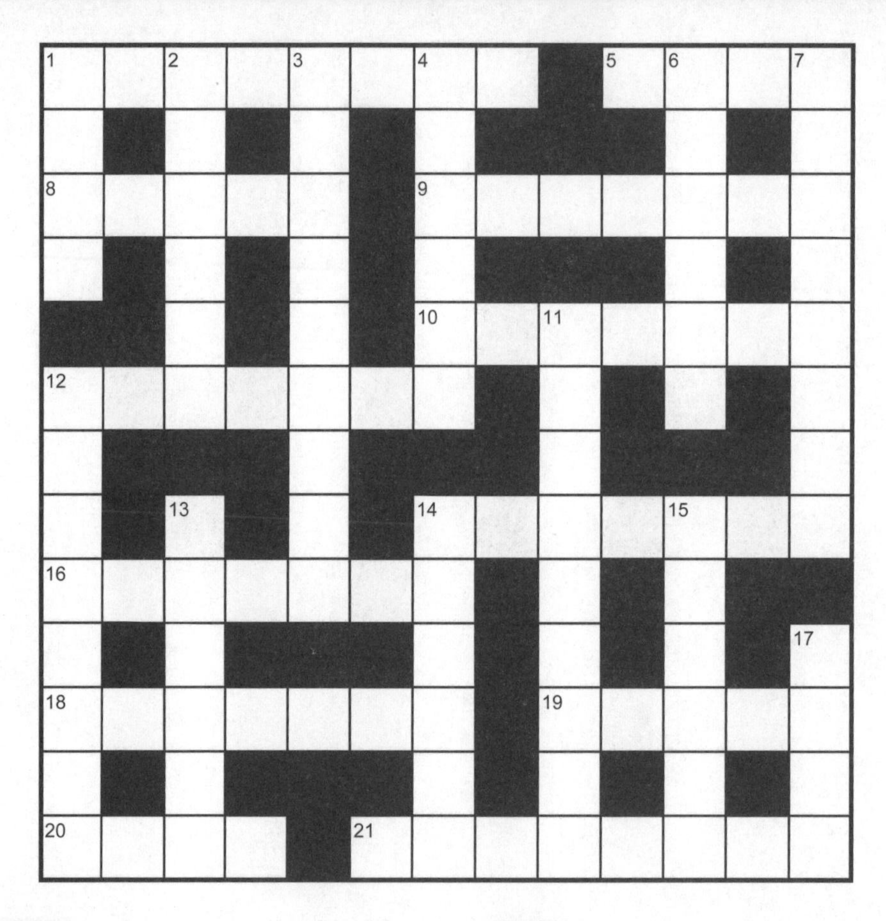

ACROSS

1. Victim of an accident (8)
5. Lofty (4)
8. Small streams (5)
9. Formal speech (7)
10. Parcels (7)
12. Provide money for (7)
14. Irregularity (7)
16. This evening (7)
18. Create a positive feeling in a person (7)
19. Selected (5)
20. Conceal (4)
21. Gathering (8)

DOWN

1. Suppress (4)
2. Mirthless (6)
3. Apportioning (9)
4. Group of touring entertainers (6)
6. Iridaceous plants (6)
7. Truly (8)
11. Record of events (9)
12. E.g. plaice (8)
13. In mint condition (6)
14. Capital of Greece (6)
15. Assurance; composure (6)
17. Wet with condensation (4)

CROSSWORD 82

ACROSS

1. Shaft on which a wheel rotates (4)
3. Pepper plant (8)
9. Tumult (7)
10. Accumulate (5)
11. Sound that a cow makes (3)
12. Flour dough used in cooking (5)
13. Should (5)
15. Adult human female (5)
17. Cut a joint of meat (5)
18. Definite article (3)
19. Published false statement (5)
20. Do repeatedly (7)
21. Young (8)
22. Scheme (4)

DOWN

1. In a reflex manner (13)
2. In a slow tempo (of music) (5)
4. In poor health (6)
5. Having an acrid wit (5-7)
6. Skeleton of a motor vehicle (7)
7. Ineptitude in running a business (13)
8. A grouping of states (12)
14. Reindeer (7)
16. One's environment (6)
18. Path to follow (5)

CROSSWORD 83

ACROSS

1. Small crude shelter (5)
4. Companion (7)
7. Long-necked birds (5)
8. Ate greedily (8)
9. Implement used for cleaning (5)
11. Whole; complete (8)
15. Suave (8)
17. Large motor vehicle (5)
19. Belonging to the past (8)
20. Leg joints (5)
21. Upward slopes (7)
22. Have an irritating effect (5)

DOWN

1. Powerful car lamp (9)
2. Smooth and soft (7)
3. Form of public worship (7)
4. Photographic equipment (6)
5. Amend; change (6)
6. Mounds of loose sand (5)
10. Cyclone (9)
12. Pushing abruptly; startling (7)
13. Powdered spice (7)
14. Assent or agree to (6)
16. Those expelled from a country (6)
18. Leases (5)

CROSSWORD 84

ACROSS

1. Portray (6)
4. Adhesive putty (6)
9. Silklike fabric (7)
10. Taught (7)
11. Young male horses (5)
12. Put into use (5)
14. Lane; passageway (5)
15. Opposite of lows (5)
17. Make thirsty (5)
18. Kind of abbreviation (7)
20. Legal inquiry (7)
21. Hesitate (6)
22. Type of muscle (6)

DOWN

1. Discover (6)
2. Trifling (8)
3. Board game (5)
5. Receptacle for cigarette residue (7)
6. Level in a hierarchy (4)
7. Without affection (6)
8. Causing sudden upheaval (11)
13. Matchless (8)
14. Unintelligent (7)
15. Warmed up (6)
16. Paler (6)
17. Wound the pride of (5)
19. Destroy (4)

CROSSWORD 85

ACROSS

1. Third awning (anag.) (11)
9. Tree (3)
10. Former name of the Democratic Republic of Congo (5)
11. Assists in a crime (5)
12. Unfortunately (5)
13. Publicly recommend (8)
16. Observer (8)
18. Group of witches (5)
20. Take illegally (5)
21. Burning (5)
22. Posed (3)
23. Respectful (11)

DOWN

2. Hankered after (5)
3. Giddy (5)
4. Showered (6)
5. Treachery (7)
6. Collection of sheets of paper (7)
7. Make in bulk (4-7)
8. Scatter widely (11)
14. Move in an exaggerated manner (7)
15. Contrast (7)
17. Resembling a horse (6)
18. Moved slowly (5)
19. View (5)

CROSSWORD 86

ACROSS

1. Holland (11)
9. Prohibited by social custom (5)
10. Argument against something (3)
11. Staple (5)
12. Sculptured symbol (5)
13. Offered (8)
16. Cloudy and dull (8)
18. Parasitic arachnids (5)
21. Food blender (5)
22. Mature (3)
23. Relating to the kidneys (5)
24. Tendency to disintegrate (11)

DOWN

2. Deleting (7)
3. Axe (7)
4. Mob (6)
5. In the company of (5)
6. Uncertain; risky (5)
7. Of considerable size (11)
8. Not having a written constitution (11)
14. Citadel in Moscow (7)
15. Mistake; blunder (4,3)
17. Occurring in spring (6)
19. Make less miserable (5)
20. Play a guitar (5)

CROSSWORD 87

ACROSS

1. A plant grows from this (4)
3. Squashing (8)
9. Strong embrace (4,3)
10. Torn apart (5)
11. Coming between two things in time (12)
14. Flightless bird (3)
16. Receive a ball in one's hands (5)
17. Droop (3)
18. Conflict of opinion (12)
21. Mistaken (5)
22. Cunning (7)
23. Curative medicines; sets right (8)
24. Parched (4)

DOWN

1. Became less intense (8)
2. Precise (5)
4. Floor mat (3)
5. Uncurled (12)
6. Requests the presence of (7)
7. Messy substance (4)
8. Cheated someone financially (5-7)
12. Consumer (5)
13. Excited or annoyed (8)
15. Identifying outfit (7)
19. Edward ___ : English composer (5)
20. Pitcher (4)
22. Use (anag.) (3)

CROSSWORD 88

ACROSS

1. Collide with (4)
3. Toughness (8)
9. A number defining position (7)
10. Small freshwater fish (5)
11. Orcas (6,6)
13. Imagined whilst asleep (6)
15. Fine cloth; type of paper (6)
17. Cameraman (12)
20. Forgo; relinquish (5)
21. More than enough (7)
22. Drink consumed before bed (8)
23. Saw; observed (4)

DOWN

1. Seal off a place (8)
2. Scale representation (5)
4. Permits (6)
5. Insistently (12)
6. Female ruler (7)
7. Utters (4)
8. Sporadic (12)
12. Informed upon (8)
14. Reverberating (7)
16. Large lizard (6)
18. Fluid made by bees (5)
19. Link a town with another (4)

CROSSWORD 89

ACROSS

4. Very brave and courageous (6)
7. Text of an opera (8)
8. Give a nickname to (3)
9. Temperate (4)
10. Soft felt hat (6)
11. Knife attached to a rifle (7)
12. Welcome (5)
15. Annoying (5)
17. West Indian musical style (7)
20. Be attractive (6)
21. Scottish lake (4)
22. Animal fodder (3)
23. Aided (8)
24. Capital of New South Wales (6)

DOWN

1. Sandstone constituent (6)
2. Severe traffic congestion (8)
3. Become rigid (7)
4. These protect you from rain (5)
5. One's twilight years (3,3)
6. E.g. Picasso or Braque (6)
13. Monarchist (8)
14. Greatest in height (7)
15. Quality in speech arousing pity (6)
16. Moved back and forth (6)
18. Kept private; unknown by others (6)
19. Make good on a debt (5)

CROSSWORD 90

ACROSS

1. Short account of an incident (8)
5. Sudden misfortune (4)
8. E.g. screwdrivers and hammers (5)
9. Sailor (7)
10. Get too big for something (7)
12. Dignified conduct (7)
14. Stem the flow of (4,3)
16. Someone who studies data (7)
18. Prior (7)
19. Pinch; squeeze (5)
20. Pulls a vehicle (4)
21. Taught (8)

DOWN

1. Adult male singing voice (4)
2. Excitingly strange (6)
3. Inequality (9)
4. Drum (3-3)
6. Passenger ships (6)
7. Monster that changes form during a full moon (8)
11. Emotionally disturbing (9)
12. Excessively self-indulgent (8)
13. Small carrying cart (6)
14. Gazed (6)
15. East (6)
17. Slide (4)

CROSSWORD 91

ACROSS

1. Go out with (4)
3. Visionary; utopian (8)
9. Brushed the coat of (an animal) (7)
10. Momentary oversight (5)
11. Junction (12)
14. Possessed (3)
16. Movable helmet part (5)
17. Long period of time (3)
18. Planned in advance (12)
21. Once more (5)
22. Grouped together (7)
23. Creative skill (8)
24. Young kangaroo (4)

DOWN

1. Fierce contest (8)
2. Game fish (5)
4. Thing that fails to work properly (3)
5. Repetition of the same sound (12)
6. Beseech (7)
7. Adolescent (abbrev.) (4)
8. Enhancements (12)
12. Became less severe (5)
13. Frankly (8)
15. Inactive (7)
19. Capital of Japan (5)
20. Facts and statistics collectively (4)
22. Distant (3)

CROSSWORD 92

ACROSS

1. Surprise results (6)
7. System of piping that provides water (8)
8. In what way (3)
9. Lessens (6)
10. Roman poet (4)
11. Flat-bottomed vessels (5)
13. Nasal cavities (7)
15. Backdrop; landscape (7)
17. Felts (anag.) (5)
21. African antelope (4)
22. Restraint (6)
23. Acquire (3)
24. Vindictive (8)
25. Discharges (6)

DOWN

1. Detach; unfasten (6)
2. Waste matter (6)
3. Malice (5)
4. Act of chasing something (7)
5. Complete (8)
6. Situated within the confines of (6)
12. Tongue (8)
14. Please or delight (7)
16. Produces an effect (6)
18. Counterfeit (6)
19. Expresses one's opinion (6)
20. Stagnant (5)

CROSSWORD 93

ACROSS

1. Rigid; stern (6)
4. Destroy (6)
9. Additions to a document (7)
10. Thieves (7)
11. Insane (5)
12. Thread-weaving machines (5)
14. Quoted (5)
15. Devout (5)
17. Animal used for riding (5)
18. Maxims (7)
20. Large tracts of land (7)
21. Become angry (6)
22. Go around (6)

DOWN

1. Spiritual meeting (6)
2. Blushing with embarrassment (3-5)
3. Shrewd (5)
5. Variegated (7)
6. Man-eating giant (4)
7. Browns bread (6)
8. Pairs of round brackets (11)
13. Small-scale musical drama (8)
14. Poison (7)
15. Took in breath (6)
16. Official population count (6)
17. Fiercely (5)
19. Period of 365 days (4)

CROSSWORD 94

ACROSS

1. Ride the waves (4)
3. Capital of Australia (8)
9. Small bone (7)
10. Gush out in a jet (5)
11. Attempt to do (3)
12. Lowest point (5)
13. Standpoint (5)
15. Snail (anag.) (5)
17. Flatten on impact (5)
18. Snow runner (3)
19. Plant hormone (5)
20. With an attitude of suspicion (7)
21. Abruptly (8)
22. Depend upon (4)

DOWN

1. Meteors (8,5)
2. Tarnished (of a metal object) (5)
4. Getting older (6)
5. Efficient (12)
6. Well balanced (of character) (7)
7. As another option (13)
8. Someone you know (12)
14. Not tense (7)
16. Country in the Middle East (6)
18. From that time (5)

CROSSWORD 95

ACROSS

1. Unrealistic (8)
5. Having inherent ability (4)
9. Heavy iron tool (5)
10. Acquire from a relative (7)
11. Supports (5)
12. Expanse of salt water (3)
13. Special reward (5)
15. Inert gas that is present in air (5)
17. Having a high temperature (3)
19. Third Greek letter (5)
20. Total amount of wages paid to employees (7)
21. Faith in another (5)
22. E.g. pecan and cashew (4)
23. Barely (8)

DOWN

1. A transient occurrence (5,2,3,3)
2. Originality (7)
3. Picture (12)
4. One of a kind (6)
6. Winged animals (5)
7. Wastefully; lavishly (13)
8. Small meteor (8,4)
14. Calculate (7)
16. Strong-smelling bulb (6)
18. Secret rendezvous (5)

CROSSWORD 96

ACROSS

1. Easy target (7,4)
9. Open disrespect (5)
10. Frying pan (3)
11. Small bodies of water (5)
12. Fashions; styles (5)
13. Pardons (8)
16. Self-operating machines (8)
18. Pipes (5)
21. Diving waterbird (5)
22. Widely cultivated cereal grass (3)
23. Nimble (5)
24. Coarse cotton gauze (11)

DOWN

2. Malady (7)
3. Adornments of hanging threads (7)
4. Pasta strip (6)
5. Fabric used to make jeans (5)
6. Intimidated and weakened (5)
7. Reason given for doing something (11)
8. Very tall buildings (11)
14. Curdle (7)
15. Costumed procession (7)
17. Tennis official (6)
19. Group of goods produced at one time (5)
20. Charming and elegant (5)

CROSSWORD 97

ACROSS

1. Raider (8)
5. Couple (4)
9. Stage play (5)
10. Female big cat (7)
11. Showed not to be true (12)
13. Cause to fall from a horse (6)
14. World's largest country (6)
17. Surrender (12)
20. Reached a destination (7)
21. Manor (anag.) (5)
22. Marine flatfish (4)
23. Sentiments (8)

DOWN

1. Created (4)
2. Explanations (7)
3. Ugly (12)
4. Catch or snare (6)
6. Very skilled at something (5)
7. Remaining (8)
8. Relating to farming (12)
12. Surpass in excellence (8)
15. Ice statues with coal for eyes (7)
16. Thick wet mud (6)
18. Danger (5)
19. Writing fluids (4)

CROSSWORD 98

ACROSS

1. Not hurtful (11)
9. Fantastic (5)
10. Athletic facility (3)
11. Stares (5)
12. Round steering device (5)
13. Conceptual thinker (8)
16. Wine container (8)
18. Saying (5)
21. Area of land (5)
22. Tree (3)
23. Unwarranted (5)
24. Extremely (11)

DOWN

2. Caresses with the nose (7)
3. Split (7)
4. Forces out (6)
5. Drinking tube (5)
6. The prevailing fashion (5)
7. Dizzy (5-6)
8. Makes better (11)
14. Oriental (7)
15. Type of alcohol (7)
17. Eluded (6)
19. Mingle with something else (5)
20. Composition for a solo instrument (5)

CROSSWORD 99

ACROSS

1. Hand clapping (8)
5. Decorated a cake (4)
9. Waterlogged area of land (5)
10. Worried and nervous (7)
11. Disturbance; act of meddling (12)
13. Concurs (6)
14. Removes from one's property (6)
17. Birds of prey (6,6)
20. Series of boat races (7)
21. Flaring stars (5)
22. Free from doubt (4)
23. Moral stories (8)

DOWN

1. Ends; goals (4)
2. Spouse (7)
3. Accomplishments (12)
4. Long sticks; supplies with personnel (6)
6. Headgear of a monarch (5)
7. Spread out (8)
8. Lavish event (12)
12. Dawdlers (8)
15. Plant of the parsley family (7)
16. State of the USA (6)
18. Beer (5)
19. Belonging to a woman (4)

CROSSWORD 100

ACROSS

1. Moral obligation (4)
3. Force lifting something up (8)
9. Strongly influencing later developments (7)
10. Mediterranean island country (5)
11. Assist (3)
12. Jumps (5)
13. Relating to Norway (5)
15. School tests (5)
17. Large body of water (5)
18. Affirmative vote (3)
19. Not with anybody (5)
20. Least difficult (7)
21. Act of hard work (8)
22. In a tense state (4)

DOWN

1. Unemotional (13)
2. Domesticated (5)
4. Steal (6)
5. Vagrancy (12)
6. Discard from memory (7)
7. Party lanterns (anag.) (13)
8. Awkward (12)
14. Absolutely incredible (7)
16. Ratio of reflected to incident light (6)
18. In front (5)

CROSSWORD 101

ACROSS

1. Unnatural and affected (6)
7. Taking away (8)
8. Amp (anag.) (3)
9. Educated (6)
10. Talk wildly (4)
11. Pierces with a horn (5)
13. Caribbean dance (7)
15. Muttered (7)
17. Aromatic plants (5)
21. Effervesce (4)
22. Increase in intensity (4,2)
23. Hog (3)
24. Surrounded on all sides (8)
25. Parts of church towers (6)

DOWN

1. Extremely annoyed (6)
2. Bird of prey (6)
3. Pulls along forcefully (5)
4. Made bare (7)
5. Orchestral piece at the beginning of an opera (8)
6. Not level (6)
12. Steal or misappropriate money (8)
14. Carry on (7)
16. Workers' groups (6)
18. E.g. Eminem (6)
19. Military blockades (6)
20. Curves (5)

CROSSWORD 102

ACROSS

1. Easily achieved (5,2,4)
9. Illegal payment (5)
10. Nevertheless (3)
11. School of thought (5)
12. Male aristocrat (5)
13. Someone paddling a light boat (8)
16. Prosperous; wealthy (4-2-2)
18. Wedding official (5)
21. Water-filled ditches around castles (5)
22. Opposite of high (3)
23. Type of leather (5)
24. Instance of buying or selling (11)

DOWN

2. Form a mental picture (7)
3. Variety show (7)
4. Pungent edible bulbs (6)
5. Free from dirt (5)
6. Skewered meat (5)
7. Boldly (11)
8. Energetically or vigorously (11)
14. Lenient (7)
15. Cigarette constituent (7)
17. Archimedes' famous cry (6)
19. Lumberjack (5)
20. Sticky sap (5)

CROSSWORD 103

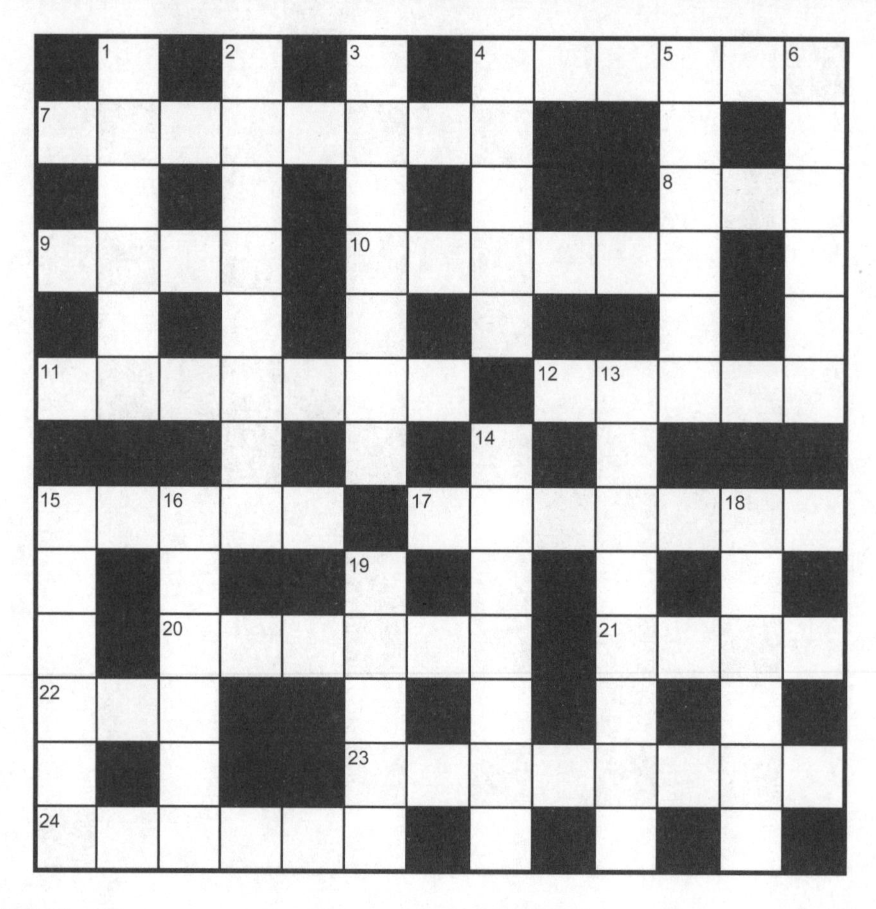

ACROSS

4. Important person (6)
7. Figure of speech (8)
8. Beam of light (3)
9. Killer whale (4)
10. Word that qualifies another (6)
11. Vehicle towed by another (7)
12. Oozes (5)
15. Erased (5)
17. Waterlogged areas of land (7)
20. Assertion (6)
21. Distort (4)
22. Method; road (3)
23. Exclamations of protest (8)
24. Amusingly eccentric (6)

DOWN

1. One who carries something (6)
2. Organism that exploits another (8)
3. Less expensive (7)
4. Courageous (5)
5. Sing in a trilling manner (6)
6. Sculptured symbols (6)
13. Opposite of westward (8)
14. Hammers (7)
15. Conical tent (6)
16. Took part in a game (6)
18. Gained deservedly (6)
19. Descend rapidly (5)

CROSSWORD 104

ACROSS

1. E.g. mallards (5)
4. Grant (7)
7. Small wood (5)
8. Protecting (8)
9. Handle a tool effectively (5)
11. Burden with too much work (8)
15. Recondite (8)
17. Skin marks from wounds (5)
19. Courteous and pleasant (8)
20. Young sheep (5)
21. Declaring to be untrue (7)
22. Trimmed (5)

DOWN

1. Medical analysis (9)
2. One who breaks the rules (7)
3. Contemptuously (7)
4. Yellowish-brown pigment (6)
5. Stress; pull a muscle (6)
6. Lived (anag.) (5)
10. Talked about (9)
12. Overly conceited and arrogant (5-2)
13. Singer (7)
14. Peevish and annoyed (6)
16. Cord (6)
18. Long for (5)

CROSSWORD 105

ACROSS

1. Helps (4)
3. Small part (8)
9. Precede (7)
10. Titles (5)
11. Not staying the same throughout (12)
13. Emotional shock (6)
15. Writing desk (6)
17. Excessively loud (12)
20. Excuse of any kind (5)
21. A rich mine; big prize (7)
22. Anxiousness (8)
23. Case (anag.) (4)

DOWN

1. Causes pain or suffering (8)
2. Style of Greek architecture (5)
4. Smelling horrible (of old food) (6)
5. Building (12)
6. Vast (7)
7. Facial feature (4)
8. Act of sending a message (12)
12. Thieves (8)
14. Subsiding (7)
16. Spherical objects (6)
18. Type of chemical bond (5)
19. Headland (4)

CROSSWORD 106

ACROSS

1. Not arranged neatly (6)
4. Confused noise (6)
9. Tuneful (7)
10. Wooden houses (7)
11. Penitent (5)
12. Eats like a bird (5)
14. Inadequately (5)
15. Increase in size (5)
17. Loosely woven cloth (5)
18. Small hardy range horse (7)
20. Ate a midday meal (7)
21. No one (6)
22. Cowers (anag.) (6)

DOWN

1. Uncover (6)
2. Put up with (8)
3. Father (5)
5. Sad (7)
6. Soft cheese (4)
7. Breaks open (6)
8. Consequently (11)
13. Collaborator on a book (8)
14. Cried plaintively (7)
15. Call for the presence of (6)
16. Piece of grassland (6)
17. Units of heredity (5)
19. Rebuff (4)

CROSSWORD 107

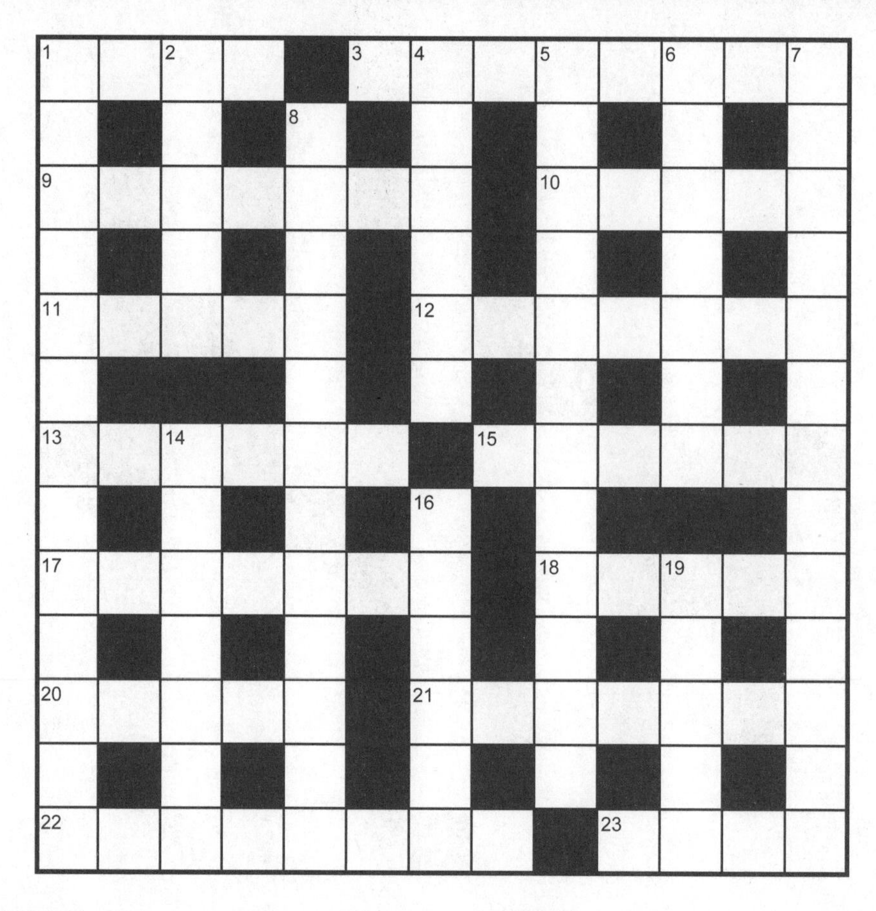

ACROSS

1. Opposite of pull (4)
3. Wristband (8)
9. Declaring (7)
10. Corpulent (5)
11. Theme for a discussion (5)
12. Scoundrels (7)
13. Referencing (6)
15. Contemplate (6)
17. River of southeastern Africa (7)
18. This follows day (5)
20. Dramatic musical work (5)
21. Tortilla rolled around a filling (7)
22. Prestigious (8)
23. Allot a punishment (4)

DOWN

1. Playful trick (9,4)
2. Exclusive newspaper story (5)
4. Pay attention to (6)
5. Long race (5-7)
6. On the sheltered side (7)
7. Hidden store of valuables (8,5)
8. Very sad (12)
14. Storm (7)
16. Feasible (6)
19. Steer (5)

CROSSWORD 108

ACROSS

4. Walk like a duck (6)
7. Type of Eurasian carp (8)
8. Sharp projection (3)
9. Mischievous god in Norse mythology (4)
10. Rut (6)
11. Let out (7)
12. Small pier (5)
15. Break into pieces (5)
17. Musical instrument (7)
20. Urges to act (6)
21. Vale (4)
22. Excavate (3)
23. Trying to heal (8)
24. Without difficulty (6)

DOWN

1. Sullen and gloomy (6)
2. Fans (8)
3. Repulsion (7)
4. Cry of excitement (5)
5. Dispirit (6)
6. Nervously (6)
13. Speed up (8)
14. Gnawing animal (7)
15. Seat on the back of a horse (6)
16. Signal (anag.) (6)
18. Country where one finds Warsaw (6)
19. Fleshy (5)

CROSSWORD 109

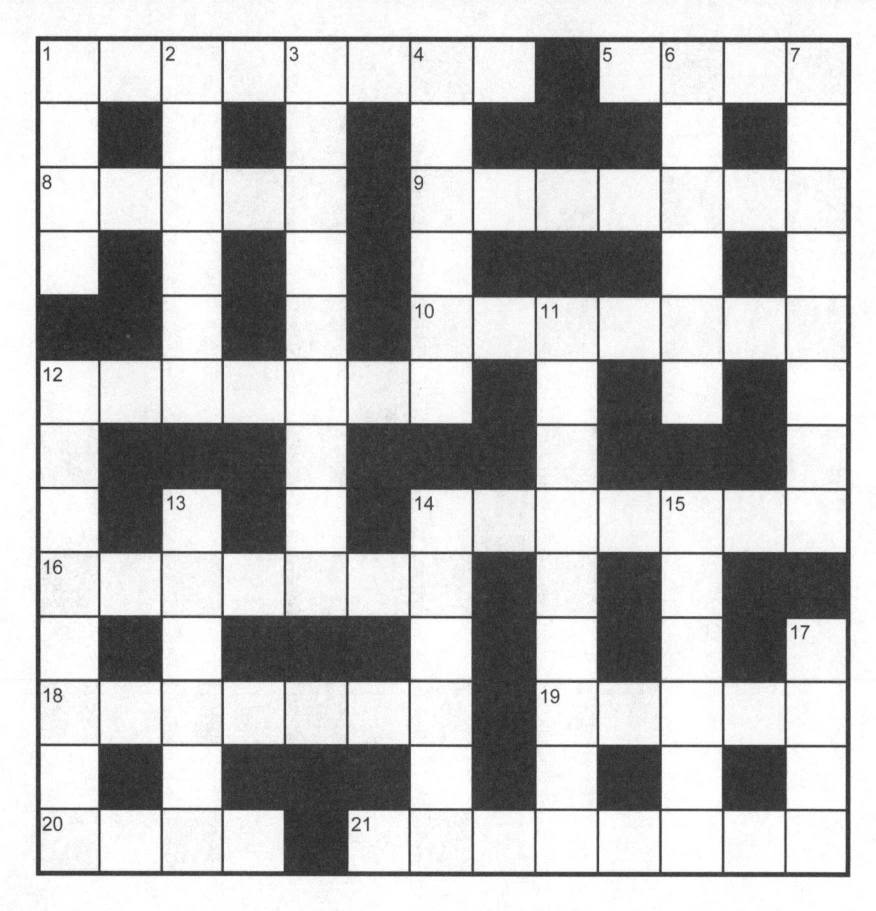

ACROSS

1. Wave or flourish a weapon (8)
5. Small particles of stone (4)
8. Tread heavily (5)
9. Copy (7)
10. Fluids (7)
12. Thing causing outrage (7)
14. Remnant (7)
16. Pig's foot (7)
18. Squabbling (7)
19. Object on which a bird roosts (5)
20. Dote (anag.) (4)
21. Unseemly (8)

DOWN

1. Hit hard (4)
2. Single-celled organism (6)
3. Contingent upon (9)
4. High-pitched (6)
6. Dried grape (6)
7. Cut across (8)
11. Fourfold (9)
12. Take away (8)
13. Language (6)
14. Starting point (6)
15. Come into view (6)
17. Stimulate the appetite (4)

CROSSWORD 110

ACROSS

1. Tears open (4)
3. Admitted (8)
9. Stimulated; urged on (7)
10. Original; new (5)
11. Break up (12)
13. Inform (6)
15. Wading birds (6)
17. Making no money (12)
20. Pulsate (5)
21. Quantities (7)
22. Reassured (8)
23. Put on an item of clothing (4)

DOWN

1. Permanent inhabitant (8)
2. Blocks a hole (5)
4. Large quantity (6)
5. Gathering of people (12)
6. Avid follower (7)
7. Aromatic herb (4)
8. Capable of being moved (12)
12. Evaluator (8)
14. Slender stemlike plant appendage (7)
16. Ablaze (6)
18. Spree (5)
19. Agitate a liquid (4)

CROSSWORD 111

ACROSS

1. Resisted (6)
4. Worldwide (6)
9. Walks for pleasure (7)
10. Film directed by Stephen Gaghan (7)
11. More secure (5)
12. Raises up (5)
14. Long poems derived from ancient tradition (5)
17. The protection of a particular person (5)
19. Staple food (5)
21. Uncovered (7)
23. Part of a church near the altar (7)
24. Spreads out and apart (6)
25. Superior (6)

DOWN

1. Type of engine (6)
2. Number after three (4)
3. All together (2,5)
5. Devices that emit light (5)
6. Large amphibian (8)
7. Opposite of winners (6)
8. Radically (11)
13. Luminous meteor (8)
15. Young pilchard (7)
16. Calculating machine (6)
18. Female sibling (6)
20. Decompose (5)
22. Door by which you leave a building (4)

CROSSWORD 112

ACROSS

1. Disturb (8)
5. Long poem (4)
9. The papal court (5)
10. Make damp (7)
11. Inclination (7)
12. Variety or kind (5)
13. Musical dramas (6)
14. Surgical knife (6)
17. Store of hoarded wealth (5)
19. Fell over (7)
20. Marked with spots (7)
21. Steer (anag.) (5)
22. Finishes (4)
23. Teaches (8)

DOWN

1. Uneasy (13)
2. Odd (7)
3. Clearness (12)
4. Boundaries (6)
6. Feign (3,2)
7. Satisfaction (13)
8. Graphical (12)
15. Guilty person (7)
16. Remained (6)
18. Egg-shaped solid (5)

CROSSWORD 113

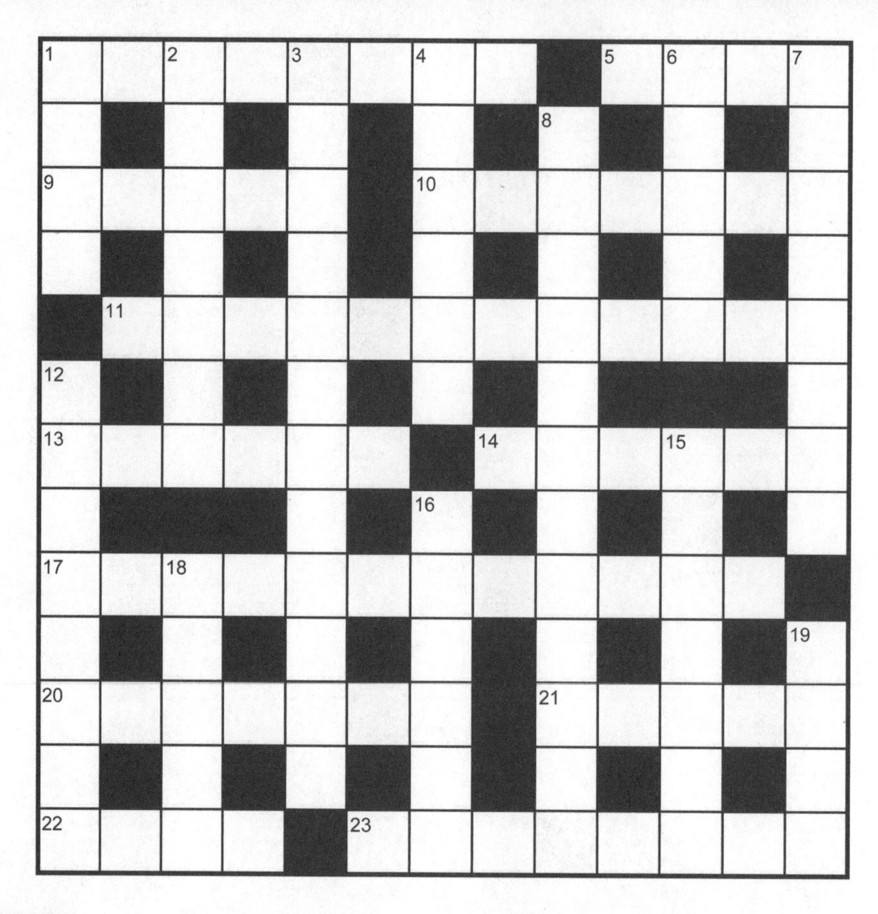

ACROSS

1. Having no worries (8)
5. Cab (4)
9. Aqualung (5)
10. Error in printing or writing (7)
11. Easy-going (4-8)
13. Outcome (6)
14. Wears away (6)
17. Intended to attract notice (12)
20. Segmented worm (7)
21. Wanderer (5)
22. Mission (4)
23. Announces formally (8)

DOWN

1. Portfolio (4)
2. Loud and hoarse (7)
3. Deceitfully (12)
4. Ten plus one (6)
6. Later (5)
7. Lacking humility (8)
8. Commensurate (12)
12. Conceited (8)
15. Percussion musician (7)
16. Manage; hold (6)
18. Holding or grasping device (5)
19. Chances of winning (4)

CROSSWORD 114

ACROSS

1. Decorate with a raised design (6)
4. Pieces of bread (6)
9. Not friendly (7)
10. Horse's fodder container (7)
11. Soothes (5)
12. Recently (5)
14. Church songs (5)
15. Fad (5)
17. Circumference (5)
18. Low protective wall (7)
20. Reaches a destination (7)
21. Resides (6)
22. Approached (6)

DOWN

1. Morals (6)
2. Roman building (8)
3. Sinks (anag.) (5)
5. Periods of instruction (7)
6. Freshwater game fish (4)
7. Unkempt (of hair) (6)
8. Nostalgic (11)
13. In any place (8)
14. Useful (7)
15. Emulated (6)
16. Pursued (6)
17. Ravine (5)
19. Symbol with magic significance (4)

CROSSWORD 115

ACROSS

4. Japanese dress (6)
7. Place (8)
8. Utter (3)
9. Present (4)
10. Pouch (6)
11. Making sore by rubbing (7)
12. Broaden (5)
15. Prison compartments (5)
17. Portions of time (7)
20. Uncover (6)
21. Doing little (4)
22. Removed from sight (3)
23. Drug that treats a disease (8)
24. Lymphoid organ (6)

DOWN

1. Burnish (6)
2. Jovial (8)
3. Tearing (7)
4. Bump into (5)
5. Expelled from office (6)
6. Gas we breathe (6)
13. Language used by an individual (8)
14. Isolate (7)
15. Official seal (6)
16. Noisily (6)
18. Multiples of twelve (6)
19. Sets of players (5)

CROSSWORD 116

ACROSS

1. Hostages (8)
5. Sent by (4)
8. Place where something happens (5)
9. Anxious and afraid (7)
10. Female deity (7)
12. Enlarge (7)
14. Neck-warming garments (7)
16. Volcanic crater (7)
18. Tallier (anag.) (7)
19. Asian pepper plant (5)
20. Regretted (4)
21. Most saccharine (8)

DOWN

1. Underground chamber (4)
2. Longing for (6)
3. Intoxicate (9)
4. Representation of a person (6)
6. Kicked or hit hard (6)
7. Thick dark syrup (8)
11. Open to question (9)
12. Brawny (8)
13. Happy; carefree (6)
14. Jaundiced (6)
15. Moral excellence (6)
17. Thin narrow piece of wood (4)

CROSSWORD 117

ACROSS

1. Abounding (8)
5. Leaf (anag.) (4)
9. Juicy fruits (5)
10. Bring a law into effect again (2-5)
11. Chopping (5)
12. Cry (3)
13. Ascended (5)
15. Cairo is in this country (5)
17. Not on (3)
19. Send someone to a medical specialist (5)
20. Helped to happen (7)
21. Type of jazz (5)
22. Having pains (4)
23. Foliage (8)

DOWN

1. The first and the last (5,3,5)
2. Dissimilar (7)
3. Unpleasant (12)
4. Jitters (6)
6. Leashes (5)
7. Account of one's own life (13)
8. Clearly evident (12)
14. Friendly (7)
16. Over there (6)
18. Burst of light (5)

CROSSWORD 118

ACROSS

1. Eye condition (8)
5. Mark left from a wound (4)
9. Indian monetary unit (5)
10. Books forming a whole work (7)
11. Easy targets (7,5)
13. Flourish (6)
14. Frail (6)
17. Heartbroken (12)
20. People insisting on adherence to traditional rules (7)
21. Ray (5)
22. Too; in addition (4)
23. Most annoyed (8)

DOWN

1. Microscopic organism (4)
2. A ripple (anag.) (7)
3. Inventiveness (12)
4. Affecting the emotions (6)
6. Funny person (5)
7. Held out against (8)
8. Heavy long-handled tool (12)
12. Country in northeastern Africa (8)
15. Emotional stability (7)
16. Make less tight (6)
18. Subdivision of an army (5)
19. Immense (4)

CROSSWORD 119

ACROSS

1. Occupancy (11)
9. Narrow opening (5)
10. Type of statistical chart (3)
11. Smash into another vehicle (5)
12. Extinct birds (5)
13. Broadcast (8)
16. Creature that eats both meat and plants (8)
18. Boasts (5)
21. Large waterbird (5)
22. Sap (anag.) (3)
23. Legal process (5)
24. Act of publishing in several places (11)

DOWN

2. Newsworthy (7)
3. Repository (7)
4. Expressions (6)
5. Put a question to (5)
6. God of love (5)
7. Disturb the status quo (4,3,4)
8. Quantification (11)
14. Lock of curly hair (7)
15. Country in northwestern Africa (7)
17. Lunatic (6)
19. Sufficiently (5)
20. Satisfied a desire (5)

CROSSWORD 120

ACROSS

1. Rodent (8)
5. Lose one's footing (4)
8. Group of activists (5)
9. Live longer than (7)
10. Issue for sale (7)
12. Respects (7)
14. Book of the Bible (7)
16. Virtuoso solo passage (7)
18. Living in water (7)
19. State of nervous excitement (5)
20. Extremities of the feet (4)
21. Unsporting activity (4,4)

DOWN

1. Gaming cubes (4)
2. Element discovered by the Curies (6)
3. In the red (9)
4. Exclusive stories (6)
6. Introduction (4-2)
7. Large jugs (8)
11. Abundant (9)
12. Flying machine (8)
13. Request earnestly (6)
14. South American cowboy (6)
15. Cry and sniffle (6)
17. Wear away (4)

CROSSWORD 121

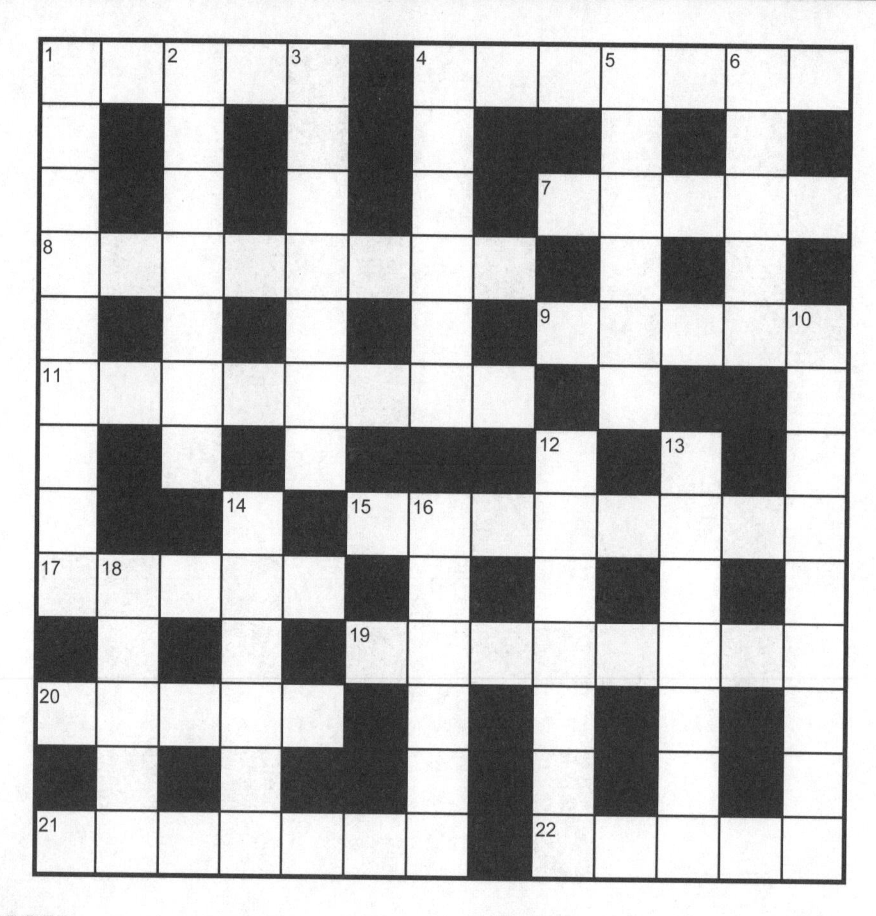

ACROSS

1. Device for sharpening razors (5)
4. Embellish (7)
7. Opposite of sink (5)
8. Fence of stakes (8)
9. Explosive devices (5)
11. Vertical flues (8)
15. Sailing vessel (8)
17. Steered a car (5)
19. Spanish dance (8)
20. Nose of an animal (5)
21. Shuns (7)
22. Spirited horse (5)

DOWN

1. Thought that (9)
2. Get back (7)
3. Gift (7)
4. Lovingly (6)
5. Scottish sheep dog (6)
6. Individual piece of snow (5)
10. Right side of a boat (9)
12. Layouts; styles (7)
13. Entrap (7)
14. Admit openly (6)
16. Hardened part of the skin (6)
18. Steps of a ladder (5)

CROSSWORD 122

ACROSS

1. Compensate for (6)
4. Falls out unintentionally (6)
9. Tenth month of the year (7)
10. E.g. from Moscow (7)
11. Paces (5)
12. Killer whales (5)
14. Delicious (5)
17. Gives out (5)
19. Head monk of an abbey (5)
21. Oval shape (7)
23. Fishermen (7)
24. Evaluate (6)
25. Accepted (6)

DOWN

1. Exaggerate (6)
2. Coniferous trees (4)
3. Creepiest (7)
5. Golf shots (5)
6. Opera texts (8)
7. State of mental strain (6)
8. Brevity in expressing oneself (11)
13. Vegetables (8)
15. Screaming (7)
16. Country in Central America (6)
18. Appeared to be (6)
20. Arduous journeys (5)
22. Fish (4)

CROSSWORD 123

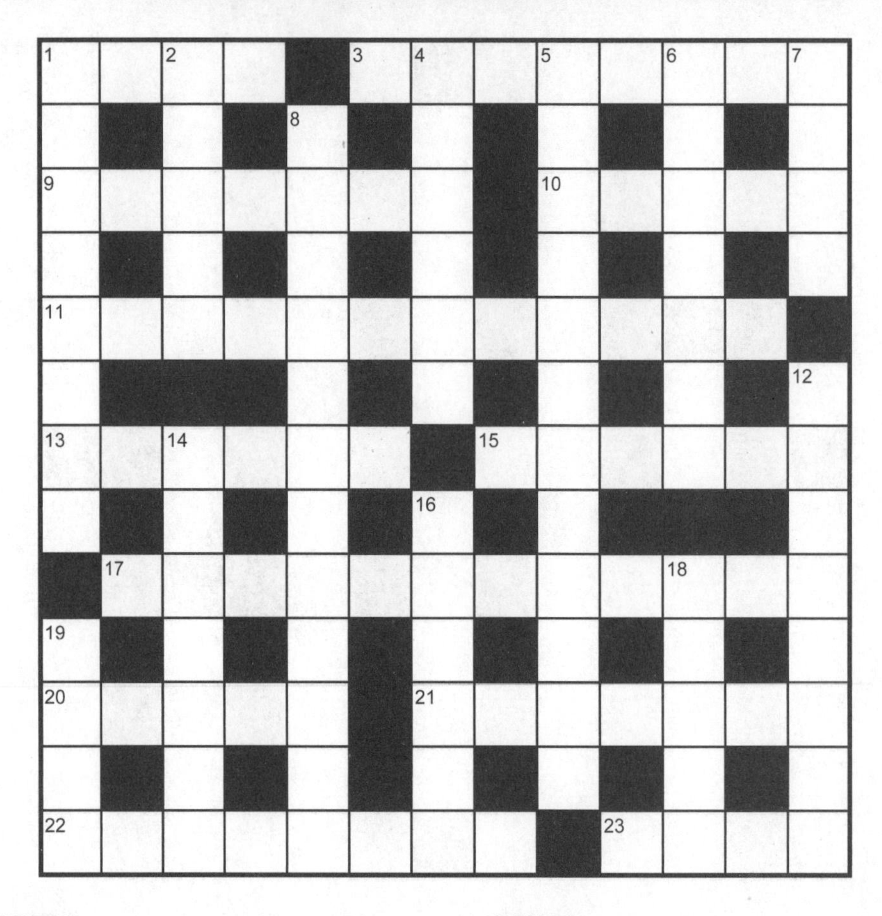

ACROSS

1. Type of starch (4)
3. Went before (8)
9. Sculptures (7)
10. Cuts slightly (5)
11. Derived from past events (12)
13. Legitimate (6)
15. Beat with the fists (6)
17. Female school boss (12)
20. Consumed (5)
21. Small-scale model (7)
22. Gratification (8)
23. Resist; refuse to obey (4)

DOWN

1. Sororal (8)
2. Seize firmly (5)
4. Hurries (6)
5. Building (12)
6. Speak rhetorically (7)
7. Run quickly (4)
8. Environment (12)
12. Alphabetical list of terms (8)
14. Grapple with (7)
16. Bit of partly burnt wood (6)
18. Fill with high spirits (5)
19. Shed tears (4)

CROSSWORD 124

ACROSS

1. Aromatic shrub (8)
5. Sudden quick movement (4)
9. Explore or examine (5)
10. Uncovers (7)
11. Public speakers (7)
12. Speed (5)
13. One of the halogens (6)
14. Firmly fixed (6)
17. Valuable thing or person (5)
19. Gets away (7)
20. Notable feat (7)
21. Ridge (5)
22. Ivy League university (4)
23. Uses again (8)

DOWN

1. Roughly (13)
2. Garment worn by dancers (7)
3. Knowledge of a future event (12)
4. Series of subject lessons (6)
6. Endures (5)
7. Blandness (13)
8. Vehemently (12)
15. Having two feet (7)
16. Fitness; condition (6)
18. Flower part (5)

CROSSWORD 125

ACROSS

1. Strong alcoholic spirit (6)
4. Treelike grass (6)
9. Sleep (4-3)
10. Clothes for washing (7)
11. Stories (5)
12. Really angry (5)
14. Leaps over a rope (5)
15. E.g. incisors and molars (5)
17. Lump or bump (5)
18. Tentacled cephalopod (7)
20. Living in another's home (7)
21. Fast (6)
22. Regime (anag.) (6)

DOWN

1. Attacks on all sides (6)
2. Like an eagle (8)
3. Sediment (5)
5. Plants that live a year or less (7)
6. Daring (4)
7. Complied with orders (6)
8. Delightfully (11)
13. Leaping up or over (8)
14. Sent by sea (7)
15. Soldiers (6)
16. Style of popular music (6)
17. Darken (5)
19. Musical or vocal sound (4)

CROSSWORD 126

ACROSS

4. Keep secret (4,2)
7. All-round view (8)
8. Animal doctor (3)
9. Thick mist (4)
10. Mark of disgrace (6)
11. Tropical disease (7)
12. Modify (5)
15. Attack on all sides (5)
17. Edge of a road (7)
20. Willow twigs (6)
21. Bone of the forearm (4)
22. Line; argument (3)
23. Wanderer (8)
24. Hay-cutting tool (6)

DOWN

1. Small pit or cavity (6)
2. Piece of furniture (8)
3. Root vegetable (7)
4. Established custom (5)
5. Capital of Cuba (6)
6. Powerful (6)
13. Upsets; agitates (8)
14. Corridor (7)
15. Promotional book descriptions (6)
16. Sedately (6)
18. Act of eating out (6)
19. Annoy (5)

CROSSWORD 127

ACROSS

1. Attach (6)
7. Based on reason (8)
8. Wet soil (3)
9. Makes amends for (6)
10. Work hard (4)
11. Study (anag.) (5)
13. Deteriorate (7)
15. Stiff and formal (7)
17. Walks up and down (5)
21. White aquatic bird (4)
22. Without pattern (6)
23. Periodic publication (abbrev.) (3)
24. Medieval weapon (8)
25. Sets of rooms (6)

DOWN

1. Nut-like seed that marzipan is made from (6)
2. Foot levers (6)
3. Male bee (5)
4. Stored away (7)
5. Mexican pancake (8)
6. Slander (6)
12. Sharpness (of taste) (8)
14. Thus; as a result (7)
16. Tall castle structures (6)
18. Dedicate (6)
19. Marsh plants (6)
20. Bites at persistently (5)

CROSSWORD 128

1		2		3		4		■	5	6		7
	■		■		■		■	8	■		■	
9					■	10						
	■		■		■		■		■		■	
11							■	12				
	■		■		■		■		■	■	■	
13						■	14			15		
	■	■	■		■	16	■		■		■	
17		18			■	19						
	■		■		■		■		■		■	
20							■	21				
	■		■		■		■		■		■	
22				■	23							

ACROSS

1. One liquid dispersed in another (8)
5. Spiritual teacher (4)
9. Largest moon of Saturn (5)
10. Attributed to (7)
11. A Roman Catholic devotion (7)
12. Tumbles (5)
13. Top aim (anag.) (6)
14. US state of islands (6)
17. Trembling poplar (5)
19. Morally right (7)
20. In the place of (7)
21. Buffalo (5)
22. Geek (4)
23. Relied on (8)

DOWN

1. Act of extending by inference (13)
2. Tense (7)
3. Very determined (6-6)
4. Serving no functional purpose (6)
6. Up to the time when (5)
7. Lacking in control (13)
8. Easy to converse with (12)
15. Charged with a crime (7)
16. Interfere (6)
18. Show-off (5)

CROSSWORD 129

ACROSS

1. Period of celebration (8)
5. Legendary story (4)
9. Obsession (5)
10. Brazilian dance (7)
11. Brusque and surly (12)
13. Not disposed to cheating (6)
14. Functional (6)
17. Constantly; always (12)
20. Dilemma (7)
21. Spin quickly (5)
22. Peas (anag.) (4)
23. Sears (8)

DOWN

1. Renown (4)
2. Reddening of the skin (7)
3. Not allowable (12)
4. Refer to indirectly (6)
6. Long for (5)
7. Broad and strongly built (8)
8. Imitator (12)
12. Yellowish edible seed (8)
15. Optimistic about something (7)
16. Infinitesimally small (6)
18. Crevices (5)
19. Unfortunately (4)

CROSSWORD 130

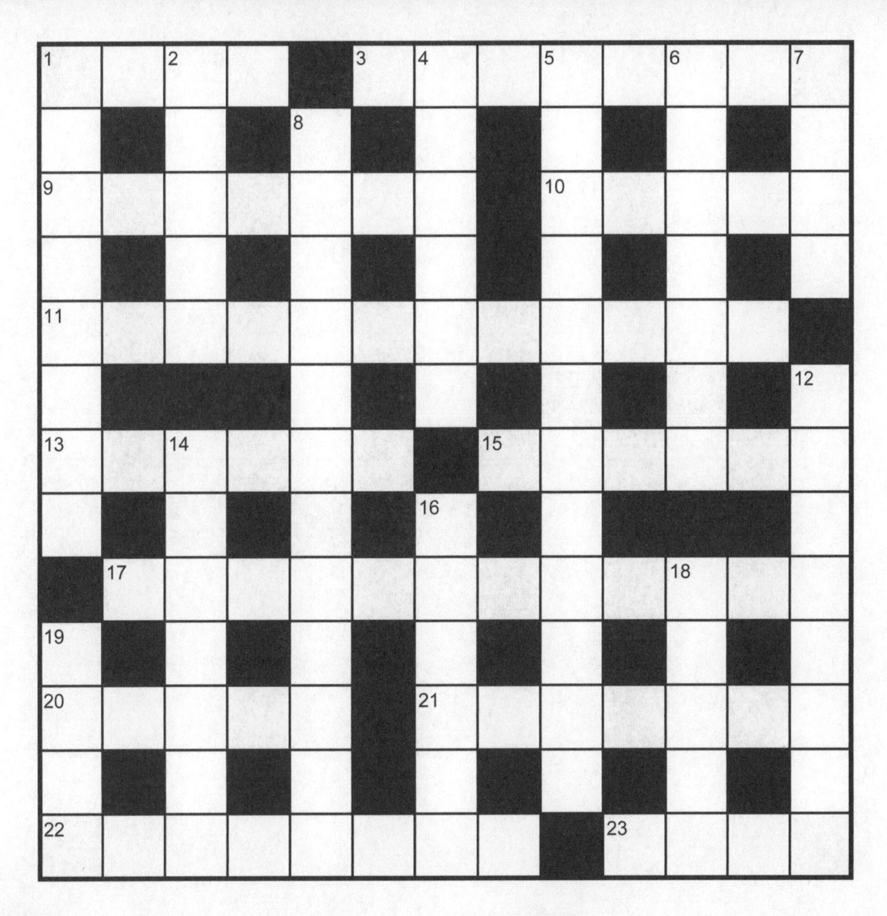

ACROSS

1. Has to (4)
3. Household warming device (8)
9. Finished (3,4)
10. Freight (5)
11. Clothing such as a vest (12)
13. Make beloved (6)
15. Pollute (6)
17. Quarrelsome and uncooperative (12)
20. Dance club (5)
21. Apparatus (7)
22. Scantily (8)
23. Flightless birds (4)

DOWN

1. Gauges (8)
2. Dish of raw vegetables (5)
4. Breathing passage (6)
5. Ineptness (12)
6. Capital of Ontario (7)
7. Underground plant part (4)
8. Unnecessarily careful (12)
12. Fabric strips for covering wounds (8)
14. Salt lake in the Jordan valley (4,3)
16. Type of living organism (6)
18. General hatred (5)
19. Lyric poems (4)

CROSSWORD 131

ACROSS

1. Device used to increase thrust (11)
9. Sticky yellowish substance (3)
10. Seeped (5)
11. Dividing boundaries (5)
12. Toy bear (5)
13. Sinking down (8)
16. Revolted (8)
18. Move out of the way (5)
20. Friendship (5)
21. Edible substances (5)
22. Small social insect (3)
23. Having good intentions (4-7)

DOWN

2. Deceived (5)
3. Dark wood (5)
4. Type of market (6)
5. Huge coniferous tree (7)
6. Cry out (7)
7. European country (11)
8. Homework tasks (11)
14. Slanting (7)
15. Humorous; done in fun (7)
17. Repeat performance (6)
18. Water container (5)
19. Looking tired (5)

CROSSWORD 132

ACROSS

1. Sweeping implements (6)
4. Fashioned (6)
9. Routine dental examination (5-2)
10. Item used by asthma sufferers (7)
11. E.g. beef and lamb (5)
12. Sour substances (5)
14. Preclude (5)
15. Close-fitting garments (5)
17. Musical note (5)
18. Harmonious relationship (7)
20. Car motors (7)
21. Spirited horses (6)
22. Subsidiary action (6)

DOWN

1. Develop into (6)
2. Uses a piece of machinery (8)
3. Creates (5)
5. Impetuous person (7)
6. Tablet (4)
7. Detritus (6)
8. Dogmatic (11)
13. Very annoying (8)
14. Shock with wonder (7)
15. As compared to (6)
16. Contemptibly small (6)
17. Not fitting closely (5)
19. Prod (4)

CROSSWORD 133

ACROSS

1. Cloth worn around the waist (4)
3. Ornamental climbing plant (8)
9. More spacious (7)
10. Nearby (5)
11. Principle of morality (5)
12. Bring to life (7)
13. Pressing keys (6)
15. Opposite of an acid (6)
17. Submarine weapon (7)
18. Identical copy (5)
20. Not concealed (5)
21. Warmest (7)
22. Closure of a system or factory (8)
23. Crazy (4)

DOWN

1. Clandestine (13)
2. Apathy (5)
4. Immature of its kind (of insects) (6)
5. A large number (12)
6. Musical composition (7)
7. Obviously (4-9)
8. Unhappy (12)
14. Upstart; one who has recently gained wealth (7)
16. Person who fails to turn up (2-4)
19. Last Greek letter (5)

CROSSWORD 134

ACROSS

1. Blow loudly (4)
3. Needed (8)
9. Jumps up suddenly (7)
10. Laud (5)
11. Street (12)
13. Outdoes (6)
15. Spanish festival (6)
17. Knowing more than one language (12)
20. Speak in public without preparation (2-3)
21. Edible jelly (7)
22. Remittances (8)
23. Sea eagle (4)

DOWN

1. Waver (8)
2. Refrain from (5)
4. Banner or flag (6)
5. Intuitively designed (of a system) (4-8)
6. Comes back (7)
7. As expected (4)
8. Unfriendly (12)
12. Way of speaking (8)
14. Normally (7)
16. Small in degree (6)
18. Complete; absolute (5)
19. Breathe convulsively (4)

CROSSWORD 135

ACROSS

1. Inspired by reverence (4)
3. Capable of being satisfied (8)
9. Astronomical units (7)
10. Dry red wine (5)
11. Group of eight (5)
12. Grating (7)
13. Innate (6)
15. Act of union (6)
17. Severely simple (7)
18. Browned bread (5)
20. Cake decoration (5)
21. Called on (7)
22. Symbols representing musical notes (8)
23. Refuse to admit (4)

DOWN

1. An inexact result (13)
2. Small heron (5)
4. State confidently (6)
5. Regardless of (12)
6. Reservation (7)
7. In an inflated manner (13)
8. Boxing class division (12)
14. Player of an instrument that is low in pitch (7)
16. Sheep known for its wool (6)
19. Foot joint (5)

CROSSWORD 136

ACROSS

1. Intertwined segment of rope (4)
3. Whipped (8)
9. Countries (7)
10. Not together (5)
11. Malfunction or fail (of an electrical device) (5-7)
13. Figure of speech (6)
15. Seem (6)
17. Sensory system used by dolphins (12)
20. Eighth Greek letter (5)
21. Diacritical marks (7)
22. Moving at speed (8)
23. Average value (4)

DOWN

1. Extra large (4-4)
2. Surpass (5)
4. Of the universe (6)
5. Intolerable (12)
6. Igneous rock (7)
7. Be foolishly fond of (4)
8. Characteristic of the present (12)
12. Male relation (8)
14. Uncertain (7)
16. Vertical pillar (6)
18. Accustom to something (5)
19. Engrave with acid (4)

CROSSWORD 137

ACROSS

1. Skin irritation (4)
3. Fantastic (8)
9. Dried grapes (7)
10. Large intestine (5)
11. Break the rules (5)
12. Taller and thinner (7)
13. Quirk (6)
15. Raised platforms (6)
17. Refills (7)
18. Hurled away (5)
20. Monster (5)
21. Word opposite in meaning to another (7)
22. Fully (8)
23. Keep away from (4)

DOWN

1. Irretrievable (13)
2. Reproach (5)
4. Frames used by artists (6)
5. Build up again from parts (12)
6. Recording on tape (7)
7. Female politician in the US (13)
8. Sound of quick light steps (6-6)
14. Chivalrous (7)
16. Attack someone (6)
19. Cattle-breeding farm (5)

CROSSWORD 138

ACROSS

1. Cosmetic treatment of the feet (8)
5. Egg-shaped (4)
9. Compassion (5)
10. The small details of something (7)
11. In a sparing manner (12)
14. Insect that can sting (3)
15. Donor (5)
16. Small green vegetable (3)
17. Inflexible (12)
20. Instructor (7)
22. Hold responsible (5)
23. Fine powder (4)
24. Disapproved of (8)

DOWN

1. Device for inflating tyres (4)
2. Very long lasting (7)
3. Science of deciphering codes (12)
4. Male sheep (3)
6. Stove (anag.) (5)
7. A period of 366 days (4,4)
8. Incurably bad (12)
12. Shifts (5)
13. Done away with (8)
16. Tapering flag (7)
18. Melts (5)
19. Transmit (4)
21. Steal (3)

CROSSWORD 139

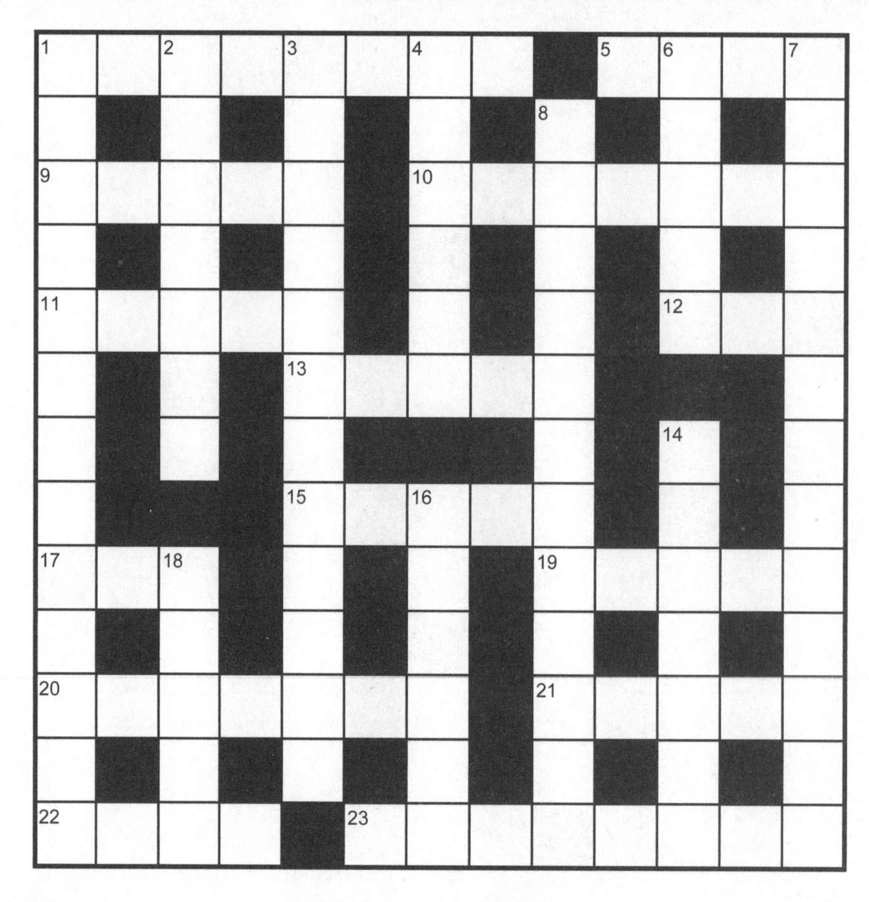

ACROSS

1. Forebear (8)
5. Product made from soya beans (4)
9. Ironic metaphor (5)
10. People who rent property (7)
11. Grasp tightly (5)
12. Not bright; darken (3)
13. Timepiece (5)
15. Folded back part of a coat (5)
17. Seabird (3)
19. Covered with water (5)
20. Person learning a skill (7)
21. Inactive (5)
22. Sweet dessert (4)
23. Inducing sleep (8)

DOWN

1. Not living up to expectations (13)
2. Stately hymn tune (7)
3. Somnambulism (12)
4. Yield (6)
6. Possessed (5)
7. Uncaring (13)
8. Complete destruction (12)
14. Least fresh (7)
16. Entirely (6)
18. Natural talent (5)

CROSSWORD 140

ACROSS

1. Conflict (6)
4. Material; textile (6)
9. Waterfall (7)
10. Inventor (7)
11. Hunt (5)
12. Curbs (5)
14. Grips with the teeth (5)
15. Freedom from war (5)
17. Bore into (5)
18. Come out on top (7)
20. Stands about idly (7)
21. Seat for two or more persons (6)
22. Striped animals (6)

DOWN

1. Arm muscle (6)
2. State of Australia (8)
3. Slender freshwater fish (5)
5. Is present at (7)
6. Public disturbance (4)
7. Cloud type (6)
8. Dishonestly (11)
13. Person who rebels (8)
14. Due to the fact that (7)
15. Small songbirds (6)
16. Advantages (6)
17. Operate a motor vehicle (5)
19. Give out (4)

CROSSWORD 141

ACROSS

1. Alert and thinking cogently (5-6)
9. Arrive at (5)
10. First woman (3)
11. The reproduction of sound (5)
12. Type of verse (5)
13. Retort (8)
16. Type of pasta (8)
18. Ascends (5)
21. Undertaking something (5)
22. Belonging to us (3)
23. Hawaiian greeting (5)
24. Act of staying away from work (11)

DOWN

2. Noisiest (7)
3. With reference to (7)
4. Interruption or gap (6)
5. Loathe (5)
6. Military opponent (5)
7. One who presides over a meeting (11)
8. Misleadingly (11)
14. Golfing measure of distance (7)
15. Reasons for action (7)
17. Classify (6)
19. Clean thoroughly; vegetation (5)
20. Tremble (5)

CROSSWORD 142

ACROSS

1. Gangs (4)
3. Capable of happening (8)
9. Long-lasting and recurrent (7)
10. Steals (5)
11. Understandably (12)
14. Title of a married woman (3)
16. Unexpected plot element (5)
17. Command to a horse (3)
18. Large grocery stores (12)
21. Breed of dog (5)
22. Stronghold (7)
23. Have a different opinion (8)
24. Require (4)

DOWN

1. Exaggerated masculinity (8)
2. Destroyed by fire (5)
4. Monstrous humanoid creature (3)
5. Narcissism (4-8)
6. Distribute illicitly (7)
7. Compass point (4)
8. Uncomplimentary (12)
12. Form of expression (5)
13. Diminished (8)
15. Multiplies a number by itself (7)
19. Expulsion (5)
20. Move fast in a straight line (4)
22. Farewell remark (3)

CROSSWORD 143

ACROSS

1. A reduction in price (8)
5. Spheres (4)
8. Swerves off course (5)
9. Type of computer (7)
10. More saccharine (7)
12. Brave (7)
14. Person who accumulates things (7)
16. Master of ceremonies (7)
18. Termite (anag.) (7)
19. Spoken for (5)
20. Turn or slide violently (of a vehicle) (4)
21. Create an account deficit (8)

DOWN

1. Relocate (4)
2. Expressing regret (6)
3. Worth having (9)
4. Broadest (6)
6. Revolve (6)
7. Higher in rank (8)
11. Large digging machine (9)
12. Coupons (8)
13. Extensive domain (6)
14. History play by Shakespeare (5,1)
15. Not as light (6)
17. Afresh (4)

CROSSWORD 144

ACROSS

1. Giant aerial (anag.) (11)
9. Silent (3)
10. Goodbye (Spanish) (5)
11. Assertion (5)
12. Suitably (5)
13. Demote (8)
16. Intestines of an animal (8)
18. Sheikhdom on the Persian Gulf (5)
20. Domesticates (5)
21. Chop meat into very small pieces (5)
22. Wager (3)
23. Leader in a race (5,6)

DOWN

2. The entire scale (5)
3. Given to disclosing secrets (5)
4. Sharp pain (6)
5. Saves from danger (7)
6. Yearbook (7)
7. Restlessly (11)
8. Mark an event (11)
14. Speak haltingly (7)
15. Rower (7)
17. Lender (6)
18. Female sovereign (5)
19. Piece of furniture (5)

CROSSWORD 145

ACROSS

1. Contract of insurance (6)
4. Of practical benefit (6)
9. Land with fruit trees (7)
10. Conquer by force (7)
11. Piece of bread (5)
12. Grew fainter (5)
14. Leaves (5)
17. Genuflected (5)
19. Expels from a position (5)
21. Of great size (7)
23. Vent for molten lava (7)
24. Constructs (6)
25. Belonging to an earlier time (6)

DOWN

1. Bribe (6)
2. Lien (anag.) (4)
3. An acted riddle (7)
5. Large bags (5)
6. Capable of being done (8)
7. Small houses (6)
8. Person who gives something (11)
13. Disintegrate (8)
15. Incomplete or lacking in detail (7)
16. Famous French museum (6)
18. Excite agreeably (6)
20. Begin (5)
22. Emperor of Rome 54-68 AD (4)

CROSSWORD 146

ACROSS

1. Refuge (8)
5. Narrow point of land projecting into water (4)
9. Lawful (5)
10. Genuine (7)
11. Firm rebuke (12)
13. Situated within a building (6)
14. Items of value (6)
17. Especially (12)
20. Set apart (7)
21. Sense experience (5)
22. Skirt worn by ballerinas (4)
23. Soft leather shoe (8)

DOWN

1. Cease moving (4)
2. Definite; unquestionable (7)
3. Extremely large (12)
4. Descend down a rock face (6)
6. Part of (5)
7. A formal exposition (8)
8. Very eager; keen (12)
12. Centre (8)
15. Signs up (7)
16. Dinner jacket (6)
18. Settle for sleep (of birds) (5)
19. Incline (4)

CROSSWORD 147

ACROSS

1. Item that measures temperature (11)
9. Smack (3)
10. Animal life of a region (5)
11. Absolute (5)
12. Enumerates (5)
13. Permeable (8)
16. Trained user of a machine (8)
18. Sorceress (5)
20. Small cabin (5)
21. Rips (5)
22. Pro (3)
23. Betray (6-5)

DOWN

2. Dislikes intensely (5)
3. Fissures (5)
4. Body of work (6)
5. Elusive (7)
6. Tallest species of penguin (7)
7. E.g. Plato (11)
8. Keyboard instrument (11)
14. Fear of heights (7)
15. Water container (7)
17. Elaborately adorned (6)
18. Smarter (5)
19. Bunches (5)

CROSSWORD 148

ACROSS

1. Helper; assistant (4)
3. A division between people (8)
9. European country (7)
10. Blunder (5)
11. Relating to numbers (12)
13. Plant with oil rich seeds (6)
15. Long and very narrow (6)
17. Strong censure (12)
20. Cuban folk dance (5)
21. Decipher (7)
22. Social insect (8)
23. Group of countries in an alliance (4)

DOWN

1. Creating needless panic (8)
2. First appearance (5)
4. Item of neckwear (6)
5. Importance (12)
6. Catch fire (7)
7. Christmas (4)
8. Middleman (12)
12. Frenzied (8)
14. Impresario (7)
16. Smear or blur (6)
18. Pastoral poem (5)
19. Curved shape (4)

CROSSWORD 149

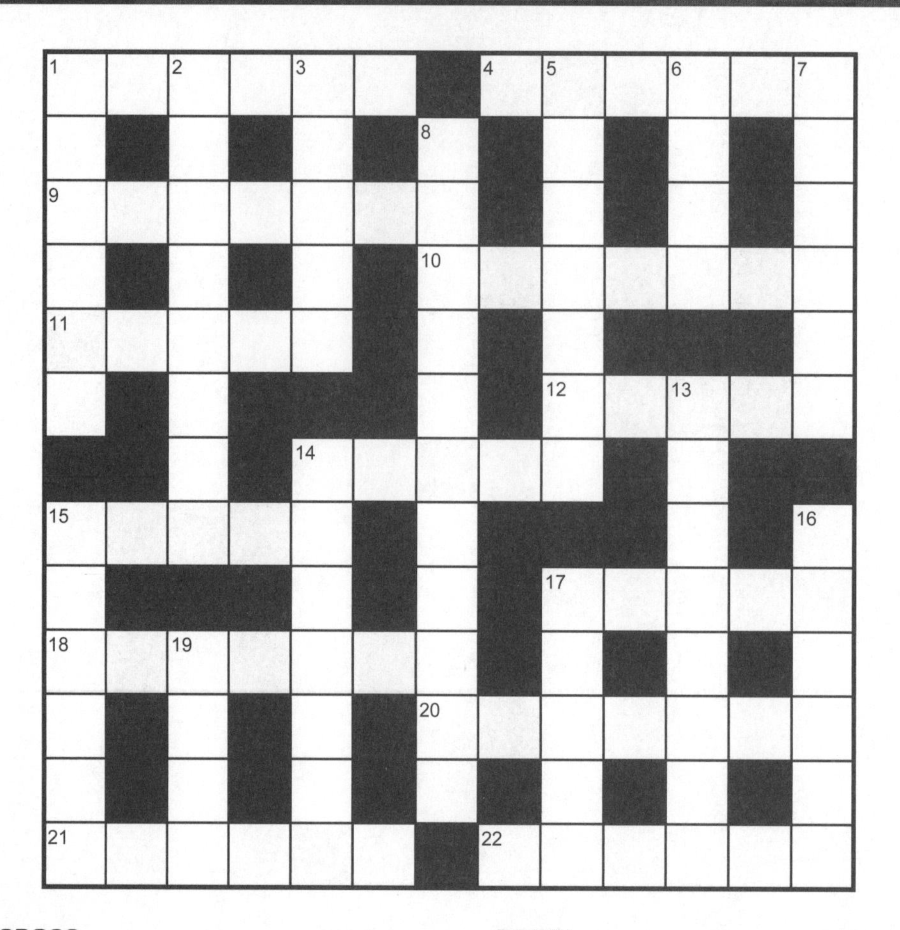

ACROSS

1. Surprise attack (6)
4. Morsels of food (6)
9. Sad and abandoned (7)
10. Sharp tooth (7)
11. Exchange of tennis strokes (5)
12. Solids with six equal square faces (5)
14. Holy person (5)
15. Craftily (5)
17. Move effortlessly through air (5)
18. Navigational instrument (7)
20. Swells (7)
21. Chaos (6)
22. Worshipped (6)

DOWN

1. Have sufficient money to pay for (6)
2. Type of crime (8)
3. Ostentatious (5)
5. Make by mixing ingredients (7)
6. Greek god of war (4)
7. Disdains (6)
8. Unrestrained (11)
13. Novice (8)
14. Junction between nerve cells (7)
15. A complex whole (6)
16. Hired out (6)
17. Looked at open-mouthed (5)
19. Type of high-energy radiation (1-3)

CROSSWORD 150

ACROSS

1. E.g. share news (11)
9. Raised floor or platform (5)
10. Mountain pass (3)
11. Sulks (5)
12. Moist stiff mixture (5)
13. Bouquets (8)
16. Person highly skilled in music (8)
18. Loose garments (5)
21. Challenged (5)
22. Burdensome charge (3)
23. Home (5)
24. Constant (11)

DOWN

2. Distant settlement (7)
3. The rubbing of muscles (7)
4. Almost (6)
5. Faint bird cry (5)
6. Small nails (5)
7. Basic entitlements for all (5,6)
8. Of noble birth (4-7)
14. Learner (7)
15. Become husky (of a voice) (7)
17. Chant; speak solemnly (6)
19. Pallid (5)
20. E.g. square or circle (5)

CROSSWORD 151

ACROSS

1. Succulent plant (6)
7. Fearless and brave (8)
8. Small truck (3)
9. Optical (6)
10. Belonging to us (4)
11. Cabs (5)
13. Mischief (7)
15. Coal bucket (7)
17. Projecting horizontal ledge (5)
21. Unwrap (4)
22. Liquid container (6)
23. Edible nut (3)
24. Unable to appreciate music (4-4)
25. Playful; energetic (6)

DOWN

1. Secret (6)
2. Opposite of concave (6)
3. Passageway of the nose (5)
4. Played for time (7)
5. Knock down (8)
6. Correspond to (6)
12. Planned (8)
14. Hit hard (7)
16. Person who imprisons another (6)
18. Expels (6)
19. Weakly (6)
20. Rigid (5)

CROSSWORD 152

ACROSS

1. Vein of metal ore (4)
3. Highly seasoned smoked beef (8)
9. Made a monarch (7)
10. Hackneyed (5)
11. Pointed tool (3)
12. Abatement (5)
13. Japanese food (5)
15. Country in southern Asia (5)
17. Sound of an emergency vehicle (5)
18. Organ of sight (3)
19. Determine the number of (5)
20. Traditional example (7)
21. Campaigner (8)
22. Pleased (4)

DOWN

1. Lazy (13)
2. Waggish (5)
4. Mixes up or confuses (6)
5. Dictatorial (12)
6. Pilot (7)
7. Wet behind the ears (13)
8. Dimly; not clearly (12)
14. Agitate (7)
16. Dancing clubs (6)
18. Tripod for an artist (5)

CROSSWORD 153

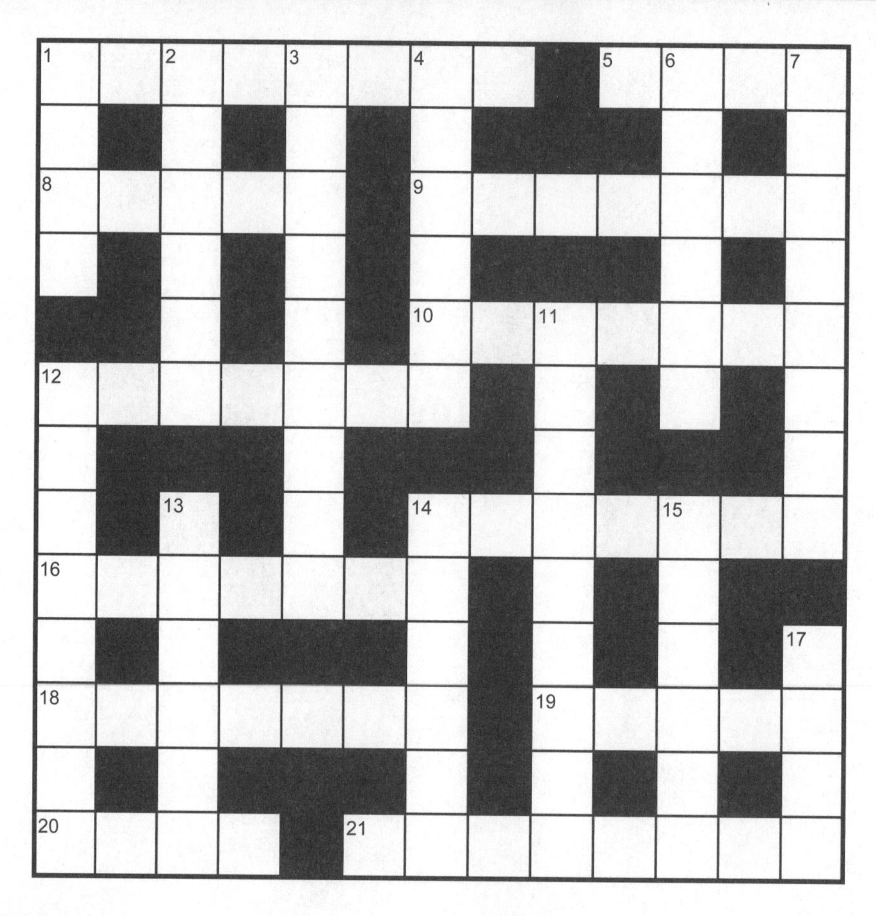

ACROSS

1. Walking heavily or noisily (8)
5. Implement for styling hair (4)
8. Ethical (5)
9. Exchanges of several strokes in tennis (7)
10. Put in someone's care (7)
12. Feeling embarrassed (7)
14. Find ace (anag.) (7)
16. Attentive (7)
18. Respire (7)
19. Hard and durable (5)
20. Lofty (4)
21. E.g. hats and helmets (8)

DOWN

1. Pack down tightly (4)
2. Continent (6)
3. Quickly finish something (6,3)
4. Cared for (6)
6. Repulsive (6)
7. Totally in love with (8)
11. Curtailed (9)
12. Letters of a language (8)
13. Expose (6)
14. Sheepskin (6)
15. Damage (6)
17. Norse god of thunder (4)

CROSSWORD 154

ACROSS

1. Entirely (5)
4. Fast-growing trees (7)
7. Manipulate dough (5)
8. Discovering; finding out (8)
9. Common green plant (5)
11. North American diving ducks (8)
15. Form the base for (8)
17. Narrow sea inlet (5)
19. Pertaining to education (8)
20. Female opera singers (5)
21. Reintegrate (7)
22. US state where one finds Houston (5)

DOWN

1. Unable to go wrong (9)
2. Molecules that bind to others (7)
3. Less old (7)
4. Hurt or troubled (6)
5. Isolationists (6)
6. Studies a subject at university (5)
10. Extends one's body (9)
12. Let in to a place again (7)
13. Confound (7)
14. Establish by law (6)
16. Pleasantly (6)
18. Liquid part of fruits (5)

CROSSWORD 155

ACROSS

1. Declines sharply (6)
7. Raised horizontal surface (8)
8. Was in first place (3)
9. Elongated rectangle (6)
10. Tools for cutting wood (4)
11. Vertical spars for sails (5)
13. Caresses (7)
15. Showed a person to their seat (7)
17. Tool for marking angles (5)
21. Amorphous shape (4)
22. Evoke a feeling (6)
23. Hairpiece (3)
24. Not closed (of an envelope) (8)
25. Entraps (6)

DOWN

1. Rarely (6)
2. Unfastens (6)
3. Item of cutlery (5)
4. Goals (7)
5. Away from land (8)
6. Look through casually (6)
12. Quivered (8)
14. Fail to repay a loan (7)
16. Soundless (6)
18. Spectator (6)
19. Giggles (6)
20. Merchandise; possessions (5)

CROSSWORD 156

ACROSS

1. Essence of something (4)
3. Shouted very loudly (8)
9. Art of paper-folding (7)
10. Exhaust gases (5)
11. Astonishing; amazing (3-9)
13. Dye used as a test of acidity (6)
15. Spanish title for a married woman (6)
17. A system of law courts (12)
20. Snag; minor problem (5)
21. Small fast ship (7)
22. Diabolically cruel (8)
23. Poses a question (4)

DOWN

1. Likely to occur (8)
2. Garbage or drivel (5)
4. Bird sounds (6)
5. Bubbling (12)
6. Keepsake; reminder (7)
7. Stage of twilight (4)
8. Poorly fed (12)
12. Wealthy and influential people (8)
14. One who holds property for another (7)
16. Sayings (6)
18. Golf clubs (5)
19. Cook (4)

CROSSWORD 157

ACROSS

1. Bonus; positive (4)
3. Unselfish concern for others (8)
9. Business establishments (7)
10. Bed covering (5)
11. Unfasten (5)
12. Limiest (anag.) (7)
13. Gambling house (6)
15. Kitchen tool to remove vegetable skin (6)
17. Deliver by parachute (3-4)
18. Period of time in history (5)
20. Data entered into a system (5)
21. Recites as a chant (7)
22. Channels of the nose (8)
23. Vases (4)

DOWN

1. Way of saying a word (13)
2. Unsuitable (5)
4. Diminish (6)
5. Demands or needs (12)
6. Existing at the beginning (7)
7. Process of transformation (of an insect) (13)
8. Creator of film scripts (12)
14. Marks of a zebra (7)
16. Difficult (6)
19. Possessor (5)

CROSSWORD 158

ACROSS

1. Freezes over (4)
3. Not genuine (8)
9. Like a bull (7)
10. At no time (5)
11. Cereal plant (3)
12. Praise highly (5)
13. European country (5)
15. Conclude (5)
17. Up and about (5)
18. Intentionally so written (3)
19. Small piece of land (5)
20. Endless (7)
21. In these times (8)
22. Not at home (4)

DOWN

1. Act of questioning (13)
2. Escape from (5)
4. Spanish rice dish (6)
5. Intense (12)
6. Remove a difficulty (7)
7. Tactically (13)
8. Joyously unrestrained (4-8)
14. Effluence (7)
16. Regalia (6)
18. Strong fibrous tissue (5)

CROSSWORD 159

ACROSS

1. Very young children (6)
7. Exploits to excess (8)
8. Mend (3)
9. Bubbles (6)
10. Arrive (4)
11. Levies (5)
13. Reasons for thinking something (7)
15. Eye protectors (7)
17. Looks after oneself (5)
21. Photographic material (4)
22. Very cold (of weather) (6)
23. Beer container (3)
24. Adolescent (8)
25. Rejoices (6)

DOWN

1. Meal where guests serve themselves (6)
2. Containerful (6)
3. Puts in order (5)
4. E.g. relating to touch or taste (7)
5. Perforate (8)
6. Shone (6)
12. Fibrous connective tissue (8)
14. Make insane (7)
16. States as one's opinion (6)
18. Five cent coin (US) (6)
19. Moves forward at speed (6)
20. Twenty (5)

CROSSWORD 160

ACROSS

1. Money that is owed (4)
3. Citing as evidence (8)
9. Joins together (7)
10. Take delight in (5)
11. Piece of wood (3)
12. ___ Agassi: former tennis star (5)
13. Removes the lid (5)
15. Red-chested bird (5)
17. Upright (5)
18. Hairstyle (3)
19. Japanese form of fencing (5)
20. Menacing (7)
21. Removing from office (8)
22. Fever or shivering fit (4)

DOWN

1. Verified again (6-7)
2. Come with (5)
4. Neglect (6)
5. Not guided by good sense (12)
6. Entered in a hostile manner (7)
7. 50th anniversary of a major event (6,7)
8. Ill-mannered (12)
14. Clear mess away (5,2)
16. Famous London clock (3,3)
18. Confuse or obscure (5)

CROSSWORD 161

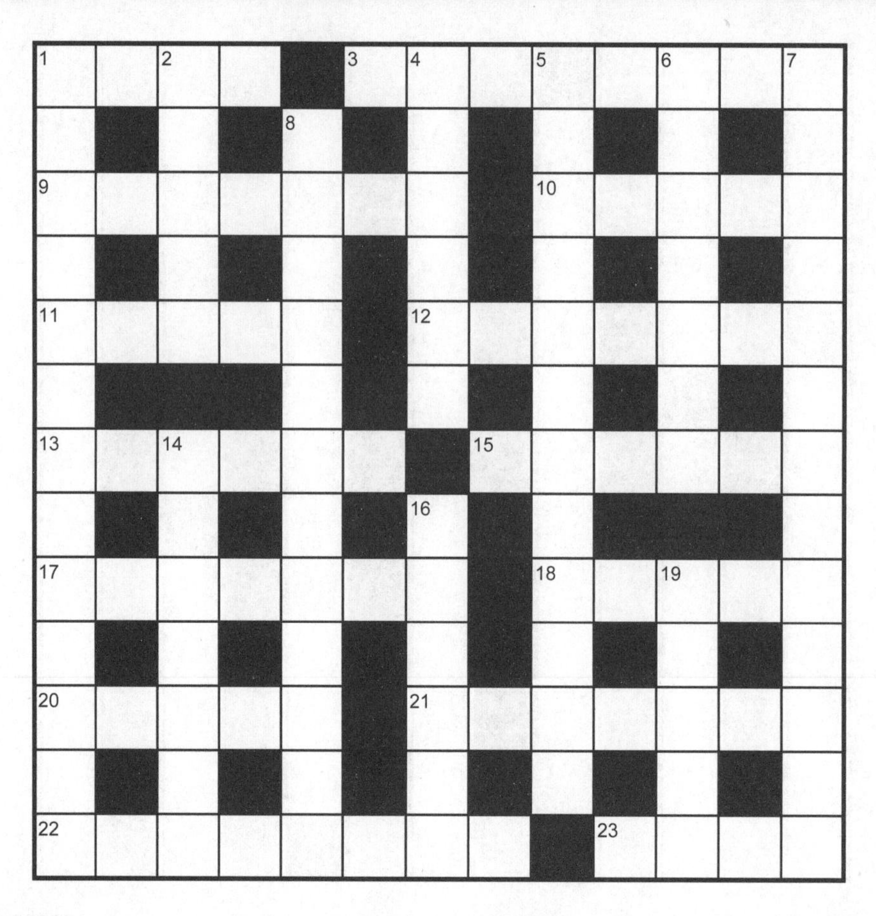

ACROSS

1. An individual thing (4)
3. Squid dish (8)
9. Have a positive impact (7)
10. Bundle of wheat (5)
11. Herb (5)
12. Large number (7)
13. Measurement of extent (6)
15. Narrow passage of water (6)
17. Coolness (7)
18. Areas; sectors (5)
20. Work spirit (5)
21. Tympanic membrane (7)
22. Delaying (8)
23. Meat from a calf (4)

DOWN

1. Not clever (13)
2. State indirectly (5)
4. Take as being true (6)
5. Lowest possible temperature (8,4)
6. United States (7)
7. Extremely small (13)
8. Incessantly (12)
14. Therein (anag.) (7)
16. Toward the rear of a ship (6)
19. Boldness; courage (5)

CROSSWORD 162

ACROSS

1. Increase rapidly (8)
5. Proofreader's mark (4)
9. Skin on top of the head (5)
10. Device that records the movements of someone (7)
11. Bump (12)
14. Evergreen coniferous tree (3)
15. Buyer (5)
16. Mouthpiece attached to a bridle (3)
17. Made poor (12)
20. Largest anthropoid ape (7)
22. Alphabetical list in a book (5)
23. Moved quickly (4)
24. Grow longer (8)

DOWN

1. Perfume ingredient (4)
2. Garden bird (7)
3. Monotonously (12)
4. Make a choice (3)
6. Symbol (5)
7. Streams of rain (8)
8. Radishes grin (anag.) (12)
12. One who makes bread (5)
13. Tubes for ejecting liquids (8)
16. Width (7)
18. Money container (5)
19. Bovine animals (4)
21. Consumed food (3)

CROSSWORD 163

ACROSS

1. Fast-flowing part of a river (6)
7. Holder of invention rights (8)
8. Small winged insect (3)
9. Meaning; purpose (6)
10. Feeling of resentment or jealousy (4)
11. Annoyed (5)
13. Solidifying (7)
15. Herb (7)
17. Wrong (anag.) (5)
21. Block a decision (4)
22. Substance present in cereal grains (6)
23. Taxi (3)
24. Shackle (8)
25. Extravagant meals (6)

DOWN

1. A palm tree (6)
2. Being nosy (6)
3. Rapidity of movement (5)
4. Stammer (7)
5. Person who puts money into something (8)
6. Opposite of hell (6)
12. Replies to a query (8)
14. European country (7)
16. Stadiums (6)
18. 16 of these in a pound (6)
19. Large dark cloud (6)
20. Drink copiously (5)

CROSSWORD 164

ACROSS

1. Crises (11)
9. Boy (3)
10. Slatted wooden box (5)
11. Cry out loudly (5)
12. Large American felines (5)
13. Wild flower (8)
16. Distinction; high status (8)
18. Type of confection (5)
20. Decaf (anag.) (5)
21. Shrill sound (5)
22. Cooking utensil (3)
23. Ongoing disagreement (11)

DOWN

2. Polite address for a woman (5)
3. Moves back and forth (5)
4. Hard tooth coating (6)
5. Tufted (7)
6. Uncovers; reveals (7)
7. Omnipotent (3-8)
8. Official agreements (11)
14. Small flute (7)
15. Receiver (7)
17. Coarse cloth (6)
18. Not true (5)
19. Deceives or misleads (5)

CROSSWORD 165

ACROSS

4. Tricky question (6)
7. Immature (8)
8. Layer of a folded material (3)
9. Capital of Ukraine (4)
10. Increase over time (6)
11. Impeded (7)
12. Raised to the third power (5)
15. Parts in a play (5)
17. Hour of going to sleep (7)
20. Emperor of Japan (6)
21. Source of inspiration (4)
22. Chain attached to a watch (3)
23. Indistinct; hazy (8)
24. Straying from the right course (6)

DOWN

1. Cause sudden excitement (6)
2. Collarbone (8)
3. Buccaneers (7)
4. Opposite of thin (5)
5. Majestic (6)
6. Had corresponding sounds (6)
13. Inopportune (8)
14. Enclosed fortification (7)
15. Shuffle playing cards (6)
16. Warm up (6)
18. Botch (4-2)
19. Inapt (anag.) (5)

CROSSWORD 166

ACROSS

1. Religious group (4)
3. Obscure (8)
9. Floating mass of frozen water (7)
10. Asserts; affirms (5)
11. Ancestors (12)
14. E.g. almond or pecan (3)
16. Armistice (5)
17. Possesses (3)
18. Freedom from control (12)
21. Form of oxygen (5)
22. Goes back on a promise (7)
23. Thinks about something continually (8)
24. Time periods (4)

DOWN

1. Leaping over a rope (8)
2. Thin pancake (5)
4. Implore (3)
5. Exceptional (12)
6. Dig out of the ground (7)
7. Not difficult (4)
8. Notwithstanding (12)
12. Display freely (5)
13. Evaluates the quality of (8)
15. Bands of connective tissue (7)
19. African country whose capital is Niamey (5)
20. Neither good nor bad (2-2)
22. Fish eggs (3)

CROSSWORD 167

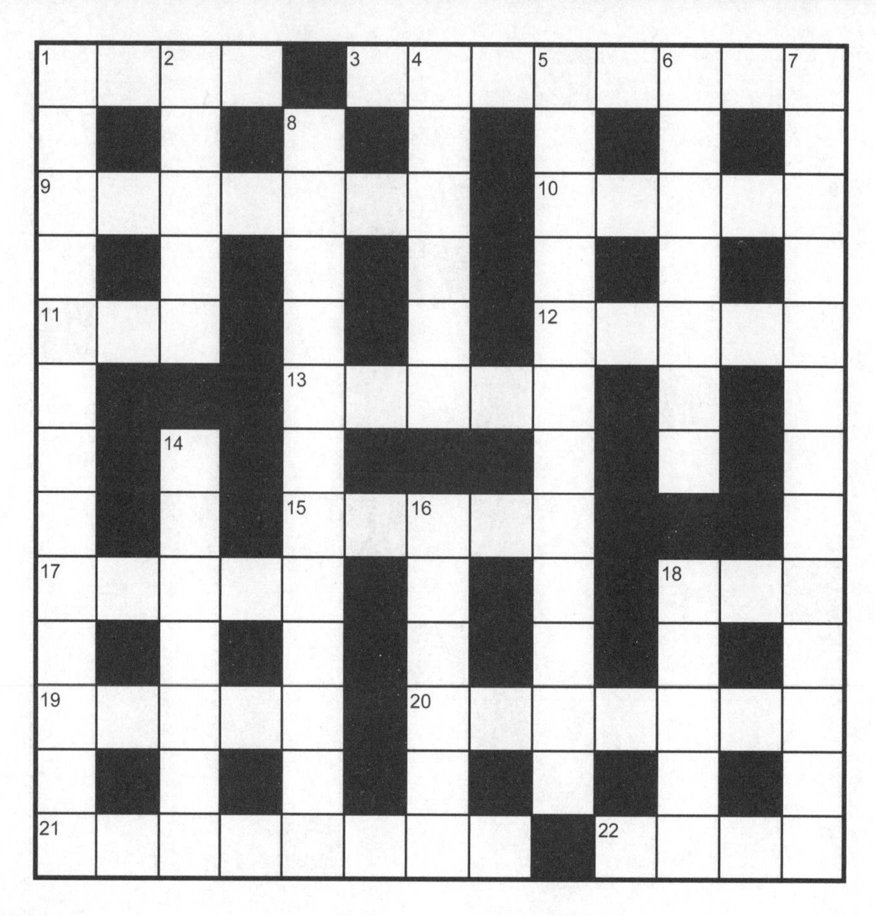

ACROSS

1. Natural oily substances (4)
3. Fleet of ships (8)
9. Rearranged letters of a word (7)
10. District council head (5)
11. Witch (3)
12. Run away with a lover (5)
13. Elevated step (5)
15. Divide; separate (5)
17. Turf out (5)
18. Draw (3)
19. Type of lizard (5)
20. Table support (7)
21. Ragged (8)
22. Allows (4)

DOWN

1. Boxing class division (13)
2. Strong ringing sound (5)
4. 11th Greek letter (6)
5. Erase trumpet (anag.) (12)
6. Give up or surrender something (3,4)
7. Pleasantness (13)
8. Swimming technique (12)
14. Coiffure (7)
16. Small (6)
18. Name of a book (5)

CROSSWORD 168

ACROSS

1. Double entendre (4,2,5)
9. Strong drink (3)
10. Strength (5)
11. Cool down (5)
12. Easy (of a job) (5)
13. Capital of Finland (8)
16. Unify (8)
18. Uneven (of a road surface) (5)
20. Relaxed; not tense (5)
21. Wild and untamed (5)
22. Range of knowledge (3)
23. Clay pottery (11)

DOWN

2. Walks awkwardly (5)
3. Delicious (5)
4. Small worry; irritate (6)
5. Social reject (7)
6. Decorative patterns (7)
7. Virtually (11)
8. Increasing greatly in number (11)
14. Balearic Island (7)
15. Advantage gained from something (7)
17. Unrefined (6)
18. Under (5)
19. Creator (5)

CROSSWORD 169

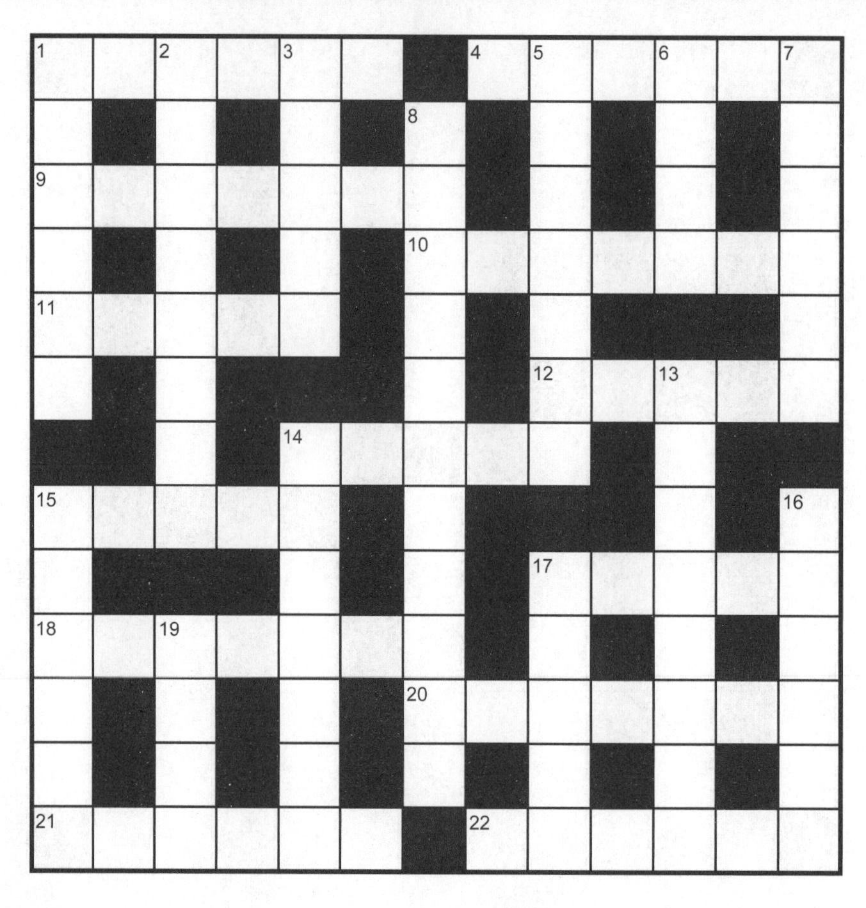

ACROSS

1. Six-legged arthropod (6)
4. Not rough (6)
9. Oscillate (7)
10. Points where edges meet (7)
11. Sailing ship (5)
12. Public transport vehicles (5)
14. Powerful forward movement (5)
15. Perspire (5)
17. Settee (5)
18. State of the USA (7)
20. Part of a gun (7)
21. Relays (anag.) (6)
22. Rounded up animals (6)

DOWN

1. Call on (6)
2. Deliberately damage (8)
3. Conflict (5)
5. Bacterium (7)
6. Seep; exude (4)
7. Makes a sibilant sound (6)
8. Give in return (11)
13. Showed indifference (8)
14. Walk with difficulty (7)
15. Gesture (6)
16. Had in common (6)
17. Culinary herb (5)
19. Comply (4)

CROSSWORD 170

ACROSS

4. Humorous television drama (6)
7. Chamber leading to a larger space (8)
8. Vehicle (3)
9. Wander (4)
10. Sporting venues (6)
11. Attacks (7)
12. Induce fear (5)
15. Enclosed (5)
17. Ostentatious (7)
20. Background actors (6)
21. Wild mountain goat (4)
22. Exclamation of amazement (3)
23. Deplorably (8)
24. Come off the tracks (6)

DOWN

1. Relishes (6)
2. Drink (8)
3. Tiny mouthfuls of food (7)
4. Besmirch (5)
5. Large homopterous insect (6)
6. Spirit of a person or group (6)
13. Careful (8)
14. Lenses in a frame that correct eyesight (7)
15. Masticated (6)
16. Long pin (6)
18. Multiply by three (6)
19. Snarl (5)

CROSSWORD 171

ACROSS

1. Type of cactus (7,4)
9. Annoy (3)
10. Bout of extravagant shopping (5)
11. Language of the Romans (5)
12. Corrodes (5)
13. Neutral particle with negligible mass (8)
16. Horrifying (8)
18. Destined (5)
20. Flower of remembrance (5)
21. Concise and full of meaning (5)
22. Obtained (3)
23. Formal evening wear (6,5)

DOWN

2. Garden tools (5)
3. Protective containers (5)
4. Immature insects (6)
5. E.g. a bishop (7)
6. Refrain from (7)
7. Magnifying instruments (11)
8. Make physically stronger (11)
14. Kettledrums (7)
15. Portable enclosure for infants (7)
17. Have a chat (6)
18. Entrance hallway (5)
19. Roman cloaks (5)

CROSSWORD 172

ACROSS

1. Evil spirit (5)
4. Cues given to performers (7)
7. Thick slice of beef (5)
8. Pleasing and captivating (8)
9. Becomes worn at the edges (5)
11. Idleness (8)
15. Commotion (8)
17. Remains (5)
19. Country in eastern Africa (8)
20. Side posts of doorways (5)
21. Serving no purpose (7)
22. Strong currents of air (5)

DOWN

1. Flippantly humorous (9)
2. Mournful (7)
3. Brave and persistent (7)
4. Quickly (6)
5. Devices that cause motion (6)
6. Sorrowful (5)
10. Moves apart (9)
12. Making the sound of a bee (7)
13. Exploit the power of (7)
14. Musical instrument (6)
16. Cooks in the oven (6)
18. Froglike amphibians (5)

CROSSWORD 173

ACROSS

1. Opposite of fast forward (6)
7. Copycat (8)
8. Month (3)
9. Fell behind (6)
10. Movable barrier (4)
11. Small canoe (5)
13. Furtiveness (7)
15. Withdraw from a commitment (4,3)
17. Abodes (5)
21. Foolish person (4)
22. Not working (6)
23. Popular edible fish (3)
24. E.g. from Tokyo (8)
25. Not so important (6)

DOWN

1. Comment (6)
2. Accost; hold up (6)
3. Drab (5)
4. Violinist (7)
5. Large marsupial (8)
6. Written in verse (6)
12. State of the USA (8)
14. Lowers the status of (7)
16. Without ethics (6)
18. Cuts up meat very finely (6)
19. Transmitter (6)
20. Speech sound (5)

CROSSWORD 174

ACROSS

1. Production (11)
9. Stiff (5)
10. Young newt (3)
11. Negatively charged ion (5)
12. Speed music is played at (5)
13. Assign (8)
16. In the open air (8)
18. Distinctive design (5)
21. Narcotics (5)
22. Type of vase (3)
23. E.g. copper or calcium (5)
24. Specialist in care for the feet (11)

DOWN

2. Ennoble (7)
3. Hot fire (7)
4. Rue doing something (6)
5. Detailed assessment of accounts (5)
6. Dairy product (5)
7. Capital of Malaysia (5,6)
8. Awfully (11)
14. Held a baby (7)
15. Guarantees (7)
17. Portable computer (6)
19. Freshwater fish (5)
20. Thigh bone (5)

CROSSWORD 175

ACROSS

1. Ill feeling (8)
5. Trudge (4)
8. Scores an exam paper (5)
9. Puzzling and obscure (7)
10. Interminable (7)
12. Warhead carried by a missile (7)
14. Satisfy; conciliate (7)
16. Dons clothes (7)
18. Visual display unit (7)
19. Talked audibly (5)
20. Not hot (4)
21. Form of makeup (8)

DOWN

1. Money given to the poor (4)
2. Make less dense (6)
3. Spreads rapidly (9)
4. Cut slightly (6)
6. Machines for shaping wood (6)
7. Resolute (8)
11. Process of scattering (9)
12. Worldwide outbreak (8)
13. Inner part of a seed (6)
14. Far from the intended target (6)
15. Border (6)
17. Dam (4)

CROSSWORD 176

ACROSS

1. Rescue (4)
3. Inconceivably large (8)
9. Fatty substance (7)
10. Minute pore in a leaf (5)
11. Insect larva (5)
12. Capital of Georgia in the US (7)
13. Crazy (6)
15. Bear witness (6)
17. Constantly present (7)
18. More recent (5)
20. Academy award (5)
21. Vague and uncertain (7)
22. Rigidly; sternly (8)
23. Increases; sums up (4)

DOWN

1. Magnificent (13)
2. Snake toxin (5)
4. Yearly (6)
5. Completeness (12)
6. Beat easily (7)
7. Bland and dull (13)
8. Using both letters and numerals (12)
14. Motorcycle attachment (7)
16. Roll of parchment (6)
19. Injury (5)

CROSSWORD 177

ACROSS

4. Small garden building (6)
7. Single-celled organisms (8)
8. Domesticated pig (3)
9. Standard (4)
10. Get by with what is available (4,2)
11. Impinges upon (7)
12. Thin fogs (5)
15. Attractively stylish (5)
17. Russian tea urn (7)
20. Scandinavian (6)
21. Inspires fear and wonder (4)
22. Carry a heavy object (3)
23. 20th-century art movement (8)
24. Walk nonchalantly (6)

DOWN

1. Type of examination (6)
2. Having no current (of a body of water) (8)
3. Horizontal angle of a compass bearing (7)
4. Ungainly (5)
5. Sound reflections (6)
6. Church instruments (6)
13. Great adulation (8)
14. Surgical knives (7)
15. Royal people (6)
16. Spore-producing organism (6)
18. Strongly opposed (6)
19. Enlighten; educate morally (5)

CROSSWORD 178

ACROSS

1. Juicy citrus fruit (6)
4. E.g. squares and triangles (6)
9. Conspire to commit a fraud (7)
10. Tiresome (7)
11. Layer (anag.) (5)
12. Make a sound expressing pain (5)
14. Humorous images that spread rapidly online (5)
15. Shallow circular dish (5)
17. Take hold of (5)
18. Small onion-like bulb (7)
20. Loving deeply (7)
21. Hate (6)
22. Journey by air (6)

DOWN

1. Happens (6)
2. Exclamation of joy (8)
3. Overly showy (5)
5. Sausages in bread rolls (3,4)
6. Game played on horseback (4)
7. E.g. summer (6)
8. Harmful (11)
13. Accommodating (8)
14. Softens with age (7)
15. Elapsed (of time) (6)
16. Measure of heaviness (6)
17. Reel for winding yarn (5)
19. Uncle's wife (4)

CROSSWORD 179

ACROSS

1. Device used to seal joints (6)
7. Promontory (8)
8. Cook in hot oil (3)
9. Day after Sunday (6)
10. Emit light (4)
11. Take away by force (5)
13. More amusing (7)
15. Courage (7)
17. Short notes (5)
21. Fibber (4)
22. Groans (anag.) (6)
23. Seed of an apple (3)
24. In a direct and frank way (3,2,3)
25. Be contingent upon (6)

DOWN

1. Laugh boisterously (6)
2. Obstruct (6)
3. Low dull sounds (5)
4. Ancient parchment (7)
5. Grace (8)
6. Unfastened (6)
12. Harshness (8)
14. Suppose to be true (7)
16. Nasal (6)
18. Long-tailed crow (6)
19. Inclined (6)
20. Crunch; wear down (5)

CROSSWORD 180

ACROSS

1. Crazy person (6)
4. Flowing back (6)
9. Unconventional (7)
10. Radioactive element (7)
11. Medicinal ointment (5)
12. Ousel (anag.) (5)
14. Religious acts (5)
17. Humped ruminant (5)
19. Facial hair (5)
21. Crush underfoot (7)
23. Relating to sight (7)
24. Send away (6)
25. Evasive; devious (6)

DOWN

1. A small handbook (6)
2. Prima donna (4)
3. Suitor (7)
5. Polishes (5)
6. Pursuit of high principles (8)
7. Water channel (6)
8. Proficiently (11)
13. Undo; loosen (8)
15. Scrape (7)
16. Soak up (6)
18. Margin of safety (6)
20. Deducts (5)
22. Light blast of wind (4)

CROSSWORD 181

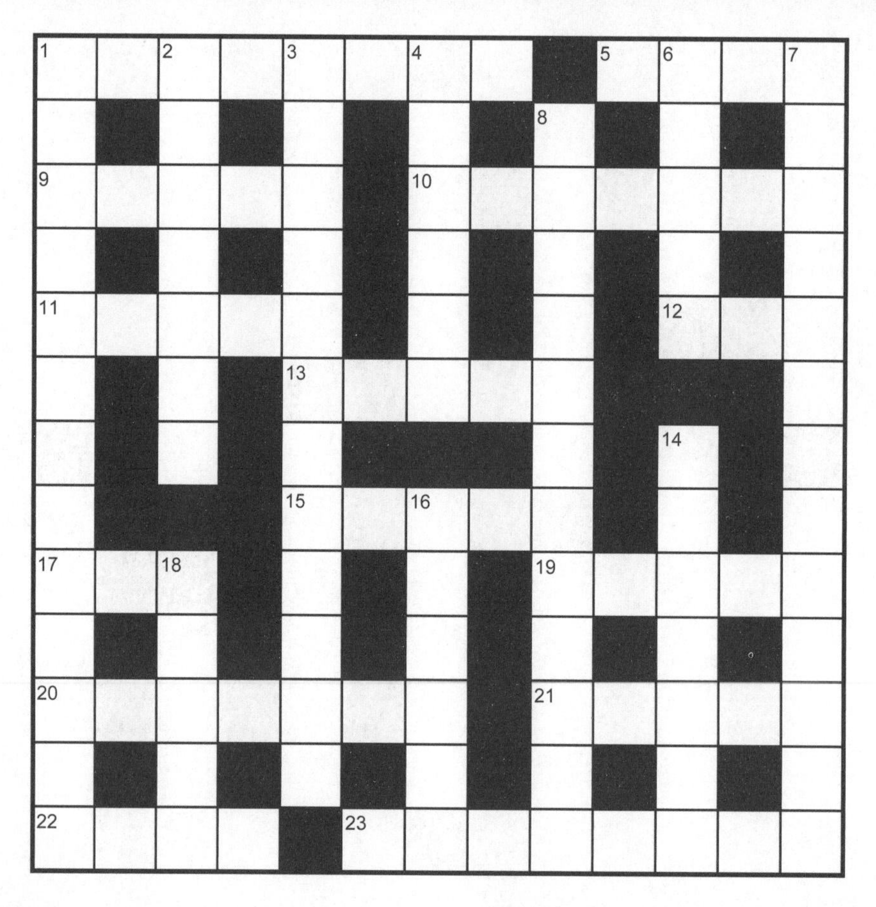

ACROSS

1. Incessant (8)
5. Drains of energy (4)
9. Assesses performance (5)
10. Disperse (5,2)
11. Latin American dance (5)
12. State of armed conflict (3)
13. Fishing net (5)
15. Stomach exercise (3-2)
17. Mock (3)
19. Very masculine (5)
20. Edges (7)
21. Words that identify things (5)
22. Consumes (4)
23. Gusty (8)

DOWN

1. Irretrievable (13)
2. Increases a deadline (7)
3. Displeased (12)
4. Cloud of gas in space (6)
6. Twisted to one side (5)
7. In a manner that exceeds what is necessary (13)
8. Changes to a situation (12)
14. Hermit (7)
16. Adornment of hanging threads (6)
18. Rupture (5)

CROSSWORD 182

ACROSS

1. Draws into the mouth (5)
4. Imprisonment (7)
7. Feeling pleased and satisfied (5)
8. Unexpectedly (8)
9. Type of small fastener (5)
11. Shows (8)
15. The bones of the body (8)
17. Range (5)
19. Sticks used as supports (8)
20. Challenges (5)
21. Very great (3-4)
22. Ball sport (5)

DOWN

1. Takes on a burden or responsibility (9)
2. Rid of something unpleasant (7)
3. Writes untidily (7)
4. Very pleasing to the eye (6)
5. Three times (6)
6. Tennis score (5)
10. Day of the week (9)
12. Sparkle (7)
13. Irritating; hankering (7)
14. Spoken form of communication (6)
16. Brandy distilled from cherries (6)
18. Fissure (5)

CROSSWORD 183

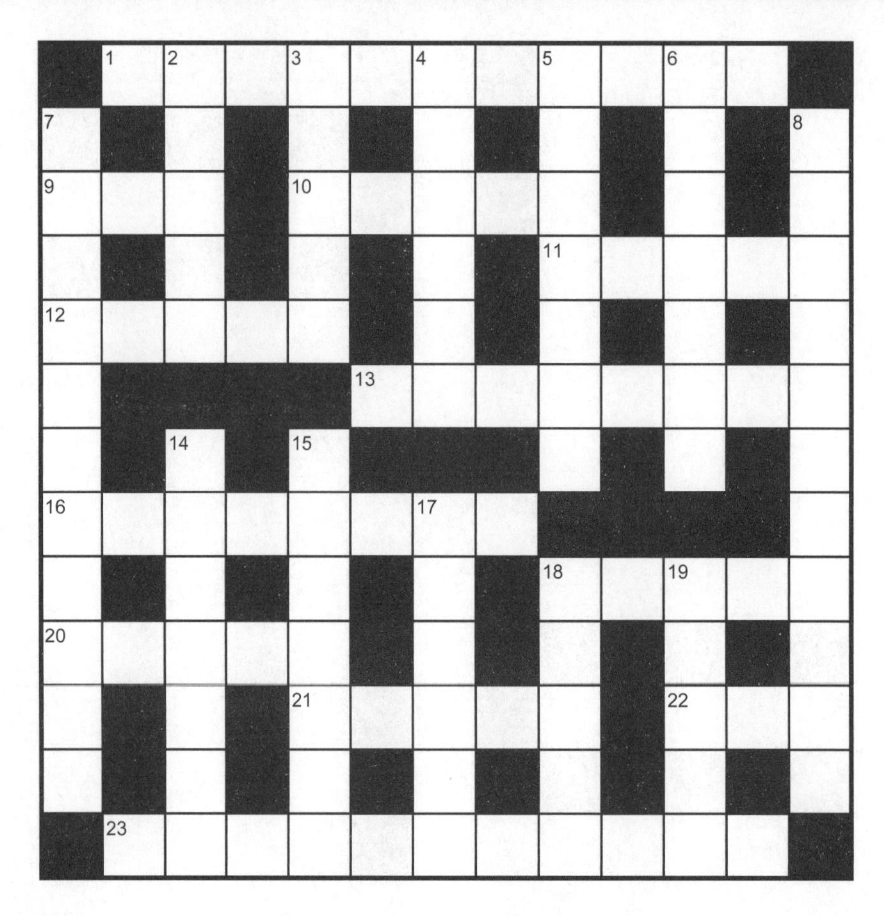

ACROSS

1. Act evasively (11)
9. Bland soft food (3)
10. Produce eggs (5)
11. One who avoids animal products (5)
12. Regulations (5)
13. Mounted guns (8)
16. Exemption (8)
18. Conceal (5)
20. Mooring for a ship (5)
21. Reversed (5)
22. Snip (3)
23. Inevitably (11)

DOWN

2. Push away (5)
3. Urns (5)
4. University lecturer (6)
5. Community of nuns (7)
6. Pulling at (7)
7. Considerable (11)
8. Give your full attention to (11)
14. Offence (7)
15. Speak excitedly of (7)
17. Buys and sells goods (6)
18. Programmer (5)
19. Pertaining to the voice (5)

CROSSWORD 184

ACROSS

4. Jumped on one leg (6)
7. Parasol (8)
8. Close-fitting hat (3)
9. Italian greeting (4)
10. Decorate (6)
11. Disturb (7)
12. Compel (5)
15. Sells (5)
17. Outfit (7)
20. Large birds of prey (6)
21. Imprint (4)
22. Roll of bank notes (3)
23. Took in (food) (8)
24. More profound (6)

DOWN

1. Controlling (6)
2. Of many different kinds (8)
3. Burrowing mammals (7)
4. Groups of animals (5)
5. Wrinkle; fold (6)
6. Remove from office (6)
13. Opposite of a pessimist (8)
14. Flower arrangement (7)
15. Watched (6)
16. Sewing instrument (6)
18. Small piece of food (6)
19. Stylishness and originality (5)

CROSSWORD 185

ACROSS

1. Potential (11)
9. Opposite of below (5)
10. Limb used for walking (3)
11. Oneness (5)
12. One of the senses (5)
13. Very capable (8)
16. Section of a train (8)
18. Swells (5)
21. Small group ruling a country (5)
22. Uncooked (of meat) (3)
23. Lessen (5)
24. Introductory (11)

DOWN

2. Quickly (7)
3. Remaining (7)
4. Change gradually (6)
5. Levels; ranks (5)
6. One-way flow structure (5)
7. Apron cutter (anag.) (11)
8. Form into a cluster (11)
14. Piece of research (7)
15. Wash and iron (7)
17. Domestic assistant (2,4)
19. Less (5)
20. Rascal (5)

CROSSWORD 186

ACROSS

1. Cuddly (8)
5. Read quickly (4)
9. Card game (5)
10. Insignificant (7)
11. Brutally; harshly (12)
14. Frozen water (3)
15. Pointed part of a fork (5)
16. Body's vital life force (3)
17. Total despair (12)
20. Standing erect (7)
22. Pungent edible bulb (5)
23. Suffers the consequences (4)
24. Written communications (8)

DOWN

1. Bird of prey (4)
2. Quick look (7)
3. Study of human societies (12)
4. Ignited (3)
6. Cutting instrument (5)
7. Country in Southeast Asia (8)
8. Insincere (12)
12. Retail stores (5)
13. Athletics event (4,4)
16. Actings (anag.) (7)
18. Lively; cheerful (5)
19. Social insects (4)
21. Golf peg (3)

CROSSWORD 187

ACROSS

1. Country one lives in (8)
5. Exchange (4)
9. Bird claw (5)
10. Slowly moving mass of ice (7)
11. Backtrack (7)
12. Shrub fence (5)
13. Son of Daedalus in Greek mythology (6)
14. Dodged (6)
17. Crime of setting something on fire (5)
19. Cherubic (7)
20. Perfectly (7)
21. Polite and courteous (5)
22. Write down (4)
23. Adventurer (8)

DOWN

1. Firmness of purpose (13)
2. Force of civilians trained as soldiers (7)
3. As a result (12)
4. Devices that illuminate (6)
6. Strange (5)
7. Upright; vertical (13)
8. Caused by disease (12)
15. Bring and hand over (7)
16. Voice box (6)
18. Slumbered (5)

CROSSWORD 188

ACROSS

1. Plant of the rose family (8)
5. Short tail (4)
9. Precious gem (5)
10. Sports ground (7)
11. Small tuned drum (5)
12. Sum charged (3)
13. Refine metal (5)
15. Ski run (5)
17. Deer (3)
19. Common edible fruit (5)
20. E.g. Iceland and Borneo (7)
21. Act of stealing (5)
22. Passionate desire for something (4)
23. Principal (8)

DOWN

1. Destroying microorganisms (13)
2. Matured (7)
3. Female singing voice (5-7)
4. Hold close (6)
6. Leader or ruler (5)
7. Unpredictable (13)
8. Lacking courage (5-7)
14. Indefinitely many (7)
16. Afternoon sleep (6)
18. Furnaces (5)

CROSSWORD 189

ACROSS

1. Domineering (11)
9. Slippery fish (3)
10. Apart from (5)
11. Counterfeit (5)
12. Encounters (5)
13. Teacher (8)
16. Strong coffee (8)
18. Group of bees (5)
20. Three-note chord (5)
21. Organ (5)
22. Trap; ensnare (3)
23. Component parts (11)

DOWN

2. Innate worth (5)
3. Large quantities of paper (5)
4. Amended (6)
5. European deer (7)
6. Mischievous (7)
7. Opposite of temporarily (11)
8. Removal of weapons (11)
14. Fifth Greek letter (7)
15. Hawker (7)
17. Answered correctly (6)
18. Tennis stroke (5)
19. Anxiety (5)

CROSSWORD 190

ACROSS

1. Strongbox (4)
3. Curved sword (8)
9. Ancestry (7)
10. Deprive of weapons (5)
11. Ascend (5)
12. Large jug (7)
13. Denial (anag.) (6)
15. One under par in golf (6)
17. Laborious (7)
18. Have in common (5)
20. Bond or connection (5)
21. Puts up with (7)
22. Pain or anguish (8)
23. Fill or satiate (4)

DOWN

1. Complete in itself (of a thing) (4-9)
2. Spore-producing organisms (5)
4. Moves very slowly (6)
5. Hillside (12)
6. Threw away (7)
7. Pitilessly (13)
8. Troublemaker (6-6)
14. Alphabetical lists (7)
16. Organic compounds (6)
19. Fourth month (5)

CROSSWORD 191

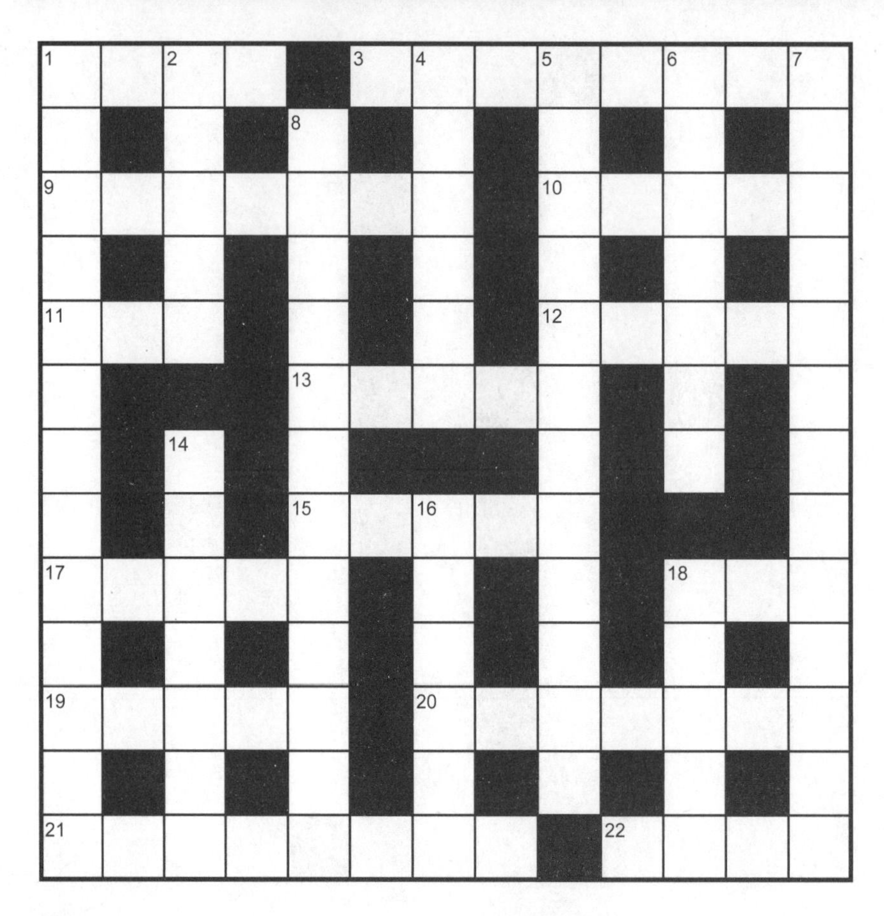

ACROSS

1. Tehran is the capital here (4)
3. Engravings (8)
9. Obtained from a source (7)
10. Stadium (5)
11. Cutting tool (3)
12. Two times (5)
13. Senior figure in a tribe (5)
15. Spike used by a climber (5)
17. Overly self-assertive (5)
18. Belonging to him (3)
19. Computer memory units (5)
20. Tenured (anag.) (7)
21. Releasing from a duty (8)
22. Chief god of ancient Greece (4)

DOWN

1. Incapable of being expressed in words (13)
2. Pointed projectile (5)
4. Cleaned up (6)
5. Very upsetting (5-7)
6. Requiring (7)
7. Brazenness (13)
8. Excessive stress (12)
14. Extremely disordered (7)
16. Connective tissue (6)
18. Dwelling (5)

CROSSWORD 192

ACROSS

1. Raised areas of land (5)
4. Navigational instrument (7)
7. Hackneyed (5)
8. Padding (8)
9. Temporary stop (5)
11. Observing (8)
15. Worm (8)
17. Frightening (5)
19. Sues arms (anag.) (8)
20. Smiles radiantly (5)
21. One-eyed giant (7)
22. Post (5)

DOWN

1. Cruelness; roughness (9)
2. Migratory grasshoppers (7)
3. Superficial area (7)
4. Large artillery gun (6)
5. Flat; two-dimensional (6)
6. Hits with the hand (5)
10. Over the top (9)
12. Small plum-like fruits (7)
13. Round building (7)
14. Fundamental; essential (6)
16. Makes a bill law (6)
18. Requiring much mastication (5)

CROSSWORD 193

ACROSS

1. Ending that leaves one in suspense (11)
9. For each (3)
10. Avocet-like wader (5)
11. Fairy (5)
12. Hazardous; dangerous (5)
13. Musical pieces for solo instruments (8)
16. Regnant (8)
18. Celestial body (5)
20. Alert (5)
21. Conveyed by gestures (5)
22. Stream of liquid (3)
23. Initiators (11)

DOWN

2. Tempts (5)
3. Hard to please (5)
4. Coiffure (6)
5. Quibble (7)
6. Cure-alls (7)
7. Fitting (11)
8. Cause to happen unexpectedly (11)
14. Organic nutrient (7)
15. Not tidy (7)
17. Spice (6)
18. Military trainee (5)
19. Army rank (5)

CROSSWORD 194

ACROSS

1. Form of energy (11)
9. Assumed proposition (5)
10. Born (3)
11. Despised (5)
12. Piece of code to automate a task (5)
13. Revealing a truth (8)
16. Taking to be true (8)
18. Aromatic resin (5)
21. Plain writing (5)
22. The gist of the matter (3)
23. Simple aquatic plants (5)
24. Testimony (11)

DOWN

2. Portable computers (7)
3. Least warm (7)
4. Continue to exist (6)
5. Beguile (5)
6. Invigorating medicine (5)
7. Accomplishment (11)
8. Try to predict an outcome (6-5)
14. Believe tentatively (7)
15. Italian rice dish (7)
17. Looked for (6)
19. Automaton (5)
20. Lift with effort (5)

CROSSWORD 195

ACROSS

1. Conventional (11)
9. Fix the result in advance (3)
10. Early version of a document (5)
11. More delicate (5)
12. Container for storing items (5)
13. Excessive amount of something (8)
16. Bewilder (8)
18. Ye old (anag.) (5)
20. Large tree (5)
21. Gate fastener (5)
22. Cup (3)
23. Highs and lows (3,3,5)

DOWN

2. Seethed with anger (5)
3. Iffy (5)
4. Go from one place to another (6)
5. Sets of clothes (7)
6. Give up (7)
7. Able to be used (11)
8. Branch of medicine dealing with skin disorders (11)
14. Patella (7)
15. Spiral cavity of the inner ear (7)
17. Acquired money as profit (6)
18. Loutish person (5)
19. Evil spirit (5)

CROSSWORD 196

ACROSS

1. Frustrated (8)
5. Fish (4)
8. Starting point (5)
9. Chaser (7)
10. Spilt (7)
12. Aircraft with two pairs of wings (7)
14. Depict in a particular way (7)
16. Compress (7)
18. Ardent (7)
19. Small garden statue (5)
20. Puts down (4)
21. Lookout (8)

DOWN

1. Bats (anag.) (4)
2. Do the dishes (4-2)
3. Reinforcement of sound (9)
4. Show up; reveal (6)
6. Takes the place of (6)
7. Extreme bitterness (8)
11. Between sunset and sunrise (9)
12. Heavenly (8)
13. Deep pit (6)
14. Grinding tool (6)
15. Revived or regenerated (6)
17. Raised area of skin (4)

CROSSWORD 197

ACROSS

1. Every (4)
3. Battered (8)
9. Coatings (7)
10. Stitched (5)
11. Evergreen shrub (12)
13. Freshest (6)
15. Taxonomic groupings (6)
17. Terrified or extremely shocked (6-6)
20. Repository (5)
21. Prescription (7)
22. Sanctions (8)
23. Sort; variety (4)

DOWN

1. Surroundings (8)
2. Showing a willingness to achieve results (3-2)
4. Reply (6)
5. Mishap (12)
6. Started an essay again (7)
7. Part of a pedestal (4)
8. One who takes part in a protest (12)
12. Make valid retrospectively (8)
14. Yelled with excitement (7)
16. Treat without seriousness (6)
18. High lending practice (5)
19. Lazy (4)

CROSSWORD 198

ACROSS

1. Catastrophe (8)
5. Mineral powder (4)
9. Small woody plant (5)
10. Connoisseur (7)
11. Scoundrel (5)
12. Eek (anag.) (3)
13. Submerged ridges of rock (5)
15. Severe (5)
17. Helpful hint (3)
19. Large crow (5)
20. People who manage college finances (7)
21. Religious book (5)
22. Fencing sword (4)
23. Innate (8)

DOWN

1. Disreputable (13)
2. Scrawny (7)
3. Underground (12)
4. Erase a mark from a surface (6)
6. Live by (5)
7. Person who writes letters regularly (13)
8. Not capable of reply (12)
14. Deserving affection (7)
16. Agreement or concord (6)
18. Clean spiritually (5)

CROSSWORD 199

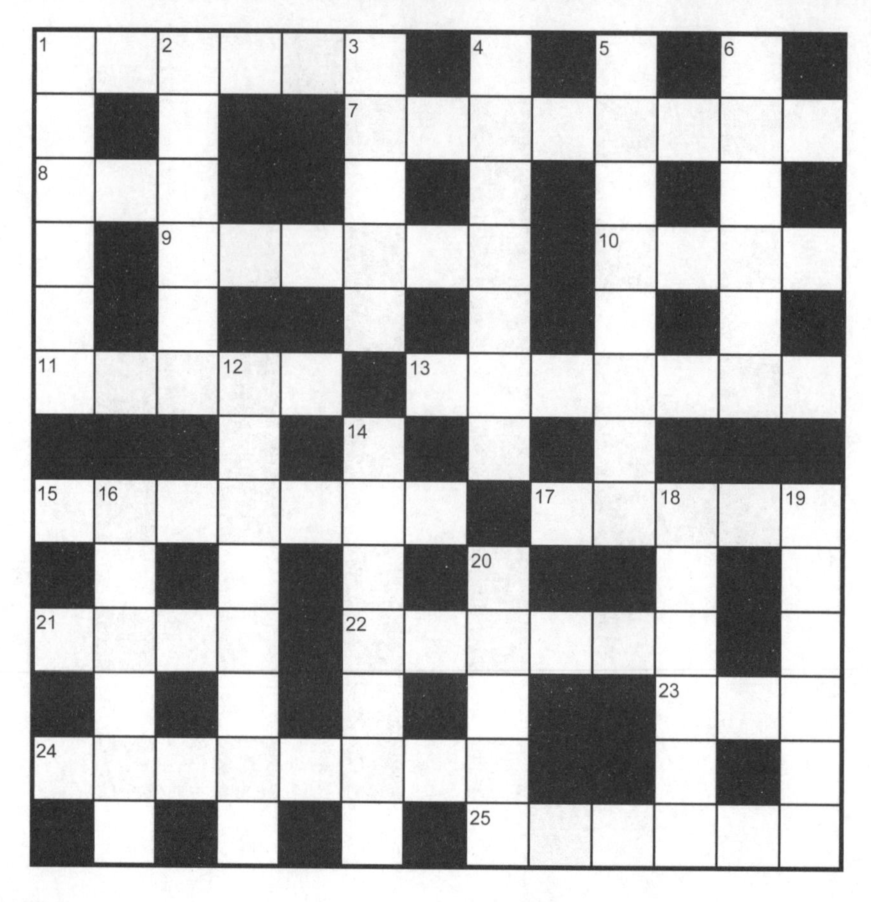

ACROSS

1. Very enthusiastic (informal) (6)
7. Made better (8)
8. Marry (3)
9. Turbulence (6)
10. Mob (4)
11. Streamlined (5)
13. Brings into action (7)
15. Art of clipping shrubs decoratively (7)
17. Recorded on video (5)
21. Repeat (4)
22. Embarrassing mistake (3-3)
23. Craze (3)
24. French bread stick (8)
25. Attack with severe criticism (6)

DOWN

1. Abilities (6)
2. Self-contained unit (6)
3. Jumps into water (5)
4. Emit spitting sounds (7)
5. Country in Central Asia (8)
6. Nastily (6)
12. Concluding section (8)
14. Official proving of a will (7)
16. Unidirectional (3-3)
18. Financial gain (6)
19. Work hard; menial worker (6)
20. Crates (5)

CROSSWORD 200

ACROSS

1. Argumentative (11)
9. Bend (5)
10. Small spot (3)
11. Petulant (5)
12. Stratum (5)
13. Furtive (8)
16. Expression of gratitude (5,3)
18. Spring flower (5)
21. E.g. an Oscar or Grammy (5)
22. Meat from a pig (3)
23. First Pope (5)
24. Ghost (11)

DOWN

2. James Joyce novel (7)
3. Use again (7)
4. Make better (6)
5. Incantation (5)
6. Insanely (5)
7. Calamity or great loss (11)
8. Having celebrities in attendance (4-7)
14. Increase in size (7)
15. Oppressive rulers (7)
17. Threat (anag.) (6)
19. West Indian dance (5)
20. Songbird (5)

CROSSWORD 201

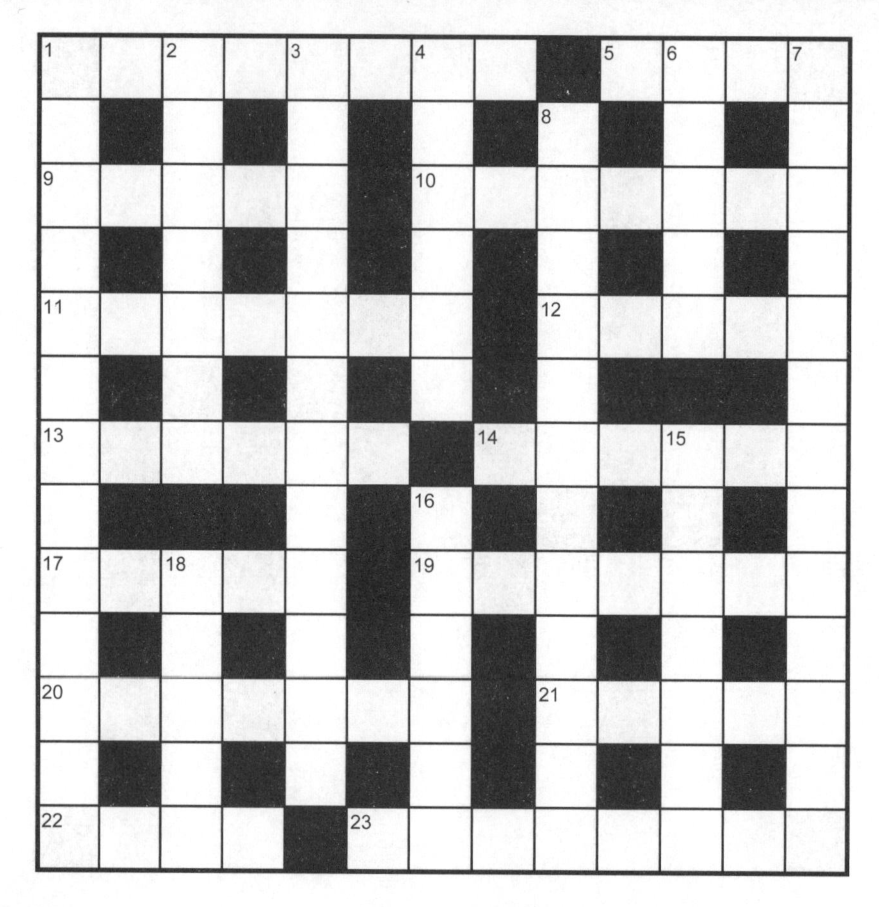

ACROSS

1. Cutting wood (8)
5. Therefore (4)
9. Female relation (5)
10. Merry (7)
11. Unlawful (7)
12. Purchaser (5)
13. Sprightliness (6)
14. Stitching (6)
17. Scope or extent (5)
19. Small ornament (7)
20. Brighten up (7)
21. Italian cathedral (5)
22. Open the mouth wide when tired (4)
23. Lack of hair (8)

DOWN

1. In a thoughtful manner (13)
2. Coincide partially (7)
3. Dictatorial (12)
4. Invalidate; nullify (6)
6. Weighty (5)
7. Sanctimonious (4-9)
8. Foolish or stupid (6-6)
15. Annoying (7)
16. Basic metrical unit in a poem (6)
18. Local authority rule (2-3)

CROSSWORD 202

ACROSS

1. Mad rush (8)
5. Large wading bird (4)
9. Rouse from sleep (5)
10. Pretended (7)
11. Penny-pinching (12)
13. Huggable (6)
14. Mouthpiece of the gods (6)
17. Strikingly (12)
20. Dirtier (7)
21. Destiny; fate (5)
22. The highest point (4)
23. Small falcons (8)

DOWN

1. Fastened with stitches (4)
2. Clumsy (7)
3. State of the USA (12)
4. Slander (6)
6. Game of chance (5)
7. Move out the way of (8)
8. Evening dress for men (6,6)
12. The scholastic world (8)
15. Unit of heat energy (7)
16. Ferocious (6)
18. Mix up (5)
19. Sham (anag.) (4)

CROSSWORD 203

ACROSS

1. Bucket (4)
3. Twist together (8)
9. Elongated rectangles (7)
10. One who steals (5)
11. Long deep track (3)
12. Proposal of marriage; bid (5)
13. Chubby (5)
15. Strangely (5)
17. Needing to be scratched (5)
18. Part of a curve (3)
19. Passage between rows of seats (5)
20. Polygon having ten sides (7)
21. Praising highly (8)
22. Motivate; desire to act (4)

DOWN

1. Defer action (13)
2. Small arm of the sea (5)
4. Capital of the Bahamas (6)
5. Branch of astronomy (12)
6. Fabled monster (7)
7. Fizz (13)
8. Joblessness (12)
14. Shrub with tubular flowers (7)
16. Deprive of force; stifle (6)
18. Tool for boring holes (5)

CROSSWORD 204

ACROSS

1. In spite of the fact (8)
5. Temporary living quarters (4)
9. Pursue in order to catch (5)
10. Strut about (7)
11. Relation by marriage (2-3)
12. Knock vigorously (3)
13. Desires (5)
15. Arboreal primate (5)
17. Bath vessel (3)
19. Church instrument (5)
20. Classifications (7)
21. Go about stealthily (5)
22. Entice (4)
23. State of the USA (8)

DOWN

1. Pertaining to building design (13)
2. Followed behind (7)
3. Irresistible (12)
4. Informal chatter (6)
6. Foresee or predict (5)
7. Miscellaneous equipment (13)
8. Person who listens into conversations (12)
14. Areas of land (7)
16. Whipped cream dessert (6)
18. Tribe (anag.) (5)

CROSSWORD 205

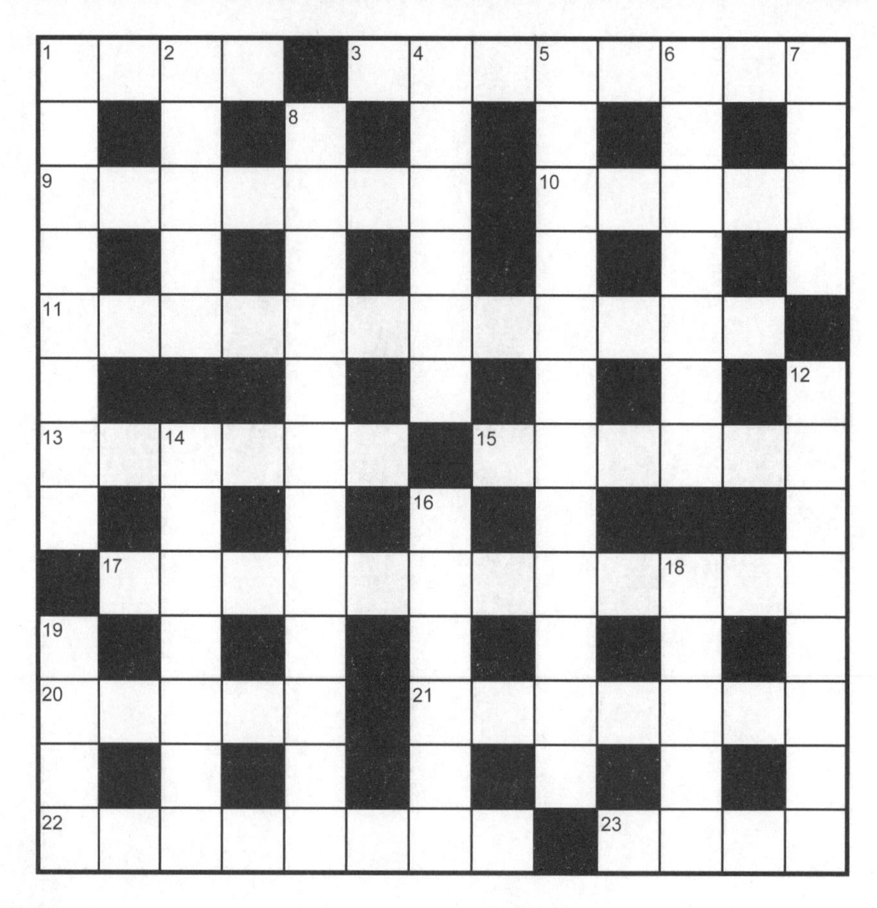

ACROSS

1. Prestigious TV award (4)
3. Disloyal people (8)
9. Blanked (7)
10. Supple (5)
11. Stretched out completely (12)
13. Strange thing (6)
15. Dual audio (6)
17. Type of cloud (12)
20. Word of farewell (5)
21. Went in (7)
22. Title of a newspaper (8)
23. Dull heavy sound (4)

DOWN

1. The production and discharge of something (8)
2. Underground worker (5)
4. Long narrow hilltops (6)
5. Unlawful (12)
6. Last longer than (of clothes) (7)
7. Noticed (4)
8. Productive insight (12)
12. Leaning at an angle (8)
14. Flowers with white petals (7)
16. Synopsis; diagram (6)
18. Deciduous coniferous tree (5)
19. Injure (4)

CROSSWORD 206

ACROSS

1. A recollection (11)
9. Committee (5)
10. Loud noise (3)
11. Cut back a tree (5)
12. Trudged through water (5)
13. Database of information (8)
16. Unmarried woman (8)
18. Speaks (5)
21. Work at a loom (5)
22. Vitality (3)
23. Astonish (5)
24. Needless (11)

DOWN

2. Erase or remove (7)
3. Cost (7)
4. Sand trap in golf (6)
5. Softly radiant (5)
6. Gave away (5)
7. Excellent (11)
8. Unintentional (11)
14. Responses (7)
15. Type of ship (7)
17. Saying (6)
19. Unit of light (5)
20. Soft type of rock (5)

CROSSWORD 207

ACROSS

1. Appease (6)
4. Uttered (6)
9. Perfect example of a quality (7)
10. Imposing a tax (7)
11. Go stealthily or furtively (5)
12. Where tennis is played (5)
14. Eccentric (5)
15. Position carefully (5)
17. Loose overall (5)
18. Fall back (7)
20. Pragmatist (7)
21. Hard to digest (6)
22. Jams tight (6)

DOWN

1. Satisfy (6)
2. Standards (8)
3. Group of birds (5)
5. Freedom from intrusion (7)
6. Flightless bird (4)
7. Gold lump (6)
8. Aircraft (pl.) (11)
13. Motionless (8)
14. Retaining (7)
15. Full of tiny holes (of a rock) (6)
16. Ice shoes (6)
17. Lean or thin (5)
19. Company symbol (4)

CROSSWORD 208

ACROSS

1. Dispatched (4)
3. Timetable (8)
9. Cosmetic liquids (7)
10. Spring flower (5)
11. Cinders (5)
12. Lift up (7)
13. Fruits with pips (6)
15. Self-supporting structures (6)
17. Ugly thing (7)
18. Tortilla topped with cheese (5)
20. Alters (5)
21. Type of natural disaster (7)
22. Splashing with water (8)
23. Sudden desire (4)

DOWN

1. Conscious knowledge of oneself (4-9)
2. Indentation; nick (5)
4. Type of nut (6)
5. Someone who sets up their own business (12)
6. Release (7)
7. Art movement (13)
8. In a carefree manner (12)
14. First in importance (7)
16. Subatomic particle such as an electron (6)
19. Type of bus (5)

CROSSWORD 209

ACROSS

1. Flight of steps (8)
5. Con; swindle (4)
9. Enthusiasm (5)
10. Bunch of flowers (7)
11. Unending (12)
13. Woody-stemmed plants (6)
14. Developed into (6)
17. Precondition (12)
20. Conquered by force (7)
21. Anxious (5)
22. Legendary creature (4)
23. Supplemental part of a book (8)

DOWN

1. Droops (4)
2. Poisonous metallic element (7)
3. Large Brazilian city (3,2,7)
4. Collections of photos (6)
6. Tiny piece of food (5)
7. Was of importance (8)
8. Most perfect example of a quality (12)
12. Elaborate musical composition (8)
15. Changed (7)
16. Arrive (4,2)
18. Pick out; choose (5)
19. Medium-sized feline (4)

CROSSWORD 210

ACROSS

1. Signs for public display (8)
5. Young sheep (4)
8. Trick or feat of daring (5)
9. Necessary (7)
10. Seed bid (anag.) (7)
12. Plant-eating aquatic mammal (7)
14. Reduce the price of (7)
16. Predatory fish (7)
18. Enduring (7)
19. Very serious (5)
20. Therefore (Latin) (4)
21. Deadlock (5-3)

DOWN

1. Monetary unit of Mexico (4)
2. Keen insight (6)
3. Care and consideration (9)
4. River in Europe (6)
6. Matter (6)
7. Official statement (8)
11. Polygon having 12 sides (9)
12. Lose (8)
13. Equipping with weapons (6)
14. Trapped (6)
15. Edible plant tuber (6)
17. A person's individuality (4)

CROSSWORD 211

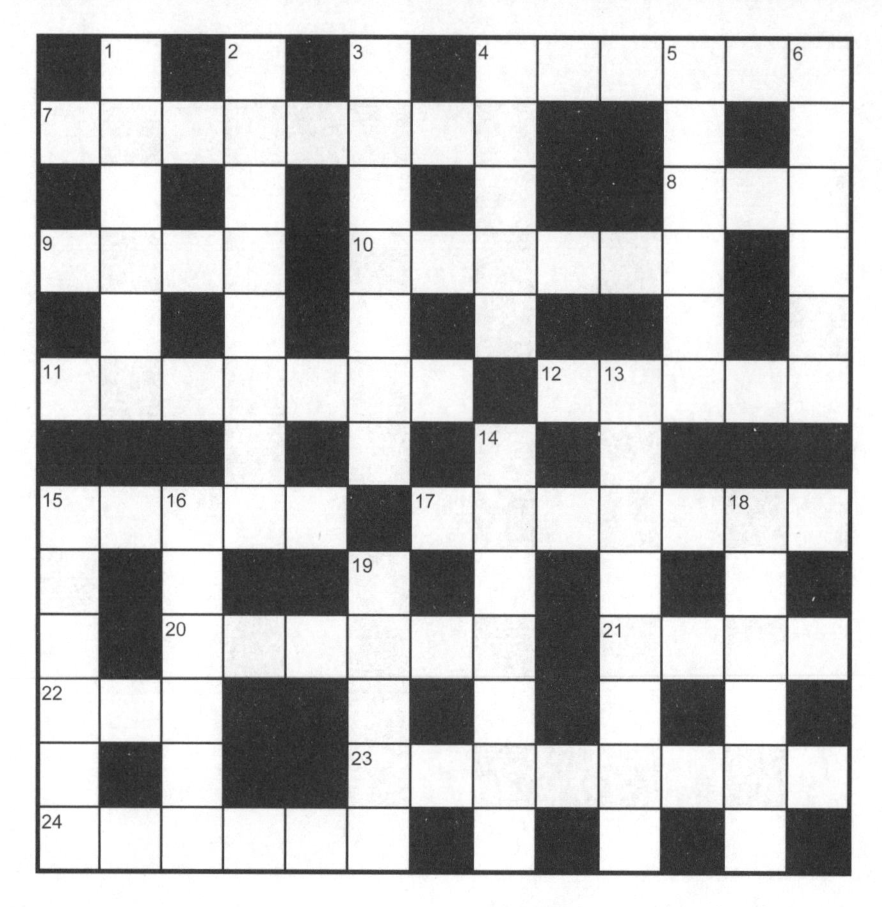

ACROSS

4. Religious leader (6)
7. Back and forth (2,3,3)
8. Broad inlet of the sea (3)
9. Having no money (4)
10. Searcher (6)
11. Moderately slow tempo (music) (7)
12. Hidden storage space (5)
15. Nocturnal insects (5)
17. Subdivision (7)
20. Shun (6)
21. Repetition to aid memory (4)
22. Precious stone (3)
23. Grandiosity of language (8)
24. Ran quickly (6)

DOWN

1. Silky case of some insect larvae (6)
2. Make gradual inroads (8)
3. Compensates for (7)
4. Spoke softly (5)
5. Set of instructions (6)
6. Wolflike wild dog (6)
13. Earlier in time (8)
14. Among (7)
15. Joined together (6)
16. Recurrent topics (6)
18. Deceive with ingenuity (6)
19. Group of notes played simultaneously (5)

CROSSWORD 212

ACROSS

1. Publisher's emblem (8)
5. Creative thought (4)
9. More pleasant (5)
10. Competitors in a sprint (7)
11. Small holes in cloth or leather (7)
12. Command (5)
13. Indulge a person (6)
14. Long-legged rodent (6)
17. First Greek letter (5)
19. Side of a coin bearing the head (7)
20. Brings about (7)
21. Woman getting married (5)
22. Sell (anag.) (4)
23. Totally uninformed (8)

DOWN

1. Very thoughtful (13)
2. Tall stand used by a preacher (7)
3. Persistence (12)
4. Female monster (6)
6. Extreme fear (5)
7. Aggressive self-assurance (13)
8. Not excusable (12)
15. Elevate (7)
16. Remains preserved in rock (6)
18. Foot-operated lever (5)

CROSSWORD 213

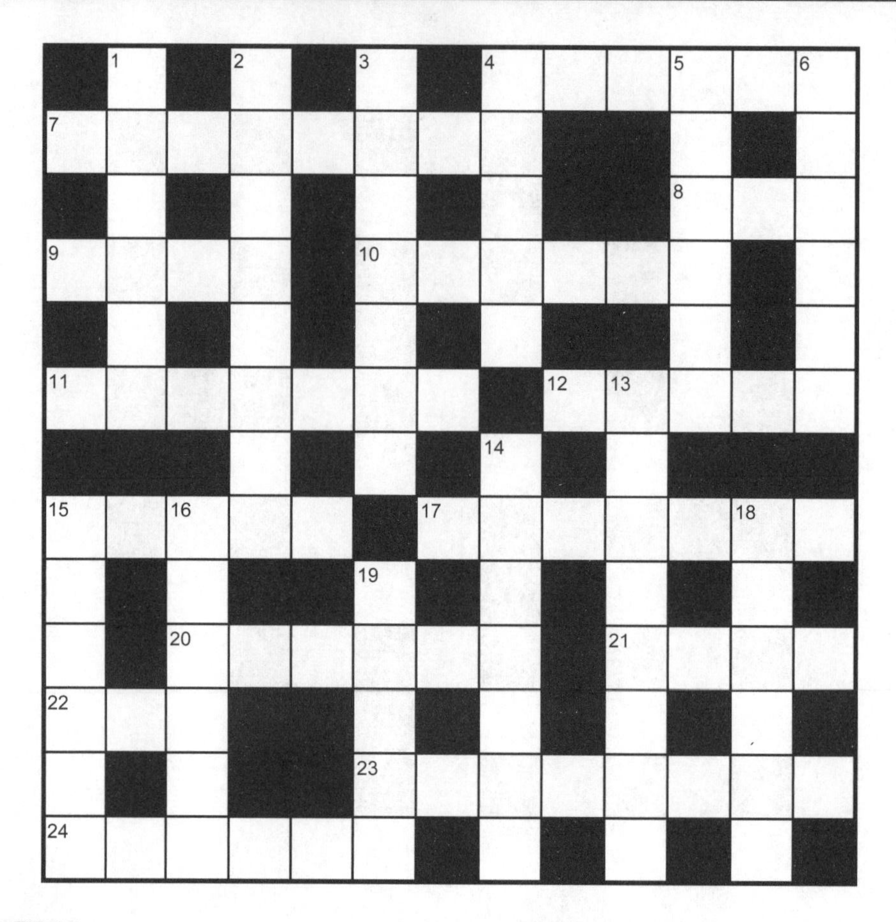

ACROSS

4. City in northeastern Italy (6)
7. Grisly (8)
8. Pear-shaped fruit (3)
9. Gossip (4)
10. Speak rapidly (6)
11. Honesty; integrity (7)
12. Obnoxiously forward (5)
15. Test or examine a metal (5)
17. Cup (7)
20. Trust or faith in (6)
21. Unit of land area (4)
22. Ground condensation (3)
23. Protrudes (8)
24. Fashions (6)

DOWN

1. Bow and arrow expert (6)
2. Segment of the spinal column (8)
3. Fails to remember (7)
4. Action words (5)
5. Deduces from evidence (6)
6. Fourscore (6)
13. Removed goods from a van (8)
14. Light fabric (7)
15. Homes (6)
16. Tunnel under a road for pedestrians (6)
18. Insertion marks (6)
19. Slips (anag.) (5)

CROSSWORD 214

ACROSS

1. Condition in an agreement (11)
9. Negligent (3)
10. Shoe ties (5)
11. Perfume (5)
12. Craftsman who uses stone (5)
13. Process of sticking to a surface (8)
16. Narrowly avoided accident (4,4)
18. Bungle (5)
20. Tarns (anag.) (5)
21. Vital organ (5)
22. Male person (3)
23. Spookiness (11)

DOWN

2. Levies (5)
3. Large mast (5)
4. Passed the tongue over (6)
5. Scuffles (7)
6. Character in Hamlet (7)
7. Poorly behaved; impolite (3-8)
8. Amazing (11)
14. Decorate food (7)
15. Breaks into pieces (7)
17. Spread out awkwardly (6)
18. Relay device (5)
19. Measures duration (5)

CROSSWORD 215

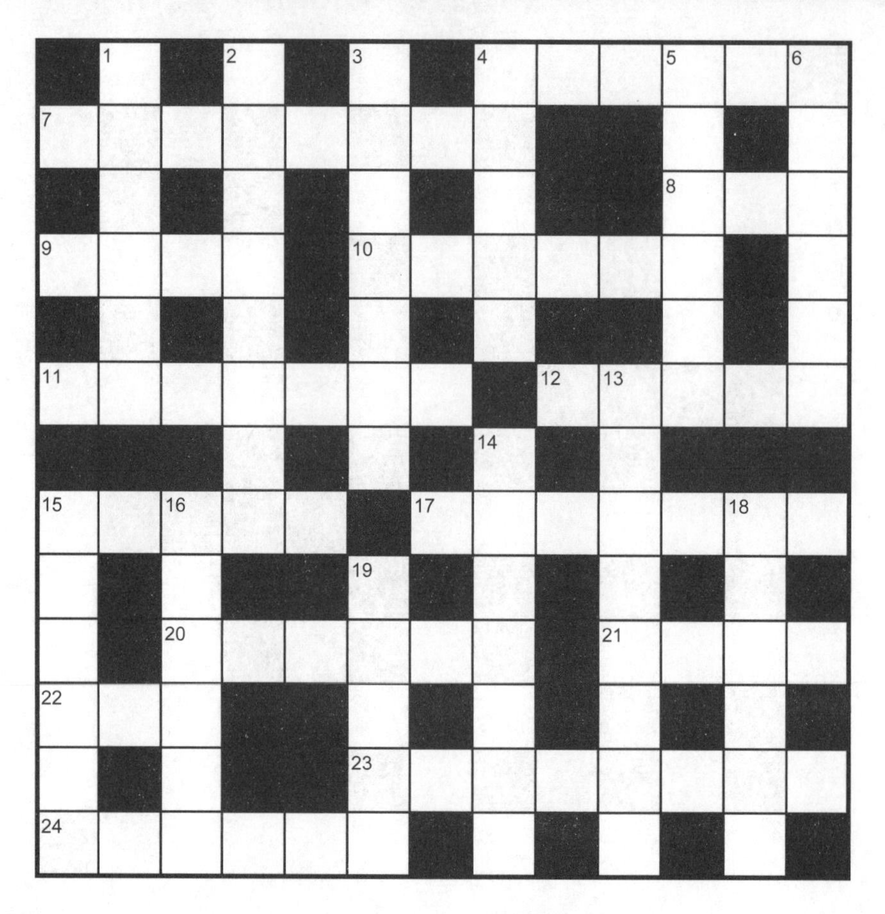

ACROSS

4. Capital of Lebanon (6)
7. Small biting fly (8)
8. Louse egg (3)
9. Brass musical instrument (4)
10. Messengers of God (6)
11. Buildings for horses (7)
12. Conveys an action without words (5)
15. Animal that uses two legs for walking (5)
17. These remove pencil marks (7)
20. Deciduous flowering shrub (6)
21. Area of a church (4)
22. Item that unlocks a door (3)
23. Opposite of positive (8)
24. Very enthusiastic (6)

DOWN

1. Vigorous; strong and healthy (6)
2. Petty quarrel (8)
3. Widened (7)
4. Tree branch (5)
5. Payment for the release of someone (6)
6. Teachers (6)
13. Madness (8)
14. Place in order (7)
15. Drinking container (6)
16. Religious act of petition (6)
18. Bring back to life (6)
19. Held on to something tightly (5)

CROSSWORD 216

ACROSS

1. Vine fruits (6)
4. Division of a group (6)
9. At the ocean floor (7)
10. Far away (7)
11. Shy (5)
12. Large pebble (5)
14. Steep slope (5)
17. Calls out loudly (5)
19. Steer (anag.) (5)
21. Raging fire (7)
23. Unrecoverable money owed (3,4)
24. Walked quickly (6)
25. Took a break (6)

DOWN

1. Classifies; sorts (6)
2. Ancient boats (4)
3. Angers (7)
5. Vault under a church (5)
6. Sleep disorder (8)
7. Tune (6)
8. Papal state (7,4)
13. Person not accepted by society (8)
15. Outline; silhouette (7)
16. Diving waterbirds (6)
18. Unemotional (6)
20. Pattern (5)
22. Crack (4)

CROSSWORD 217

ACROSS

1. Speck (4)
3. Surpass (8)
9. Less quiet (7)
10. Type of tooth (5)
11. Top degree mark (5)
12. Flat highland (7)
13. Large strong boxes (6)
15. Superior of a nunnery (6)
17. Endure (7)
18. Rope used to catch cattle (5)
20. Our planet (5)
21. Japanese dish of raw fish (7)
22. Most precipitous (8)
23. Lift something heavy (4)

DOWN

1. Makers (13)
2. Person who always puts in a lot of effort (5)
4. Not ready to eat (of fruit) (6)
5. Sleepwalking (12)
6. Release someone from duty (7)
7. Musician (13)
8. Absolute authority in any sphere (12)
14. Approve or support (7)
16. Loops with running knots (6)
19. Sharp peak (5)

CROSSWORD 218

ACROSS

1. Avarice (5)
4. Debate (7)
7. Common cause of an illness (5)
8. Line joining corners of a square (8)
9. Light downy particles (5)
11. Curiosity (8)
15. Flying an aircraft (8)
17. Very unpleasant (5)
19. Prevent heat loss (8)
20. Concentrate on (5)
21. Vital content (7)
22. Seed cases (5)

DOWN

1. Cultivation of plants (9)
2. Diplomatic building (7)
3. Refuses to acknowledge (7)
4. Decomposes (6)
5. Cools down (6)
6. Cram (5)
10. Breaks into pieces (9)
12. Mischievous (7)
13. Magicians (7)
14. Sagacious (6)
16. Inborn (6)
18. Chambers (5)

CROSSWORD 219

ACROSS

1. Thick cord (4)
3. Fact of being irreversible (8)
9. Travel somewhere (7)
10. Grape (anag.) (5)
11. Skilled joiner (12)
14. What a hen lays (3)
16. Wipe (5)
17. Home for a pig (3)
18. Lost in thought (6-6)
21. Be alive; be real (5)
22. Hair-cleansing product (7)
23. Collapse disastrously (4,4)
24. Computer memory unit (4)

DOWN

1. Rebuffed (8)
2. Ball of lead (5)
4. Climbing vine (3)
5. Pertaining to letters (12)
6. Act of entering (7)
7. Spun thread used for knitting (4)
8. Indifferent to (12)
12. Distinguishing characteristic (5)
13. Group of symptoms which occur together (8)
15. One of the archangels (7)
19. Very foolish (5)
20. Hold as an opinion (4)
22. Fasten with stitches (3)

CROSSWORD 220

ACROSS

1. Unyielding (8)
5. Heat up (4)
9. Pertaining to warships (5)
10. Runs out (7)
11. Farm vehicle (7)
12. Body of rules (5)
13. Wildcat (6)
14. Maples (anag.) (6)
17. Quartzlike gems (5)
19. Speak to (7)
20. Suggested but not stated explicitly (7)
21. Musical instrument (5)
22. Golf pegs (4)
23. Classic US comedy TV series (8)

DOWN

1. Zoologist who studies birds (13)
2. Turn aside from a course (7)
3. Connection or association (12)
4. Belonging to them (6)
6. Protective garment worn in the kitchen (5)
7. Misinterpreted (13)
8. Spotless (5-3-4)
15. Get ready (7)
16. Stick of wax (6)
18. Plentiful (5)

CROSSWORD 221

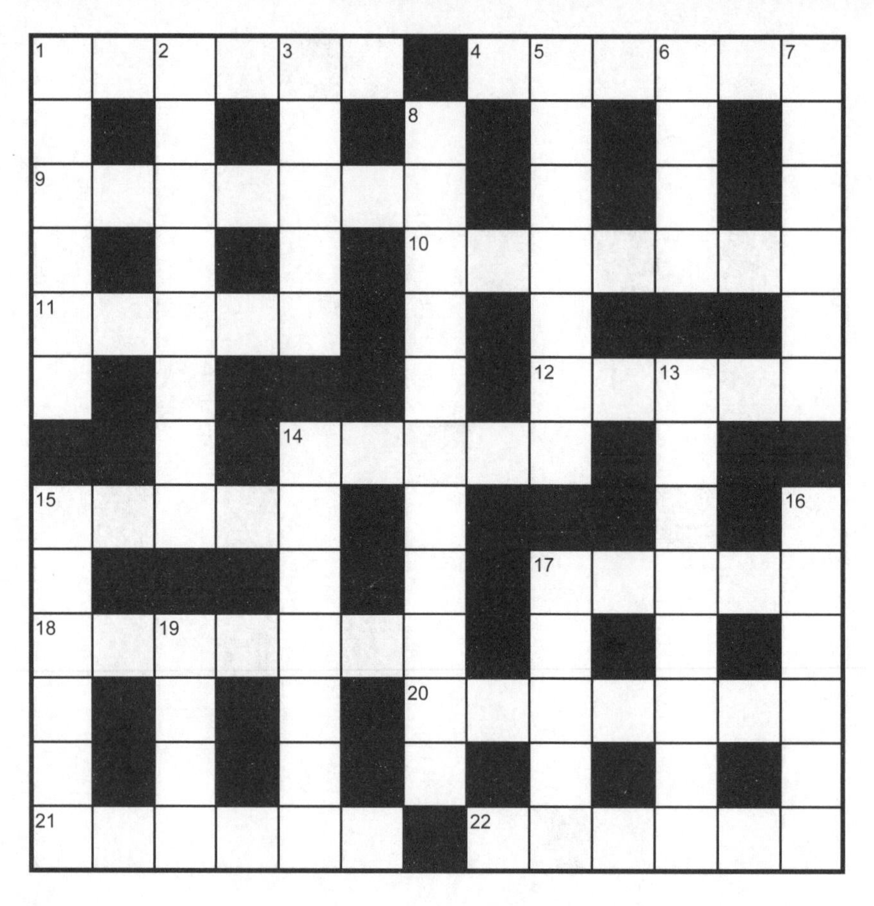

ACROSS

1. Wicked people (6)
4. Mottled marking (6)
9. Easier to understand (7)
10. Streets (7)
11. Short simple song (5)
12. Russian emperors (5)
14. Temporary lodgings (5)
15. Hit with the fist (5)
17. Bed cover (5)
18. Thoroughly (2,5)
20. Escaping (7)
21. Pointed weapons (6)
22. E.g. Borneo (6)

DOWN

1. Front of a building; false display (6)
2. Elementary negatively charged particle (8)
3. Grimy (5)
5. Characteristics (7)
6. South American country (4)
7. Deletes (6)
8. Female relation (11)
13. Aromatic plant used in cooking (8)
14. Cut pieces off something hard (7)
15. Groups of lions (6)
16. Put on a production (6)
17. Becomes acrimonious (5)
19. Bond movie (2,2)

CROSSWORD 222

ACROSS

1. Films (6)
7. Sanctity (8)
8. Remuneration (3)
9. Quantity you can hold (6)
10. Appendage (4)
11. Talk (5)
13. Rubbish (7)
15. Collate (7)
17. Tidily kept (5)
21. Popular martial art (4)
22. Throes (anag.) (6)
23. Aggressive dog (3)
24. Lover (8)
25. Show-off (6)

DOWN

1. Trees with lobed leaves (6)
2. Journey by sea (6)
3. Move from one place to another (5)
4. Blank page in a book (7)
5. Unsteady (8)
6. Putting a question to (6)
12. Consent (8)
14. Intoxicating element in wine (7)
16. Of the eye (6)
18. Mistake in snooker; blunder (6)
19. Great fear (6)
20. Pointed; acute (5)

CROSSWORD 223

ACROSS

1. Eternal (11)
9. Partly digested animal food (3)
10. Opposite of lower (5)
11. Natural yellow resin (5)
12. Flat surface (5)
13. And so on (2,6)
16. Cigars (8)
18. Large fruit with pulpy flesh (5)
20. Relating to a city (5)
21. Remove errors from software (5)
22. Finish first (3)
23. Without guilt (11)

DOWN

2. Russian spirit (5)
3. Red cosmetic powder (5)
4. Feature (6)
5. Vehement denunciations (7)
6. Took small bites out of (7)
7. Type of treatment using needles (11)
8. Menacing (11)
14. Wordy (7)
15. A placeholder name (2-3-2)
17. Biters (anag.) (6)
18. Tycoon (5)
19. Areas of mown grass (5)

CROSSWORD 224

ACROSS

1. Mischievous fairies (4)
3. Restored (8)
9. Trailblazer (7)
10. Natural underground chambers (5)
11. Remote in manner (5)
12. Capital of Kenya (7)
13. Type of bicycle (6)
15. Observing (6)
17. Variety of rummy (7)
18. Musical speeds (5)
20. Cleanse the body (5)
21. Gloss (7)
22. Publicity (8)
23. Sued (anag.) (4)

DOWN

1. Unfeasible (13)
2. Camera image (abbrev.) (5)
4. Short trip to perform a task (6)
5. Practice of designing buildings (12)
6. Pasta pockets (7)
7. Successful and eminent (13)
8. Altruism (12)
14. Without interruption (3-4)
16. Sculptor (6)
19. Sends out in the post (5)

CROSSWORD 225

ACROSS

1. Very crowded (of a place) (6)
7. Opposite of departures (8)
8. Group of whales (3)
9. Fishes (6)
10. Space; part of a building (4)
11. Role; office (5)
13. Stated the meaning of (7)
15. Symbols of disgrace (7)
17. Hits swiftly (5)
21. Country whose capital is Havana (4)
22. Yellow fruit (6)
23. School of Mahayana Buddhism (3)
24. Window in a roof (8)
25. Moves smoothly (6)

DOWN

1. Matures (of fruit) (6)
2. Title used for a French woman (6)
3. Every 24 hours (5)
4. Clad (7)
5. Summary (8)
6. Recess (6)
12. Debatably (8)
14. Vegetable (7)
16. Main tree stems (6)
18. Astonished (6)
19. Supplies sparingly (6)
20. Midges (5)

CROSSWORD 226

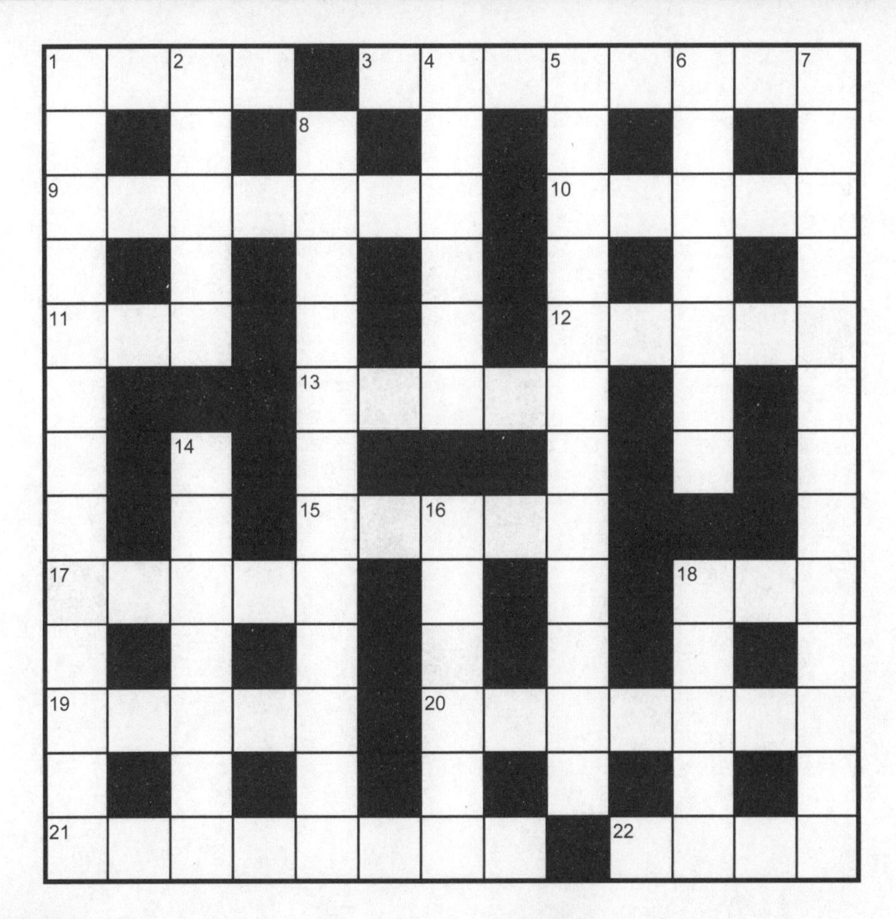

ACROSS

1. Catholic leader (4)
3. Rebuke (8)
9. One of the planets (7)
10. Dreadful (5)
11. Pay (anag.) (3)
12. Roofed entrance to a house (5)
13. Important topic (5)
15. Religious table (5)
17. Mark of insertion (5)
18. Statute (3)
19. Bring on oneself (5)
20. Excited agreeably (7)
21. Muttering angrily (8)
22. Askew (4)

DOWN

1. Miserly (5-8)
2. Appear suddenly (3,2)
4. Votes into office (6)
5. Re-emergence (12)
6. Yields a supply of (7)
7. Unenthusiastically (4-9)
8. Agreed upon by several parties (12)
14. Hot wind blowing from northern Africa (7)
16. Fabric associated with Scotland (6)
18. Permit (5)

CROSSWORD 227

ACROSS

1. Married men (8)
5. One of two equal parts (4)
9. Wound from a wasp (5)
10. Extremely cold (7)
11. Jail term without end (4,8)
14. Unit of energy (3)
15. Small branch (5)
16. Lyric poem (3)
17. Separately (12)
20. Short close-fitting jacket (7)
22. Person who goes on long walks (5)
23. Piece of office furniture (4)
24. Competition participants (8)

DOWN

1. Silence (4)
2. Grabbing hold of (7)
3. In a hostile manner (12)
4. Excavated soil (3)
6. Pertaining to birds (5)
7. Started to lose strength (8)
8. Mapmaker (12)
12. Made a mistake (5)
13. Prompted to think of (8)
16. Waterproof fabric (7)
18. Percussion instruments (5)
19. Part of the eye (4)
21. Not (anag.) (3)

CROSSWORD 228

ACROSS

4. Safety device in a car (6)
7. Recurring at intervals (8)
8. Chatter (3)
9. Clench (4)
10. Popular winter sport (6)
11. Piece of furniture (7)
12. Give a solemn oath (5)
15. Shade (anag.) (5)
17. Sneaky (7)
20. Made amends for (6)
21. Stride; rate of moving (4)
22. Man's best friend (3)
23. Bridge above another road (8)
24. Tempestuous (6)

DOWN

1. Closer (6)
2. Inclined; got rid of (8)
3. Epic poem (7)
4. Bitterly pungent (5)
5. Cause bafflement (6)
6. Speak unintelligibly (6)
13. Trachea (8)
14. Confused (7)
15. Throngs (6)
16. In slow tempo (of music) (6)
18. Most pleasant (6)
19. Harass; frustrate (5)

CROSSWORD 229

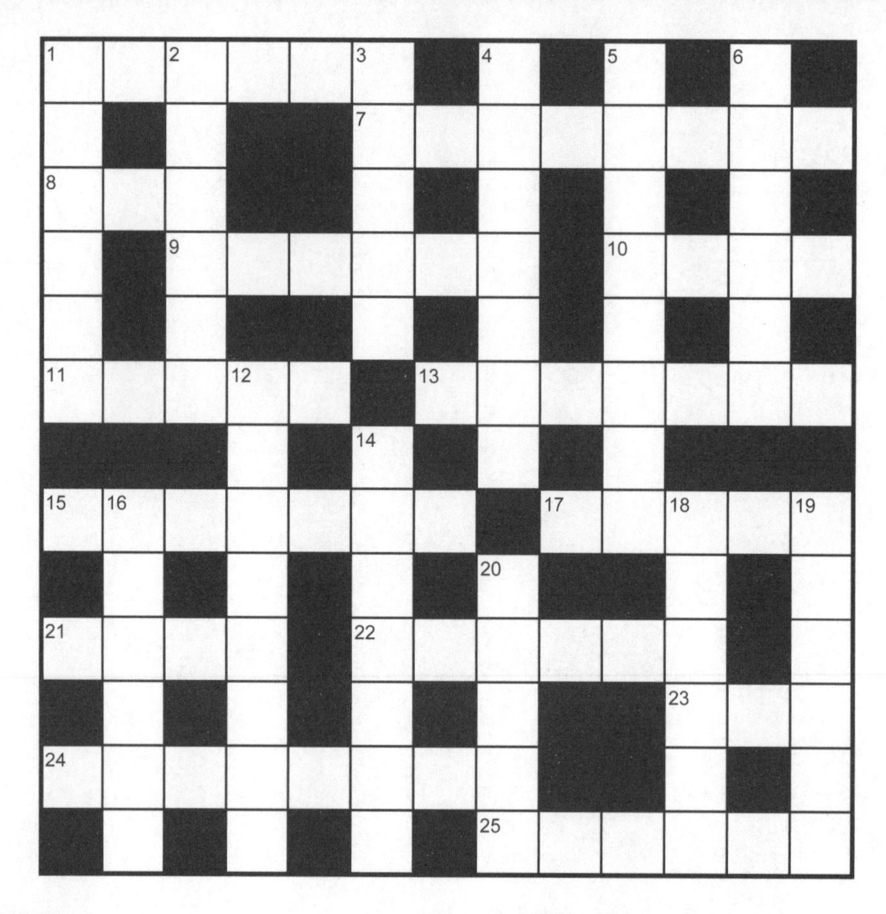

ACROSS

1. Checked; examined (6)
7. Lifts up (8)
8. Fellow (3)
9. Impart knowledge (6)
10. Cultivated (4)
11. Droopy (5)
13. Dressed in a vestment (7)
15. Friendless (7)
17. Gaped (anag.) (5)
21. Melody (4)
22. Factory siren (6)
23. Father (3)
24. Took temporary possession of (8)
25. Garment part that covers an arm (6)

DOWN

1. Large solitary cats (6)
2. Maxim (6)
3. Lure an animal into a trap (5)
4. Stir up trouble (7)
5. Symmetrical open plane curve (8)
6. End a dispute (6)
12. Mathematics of points and lines (8)
14. Brother's children (7)
16. Nerve cell (6)
18. Belt worn round the waist (6)
19. Remove silt from a river (6)
20. Incites (5)

CROSSWORD 230

ACROSS

1. Sport popular in America (8)
5. Arguments against (4)
8. Effluent system (5)
9. Apprentice (7)
10. Look into (7)
12. Monumental Egyptian structure (7)
14. Not level (7)
16. Opposite of thinner (7)
18. Plant with starchy tuberous roots (7)
19. Lying flat (5)
20. Covers; tops (4)
21. Intellectual (8)

DOWN

1. Person in charge at work (4)
2. Woodcutter (6)
3. Skin blemish (9)
4. Drank with the tongue (6)
6. State of the USA (6)
7. Emaciated (8)
11. Tropical fruit (9)
12. Etiquette (8)
13. Failed to hit the target (6)
14. Refined in manner (6)
15. Turmoil (6)
17. In a good way (4)

CROSSWORD 231

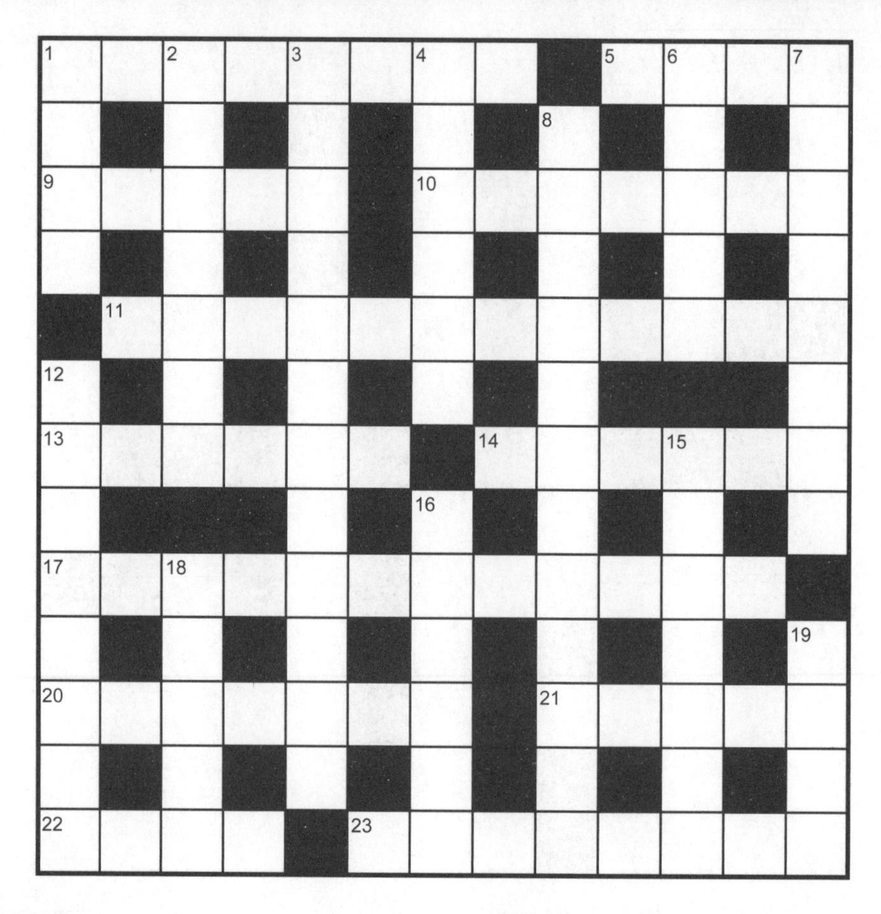

ACROSS

1. Withdraws (8)
5. Small flake of soot (4)
9. Put an idea in someone's mind (5)
10. Treated unjustly (7)
11. Relating to horoscopes (12)
13. Insect larvae (6)
14. Agree (6)
17. Calculations of dimensions (12)
20. Windpipe (7)
21. Continuing in existence (5)
22. Reduce one's food intake (4)
23. Beat out grain (8)

DOWN

1. Ready to eat (4)
2. Wooden bar across a window (7)
3. Reconsideration; item added later (12)
4. Absorbent cloths (6)
6. Conjuring trick (5)
7. Children beginning to walk (8)
8. Bring together into a mass (12)
12. Excited; lively (8)
15. Aquatic creature with prominent barbels (7)
16. Angel of the highest order (6)
18. Pure love (5)
19. Dame (anag.) (4)

CROSSWORD 232

ACROSS

1. Where one finds Kabul (11)
9. Cooking appliance (3)
10. Number of deadly sins (5)
11. Flow with a whirling motion (5)
12. Lines (anag.) (5)
13. Cervine (8)
16. Journey across (8)
18. Value (5)
20. Competes in a speed contest (5)
21. Hushed (5)
22. Measure of length (3)
23. Well-known sentence (11)

DOWN

2. Legend (5)
3. TV presenters (5)
4. Beginner (6)
5. Detection devices (7)
6. Drug that relieves pain (7)
7. Type of fat (11)
8. Orca (6,5)
14. Eyelash cosmetic (7)
15. Of enormous effect (7)
17. Stop talking (4,2)
18. Less narrow (5)
19. Staggers (5)

CROSSWORD 233

ACROSS

1. Large washing bowl (4)
3. Grammatical case (8)
9. Fish-eating birds of prey (7)
10. Concealing garments (5)
11. Inharmoniously (12)
13. Fleet of ships (6)
15. Notable inconvenience (6)
17. Incomprehensibly (12)
20. Friend (Spanish) (5)
21. Nation (7)
22. Underground cells (8)
23. Among (4)

DOWN

1. Famous street in Manhattan (8)
2. Sorts (5)
4. Next to (6)
5. Beneficial (12)
6. Frozen water spears (7)
7. Otherwise (4)
8. Without parallel (6,2,4)
12. Naive or sentimental (4-4)
14. Stately residence (7)
16. Visible warning device (6)
18. ___ pole: tribal emblem (5)
19. Pointer on a clock (4)

CROSSWORD 234

ACROSS

1. Massaged (6)
4. Arched shape of a road (6)
9. Rowdy (7)
10. Country in western Africa (7)
11. Amphibians (5)
12. Tool used for digging (5)
14. Grain storage chambers (5)
17. Mortal (5)
19. Spacious (5)
21. Final stage of a process (7)
23. Model of the body (7)
24. Cease (6)
25. Entreated; beseeched (6)

DOWN

1. Domains (6)
2. Sharp bristle (4)
3. Comes into view (7)
5. Furnish; decorate (5)
6. Person devoted to reading (8)
7. Oppose (6)
8. Semi-transparent (11)
13. Amazes (8)
15. Quiver (7)
16. Prepared (6)
18. Required (6)
20. Bonds of union (5)
22. Breezy (4)

CROSSWORD 235

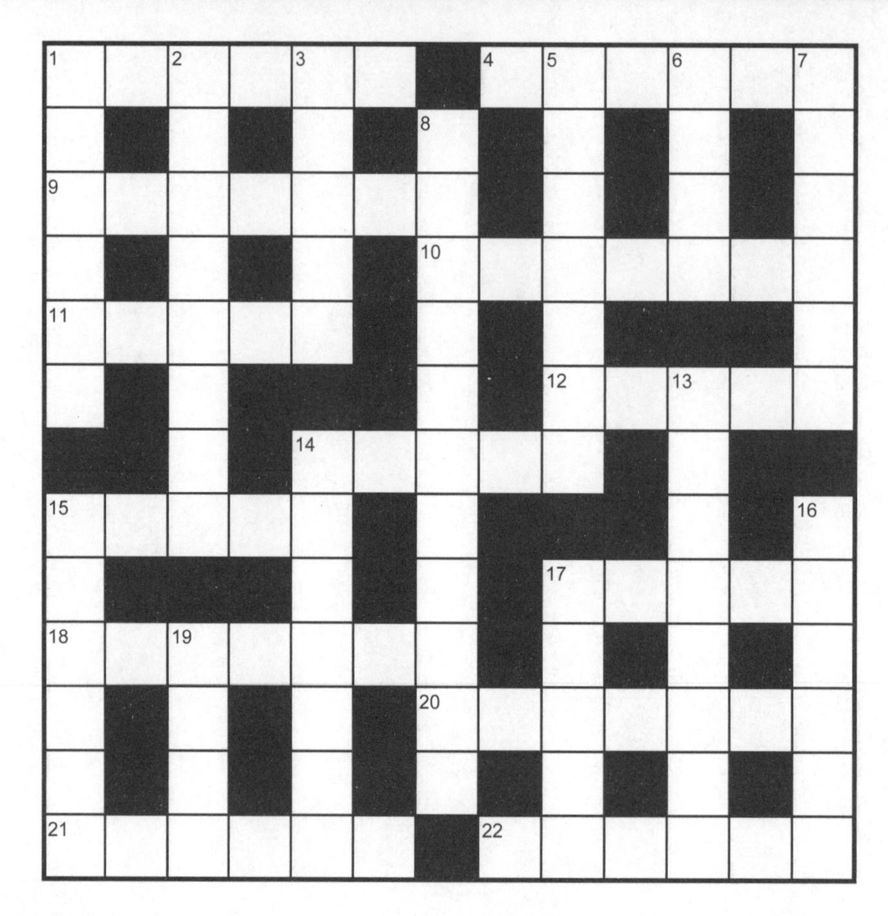

ACROSS

1. Sinful (6)
4. Pointed projectiles (6)
9. Lack of (7)
10. Becomes less wide (7)
11. Judges (5)
12. Doctrine (5)
14. Disregard the rules (5)
15. Propose; utter (5)
17. Jittery (5)
18. Storage tank (7)
20. Oppose an argument (7)
21. Mock (6)
22. Fixed (6)

DOWN

1. Country in Africa with capital Kampala (6)
2. Exaggerated emotion (8)
3. Joins together (5)
5. Deflect light (7)
6. Upon (4)
7. Perceived (6)
8. Goodwill (11)
13. Freed from doing (8)
14. Highly excited (7)
15. Dismissed from a job (6)
16. Composite of different species (6)
17. Unit of energy (5)
19. Not sweet (4)

CROSSWORD 236

ACROSS

1. Treatment of the hands (8)
5. Flaring star (4)
9. Brief appearance in a film by someone famous (5)
10. Enunciation of speech (7)
11. Modestly (12)
13. Massive system of stars (6)
14. Fighting instrument (6)
17. Crucial (3,9)
20. Plans to do something (7)
21. Exit (5)
22. Immediately following (4)
23. Two-wheeled vehicles (8)

DOWN

1. Manure (4)
2. Existing solely in name (7)
3. Question in great detail (5-7)
4. Bone in the forearm (6)
6. Outstanding (of a debt) (5)
7. Irritating (8)
8. Not on purpose; inadvertently (12)
12. Rural (8)
15. Game played on a sloping board (7)
16. Dwarfed tree (6)
18. Milky fluid found in some plants (5)
19. Wagers (4)

CROSSWORD 237

ACROSS

1. Price (4)
3. Spherical (8)
9. Newspaper audience (7)
10. Attendant upon God (5)
11. Unit of resistance (3)
12. Shallow recess (5)
13. Equip (5)
15. Annoying insects (5)
17. Pertaining to the ear (5)
18. Bleat of a sheep (3)
19. Where one finds Rome (5)
20. Stinted (anag.) (7)
21. Refer to famous people one knows (4-4)
22. Ale (4)

DOWN

1. Confirmation (13)
2. Sudden contraction (5)
4. Endured (6)
5. Forcible indoctrination (12)
6. Rational; reasonable (7)
7. Amusement park ride (6,7)
8. Working for oneself (4-8)
14. Prepare beforehand (7)
16. Room where an artist works (6)
18. Seawater (5)

CROSSWORD 238

ACROSS

1. Crimes (8)
5. Takes to court (4)
8. Climb onto (5)
9. Drive back by force (7)
10. Not attached or tied together (7)
12. Pertaining to matrimony (7)
14. Clutching (7)
16. Person proposed for office (7)
18. Coped (7)
19. Device used to give support (5)
20. Corrode (4)
21. Unskilled; amateur (8)

DOWN

1. Seethe (4)
2. Less quiet (6)
3. Food (9)
4. Loud blast of sound (6)
6. Diacritical mark of two dots (6)
7. Paying out money (8)
11. Container for voting slips (6,3)
12. Inaccurate name (8)
13. Modifies (6)
14. Involving direct confrontation (4-2)
15. Breathe in (6)
17. Warm up (4)

CROSSWORD 239

ACROSS

1. Person invited to one's house (5)
4. Dead end (7)
7. Go to see (5)
8. Wedge to keep an entrance open (8)
9. Attempts (5)
11. Without fortune (8)
15. Until now (8)
17. Precipitates (5)
19. Raised (8)
20. Criminal deception (5)
21. Complex wholes (7)
22. Small valley (5)

DOWN

1. Venetian boatman (9)
2. Impose one's will (7)
3. Scottish national emblem (7)
4. Blocks of metal (6)
5. Where bees are kept (6)
6. Grin (5)
10. Of lesser importance (9)
12. Removing hair (7)
13. Visibly anxious (7)
14. Admit to a post (6)
16. Relations by marriage (2-4)
18. Ordered arrangement (5)

CROSSWORD 240

ACROSS

1. Woes (4)
3. Fortify against attack (8)
9. Swift-flying songbird (7)
10. Rule (5)
11. In a persuasive manner (12)
14. Rodent (3)
16. Coarse (5)
17. Excessively (3)
18. Unseen observer (3,2,3,4)
21. Complete trust (5)
22. Allowing (7)
23. Official list of names (8)
24. So be it (4)

DOWN

1. Lacking confidence (8)
2. Gain knowledge (5)
4. Cut grass (3)
5. Agreements; plans (12)
6. Set of three things (7)
7. Volcano in Sicily (4)
8. Ordinary dress (5,7)
12. Small container (5)
13. Young ruffian (8)
15. Leaning at an angle (7)
19. Self-evident truth (5)
20. From a distance (4)
22. Sheltered side (3)

CROSSWORD 241

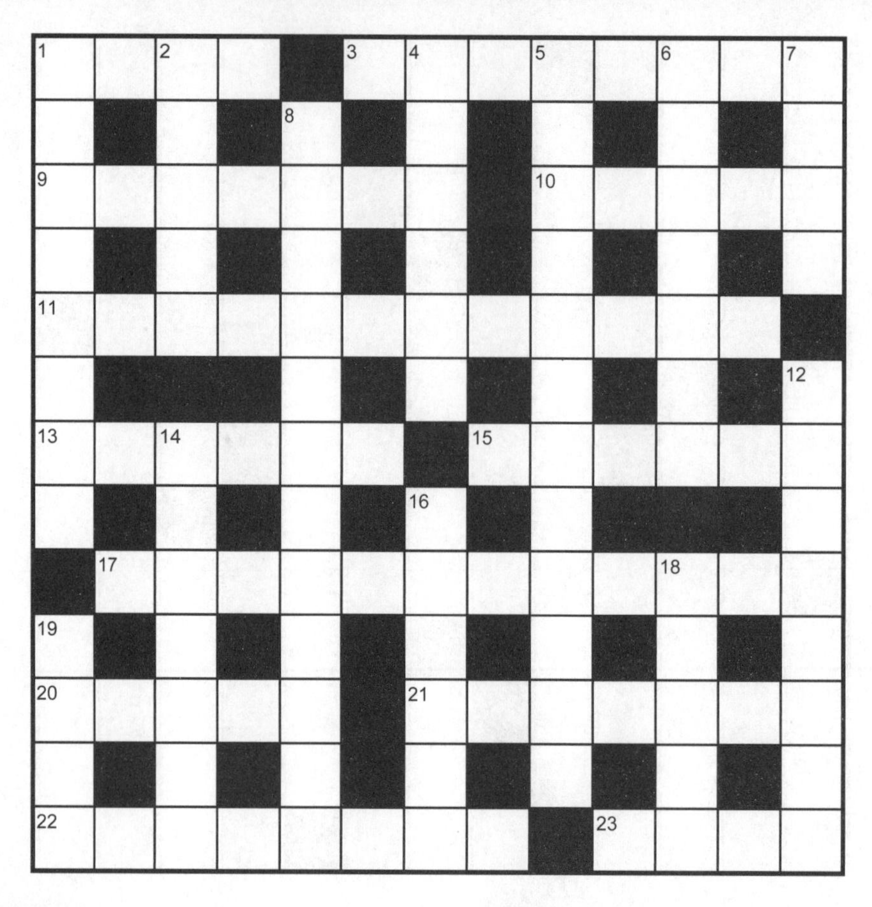

ACROSS

1. Rank (4)
3. Barely adequate (8)
9. Without flaws (7)
10. Felony (5)
11. Total confusion (12)
13. Time of widespread glaciation (3,3)
15. Third sign of the zodiac (6)
17. Give a false account of (12)
20. Connection; link (3-2)
21. Provokes (7)
22. Assembled (8)
23. Correct; accurate (4)

DOWN

1. Type of state (8)
2. Lose a contest intentionally (5)
4. Book of the Bible (6)
5. Ineptness (12)
6. Dry red table wine of Italy (7)
7. Flat and smooth (4)
8. Hostile aggressiveness (12)
12. Mild aversion (8)
14. Distinguished (7)
16. Join together (6)
18. Go inside (5)
19. Adult male deer (4)

CROSSWORD 242

ACROSS

1. Defame (6)
7. Formal speeches (8)
8. Swish (of an animal's tail) (3)
9. Flashy (6)
10. Plunder; take illegally (4)
11. Wander off track (5)
13. Nestle up against (7)
15. Rushing (7)
17. Wheels that move rudders on ships (5)
21. Edible fruit with a distinctive shape (4)
22. Type of ski race (6)
23. Soak up; wipe away (3)
24. Synthetic polymeric substances (8)
25. Wiped out (6)

DOWN

1. Letters like 'a' and 'e' (6)
2. Lumberjack (6)
3. Period between childhood and adulthood (5)
4. Changing (7)
5. Conversation (8)
6. Unfurl (6)
12. Pithy saying (8)
14. Costing (anag.) (7)
16. Ancient or well established (3-3)
18. Assumed propositions (6)
19. Oozed (6)
20. Bring about (5)

CROSSWORD 243

ACROSS

1. Impersonations (11)
9. Signal assent with the head (3)
10. Short and sweet (5)
11. Wrong (5)
12. Bottomless pit (5)
13. Person with an appreciation of beauty (8)
16. Copied (8)
18. Muscular strength (5)
20. Comic dramatic work (5)
21. Breathing organs (5)
22. Scarf of feathers or fur (3)
23. Tolerant in one's views (5-6)

DOWN

2. Dirty (5)
3. Loose outer garments (5)
4. Evening party (6)
5. Young children (7)
6. People born in a particular area (7)
7. Not necessary (8,3)
8. Relation by marriage (6-2-3)
14. One of four equal parts (7)
15. Kneecap (7)
17. US rapper (6)
18. Subatomic particle (5)
19. Stroll (5)

CROSSWORD 244

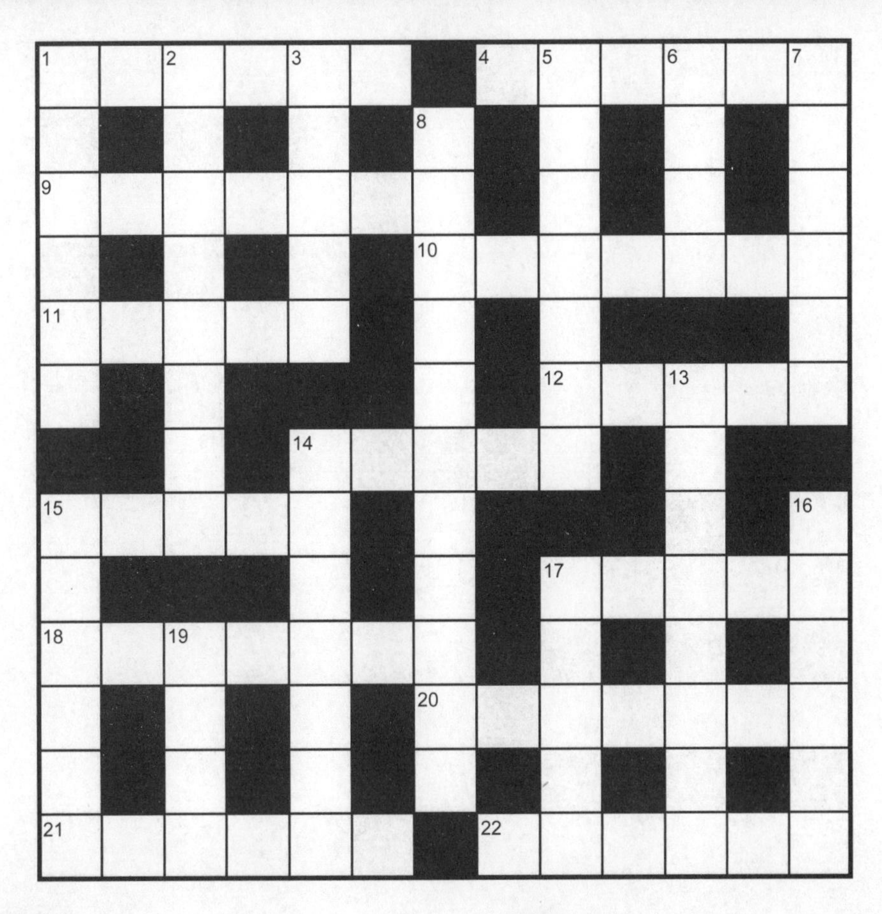

ACROSS

1. State of sleep (6)
4. Dung beetle (6)
9. Untanned leather (7)
10. Wears away (7)
11. Songbirds (5)
12. Fills a suitcase (5)
14. Only just able to be seen (5)
15. Nonsense (5)
17. Main (5)
18. Prepare for printing (7)
20. Keep out (7)
21. Live in (6)
22. Cruel ruler (6)

DOWN

1. Seldom (6)
2. Potent (8)
3. Reads quickly (5)
5. Willing to act dishonestly (7)
6. Thoroughfare (4)
7. Strong gusts of wind (6)
8. Switched off (11)
13. A Roman emperor (8)
14. Ate an extravagant meal (7)
15. This is spread on toast (6)
16. Be aggrieved by (6)
17. Finicky (5)
19. Nips (anag.) (4)

CROSSWORD 245

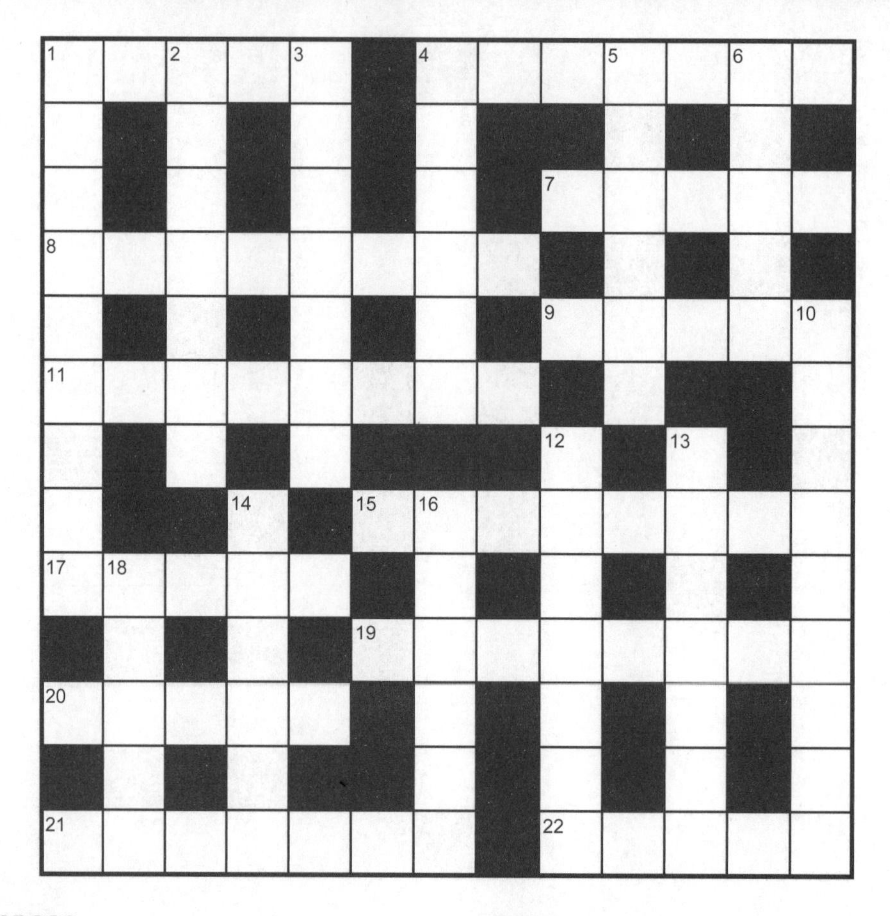

ACROSS

1. Fire (5)
4. Nearest (7)
7. Moist (of air) (5)
8. Low-cost travel package (2-6)
9. Released from jail (5)
11. Pertaining to cooking (8)
15. Dismiss as unimportant (5,3)
17. Ghost (5)
19. Giant ocean waves (8)
20. Indian garments (5)
21. Reconstruct (7)
22. Harsh and serious in manner (5)

DOWN

1. Marine crustaceans (9)
2. Fulmars (anag.) (7)
3. Banners or flags (7)
4. Less warm (6)
5. Writhe (6)
6. Shoot with great precision (5)
10. Dispersal (9)
12. Destructive (7)
13. French territorial division (7)
14. Gaming tile (6)
16. Provider of cheap accommodation (6)
18. Stage (5)

CROSSWORD 246

ACROSS

1. Plant containers (4)
3. Supported (8)
9. Got too big for something (7)
10. Amusing people (5)
11. Binoculars (5,7)
14. Relieve or free from (3)
16. Trunk of the body (5)
17. Small shelter (3)
18. Showing gratitude (12)
21. Capital of Vietnam (5)
22. Asserted without proof (7)
23. Respondent (8)
24. Metal fastener (4)

DOWN

1. Puts forward for acceptance (8)
2. Levy (5)
4. Of recent origin (3)
5. Now and then (12)
6. Piercing cry (7)
7. Shallow food container (4)
8. Decide in advance (12)
12. Expressing emotions (of poetry) (5)
13. Went along to an event (8)
15. Relies upon (7)
19. Gold block (5)
20. Ostrich-like bird (4)
22. Wonder (3)

CROSSWORD 247

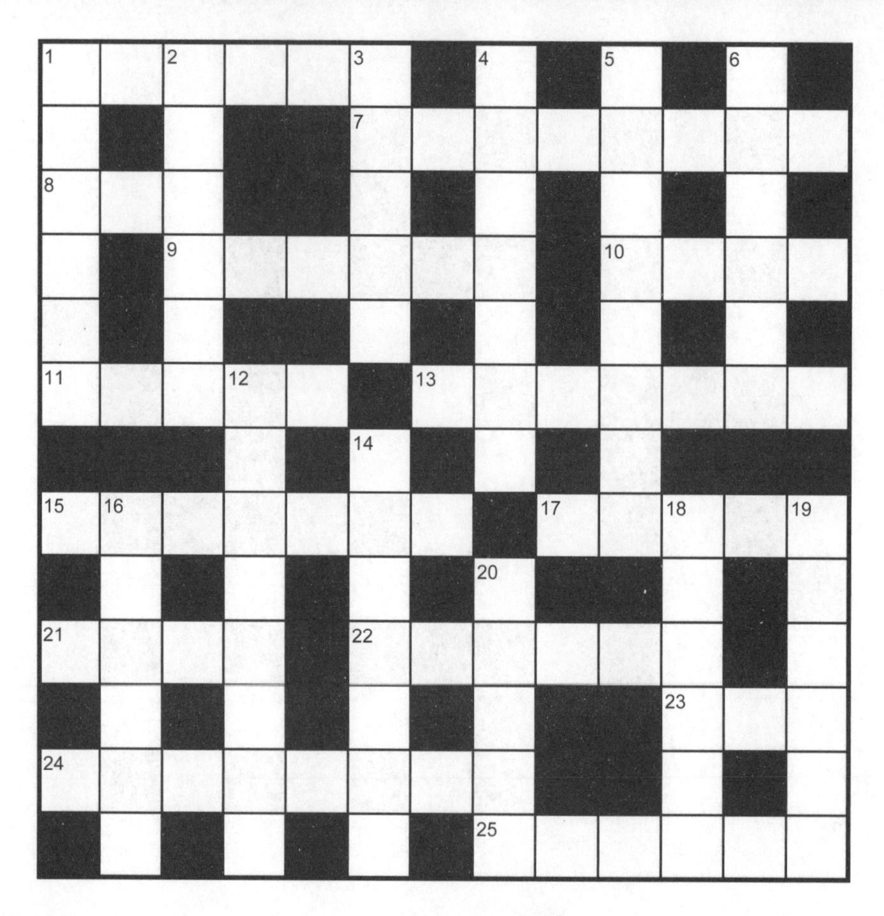

ACROSS

1. Weak through age or illness (6)
7. Arriving (8)
8. Extend out (3)
9. Turn to ice (6)
10. Large stone (4)
11. Screams (5)
13. Be made of (7)
15. Framework (7)
17. Supports (5)
21. A group of three (4)
22. Be unbearably loud (6)
23. Deviate off course (3)
24. Illegal (8)
25. Wrongdoer (6)

DOWN

1. Physical wound (6)
2. Recurring irregularly (6)
3. Blended (5)
4. Formation of troops (7)
5. Food of the gods (8)
6. Acquired skills (6)
12. On the shore of a sea (8)
14. Make sour (7)
16. Protective kitchen garments (6)
18. Deep gorge (6)
19. Plumbing fixture; brief fall of rain (6)
20. Buckets (5)

CROSSWORD 248

ACROSS

1. Makes remote; cuts off (8)
5. Unfasten (4)
9. Imbibe (5)
10. Release from captivity (3,4)
11. Group of three plays (7)
12. Regions (5)
13. Fester (6)
14. Instrumental piece of music (6)
17. Epic poem ascribed to Homer (5)
19. Cold-blooded vertebrate like a crocodile (7)
20. In a nimble manner (7)
21. Decay (5)
22. Spool-like toy (4)
23. Person who supports a cause (8)

DOWN

1. Vagueness (13)
2. Point of view (7)
3. Generally accepted (12)
4. Pieces of writing (6)
6. Care for; look after (5)
7. Exaggeration (13)
8. Atmospheric layer (12)
15. Used for the storage of fat (of tissue) (7)
16. Made a victim of (6)
18. Coldly (5)

CROSSWORD 249

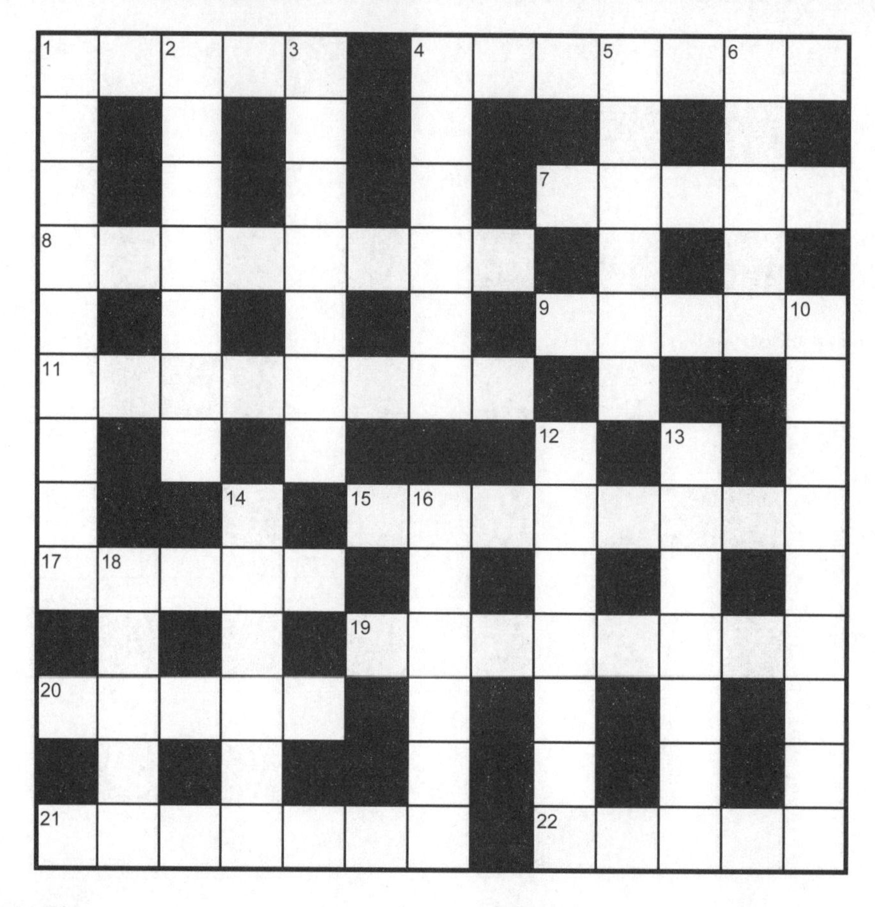

ACROSS

1. Believer in a supreme being (5)
4. Opposite of failure (7)
7. Extra advantage (5)
8. Animal (8)
9. Suppress (5)
11. Singer (8)
15. Sheath for a sword (8)
17. Issue forth with force (5)
19. Formerly Ceylon (3,5)
20. Views; observes (5)
21. Choose and follow (7)
22. Retains (5)

DOWN

1. Detects or finds (9)
2. Bring an accusation against (7)
3. Fabric (7)
4. Gazes at (6)
5. Perennial flowering plant (6)
6. Bony structure in the head (5)
10. Objects easily seen from a distance (9)
12. Tapering stone pillar (7)
13. Wealthy businessperson (7)
14. Harbinger of spring; crazy (6)
16. Coagulate (6)
18. Groups together (5)

CROSSWORD 250

ACROSS

1. Cracks (8)
5. Accompanied by (4)
8. High up (5)
9. People in jail (7)
10. Improve (7)
12. Worked out logically (7)
14. Storehouse for grain (7)
16. E.g. Tuesday (7)
18. Sheer dress fabric (7)
19. Oak tree nut (5)
20. Period of imprisonment (4)
21. Pertinent (8)

DOWN

1. Anxiety; dread (4)
2. Decreased one's speed (6)
3. Pristine; in mint condition (9)
4. Banished (6)
6. Have as a purpose (6)
7. Inn (8)
11. Mankind (5,4)
12. Lasting longer than required (5-3)
13. Mendicant (6)
14. Revolve quickly (6)
15. Atmospheric phenomenon (6)
17. Make a garment using wool (4)

CROSSWORD 251

ACROSS

1. Currency of Italy and Spain (4)
3. Afternoon performances (8)
9. Speaking (7)
10. Record on tape (5)
11. Auction offer (3)
12. Type of herring (5)
13. Start of (5)
15. Unspecified object (5)
17. Hang in the air (5)
18. Cooling tool (3)
19. Declaration (5)
20. Fond of reading and studying (7)
21. Value greatly (8)
22. Bypass (4)

DOWN

1. Institution (13)
2. Angered; irritated (5)
4. Infuriates (6)
5. Detective (12)
6. Old (7)
7. Fairness in following the rules (13)
8. Type of cloud (12)
14. Type of bill (7)
16. Line of equal pressure on a map (6)
18. Search a person; leap playfully (5)

CROSSWORD 252

ACROSS

4. Melodious (6)
7. Small window on a ship (8)
8. Wild ox (3)
9. Mother (4)
10. Sightseeing trip in Africa (6)
11. Cleanliness (7)
12. Road information boards (5)
15. Sudden sharp pains (5)
17. Exposes (7)
20. US monetary unit (6)
21. Hens lay these (4)
22. Flower that is not yet open (3)
23. Delicate ornamental work (8)
24. Fervent (6)

DOWN

1. Series of prayers (6)
2. Robbing (8)
3. Throwing a coin in the air (7)
4. Make a god of (5)
5. Weeping (6)
6. Streak (anag.) (6)
13. Floating masses of frozen water (8)
14. Oceanic birds (7)
15. Irrational fear (6)
16. Inclined one's head to show approval (6)
18. Carried with difficulty (6)
19. Divided into two (5)

CROSSWORD 253

ACROSS

1. Buckles (4)
3. Political meetings (8)
9. Zeppelin (7)
10. Unabridged (5)
11. Chatter (6-6)
14. Wetland (3)
16. Useful (5)
17. Flee (3)
18. Extremely harmful (12)
21. Implied (5)
22. Part exchange for something new (5-2)
23. Living in (8)
24. Continent (4)

DOWN

1. Launch with great force (of a rocket) (5,3)
2. Opposite of best (5)
4. Unit of current (3)
5. Female fellow national (12)
6. Not spiritual or sacred (7)
7. Takes an exam (4)
8. Showing total commitment (12)
12. Principle or belief (5)
13. Large snake (8)
15. Subtleties (7)
19. Listens to (5)
20. Heavenly body (4)
22. Net (anag.) (3)

CROSSWORD 254

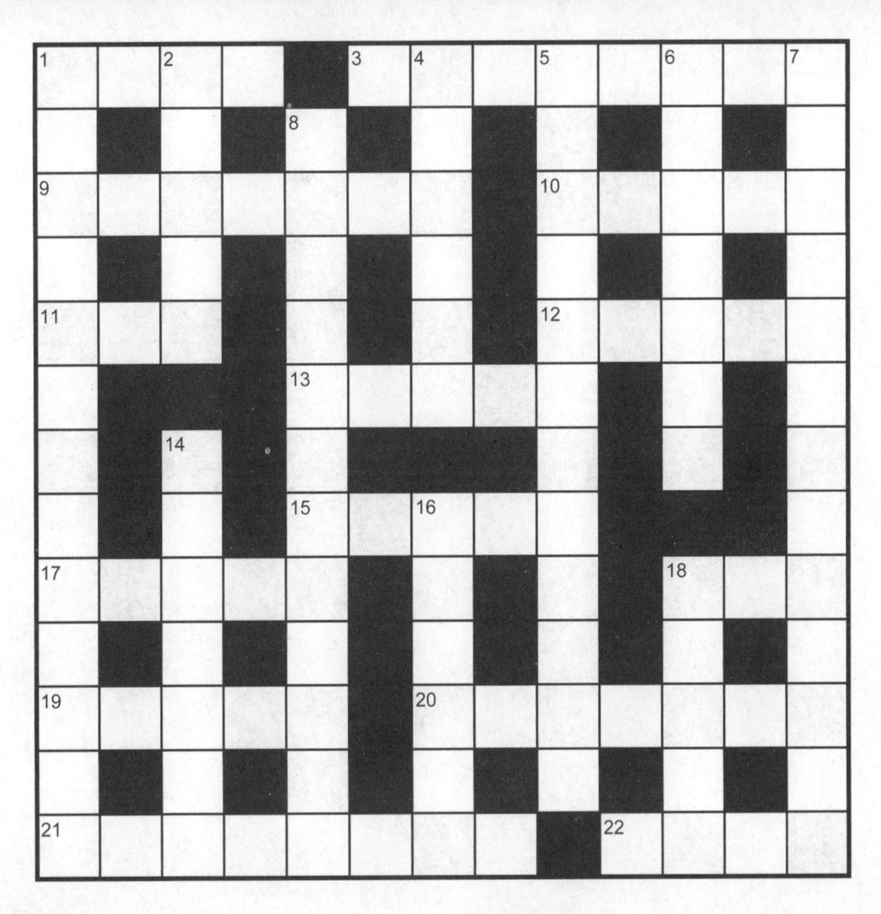

ACROSS

1. Official language of Pakistan (4)
3. Bedrooms (8)
9. Illness (7)
10. Acer tree (5)
11. Bed for a baby (3)
12. Prod with the elbow (5)
13. Individual things (5)
15. Sea duck (5)
17. Teacher (5)
18. One circuit of a track (3)
19. Element with atomic number 5 (5)
20. Sour in taste (7)
21. Evacuating (8)
22. Spherical object (4)

DOWN

1. Inexplicable (13)
2. Glazed earthenware (5)
4. Dull (6)
5. Showed (12)
6. Hindered (7)
7. Lacking originality (13)
8. Hostility (12)
14. The exposure of bedrock (7)
16. Keep hold of (6)
18. Sign of the zodiac (5)

CROSSWORD 255

ACROSS

1. An instant in time (6)
7. Difficult to move because of its size (8)
8. Sorrowful (3)
9. Glowing remains of a fire (6)
10. Slender woody shoot (4)
11. Flinch away in pain (5)
13. An oral communication (7)
15. Grotesque monster (7)
17. Breaks in two (5)
21. Sullen (4)
22. Flatfish (6)
23. Item for catching fish (3)
24. Orange pigment found in carrots (8)
25. Small oval plum (6)

DOWN

1. Capital of Russia (6)
2. Contemporary (6)
3. Melodies (5)
4. Gnarled (7)
5. Discard (8)
6. Summing together (6)
12. Country in Africa (8)
14. Soothsayer (7)
16. Hurrah (6)
18. Representatives (6)
19. Make less hard (6)
20. E.g. covered with bricks (5)

CROSSWORD 256

ACROSS

1. Outlet for excess water (8)
5. Argues (4)
8. Genuflect (5)
9. Island in the West Indies (7)
10. Imply as a condition (7)
12. Random criticism (7)
14. Unit of sound intensity (7)
16. Firmly (7)
18. Musical wind instrument (7)
19. Store in a secret place (5)
20. Profound (4)
21. Male riders (8)

DOWN

1. Trees that bear acorns (4)
2. Absolve (6)
3. Lie (9)
4. Physical item (6)
6. Prayer (6)
7. Disgraceful (8)
11. Bulbous plant (9)
12. Access code (8)
13. Split along a natural line (6)
14. Extremely energetic person (6)
15. Pacify (6)
17. Cut of beef from the foreleg (4)

CROSSWORD 257

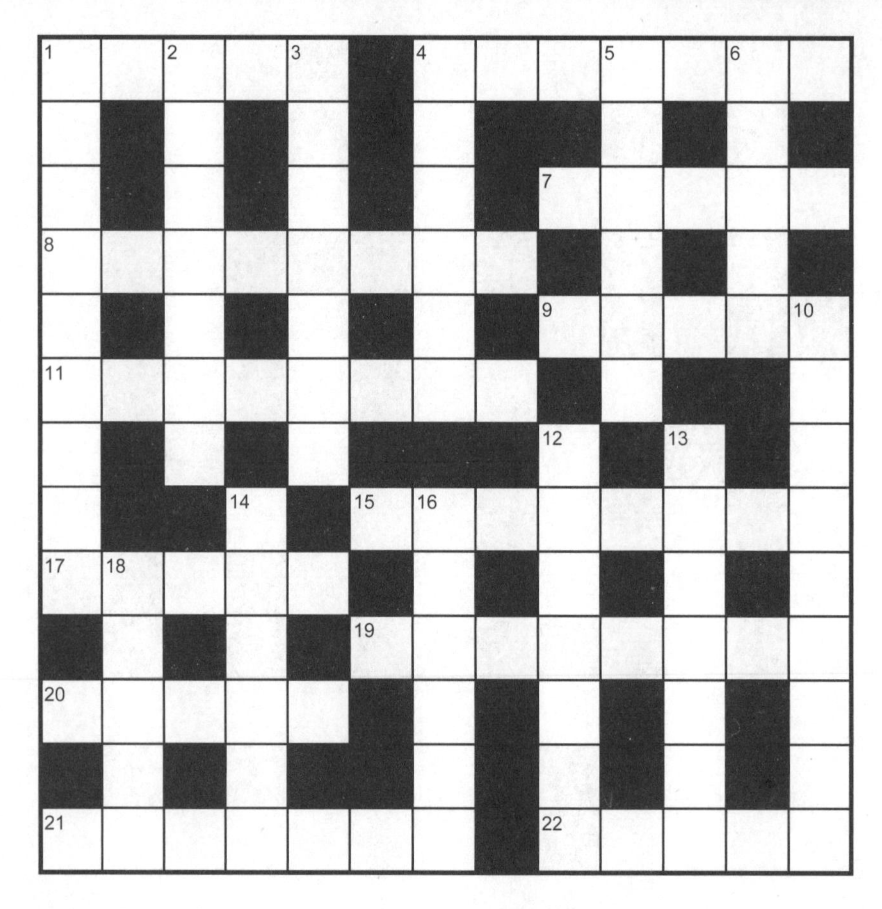

ACROSS

1. Chairs (5)
4. Strong reaction of anger (7)
7. Go swiftly (5)
8. Household chore (8)
9. Tree part left after it is cut down (5)
11. Portend (8)
15. Beekeeper (8)
17. Backbone (5)
19. Small bays (8)
20. Of sedate character (5)
21. Increased efficiency by working together (7)
22. Felt concern or interest (5)

DOWN

1. Defines clearly (9)
2. Money owed that should have been paid (7)
3. Substitute (7)
4. Took the lid off a jar (6)
5. Repeat from memory (6)
6. Darkness (5)
10. Expressed dissent (9)
12. Large ocean (7)
13. More foolish (7)
14. Provoke (6)
16. Brave; courageous (6)
18. Soft paste (5)

CROSSWORD 258

ACROSS

1. Built (11)
9. Plantain lily (5)
10. Ruction (3)
11. Wireless (5)
12. Frustrated and annoyed (3,2)
13. Unnecessary (8)
16. Universal in extent (8)
18. Rocky; harsh (5)
21. Fastening device (5)
22. Short cylindrical piece of wood (3)
23. Longest river in Europe (5)
24. Serving to enlighten; instructive (11)

DOWN

2. Exceeds; surpasses (7)
3. Learning institutions (7)
4. Rinses (anag.) (6)
5. Finely cut straw (5)
6. Large African antelope (5)
7. Accurate timer (11)
8. Difficult and intricate (11)
14. The Windy City (7)
15. Country in northwestern Africa (7)
17. Good luck charm (6)
19. Advised; encouraged (5)
20. Total disorder (5)

CROSSWORD 259

ACROSS

1. Remedy to a poison (8)
5. Country in western Africa (4)
9. Marrying man (5)
10. Caused by motion (7)
11. Follows orders (5)
12. Violate a law of God (3)
13. Taut (5)
15. Relating to a city (5)
17. Trouble in body or mind (3)
19. At that place; not here (5)
20. Writing fluid holder (7)
21. Strong lightweight wood (5)
22. Dons (anag.) (4)
23. Participant in a meeting (8)

DOWN

1. Assemblage (13)
2. Gardening tools (7)
3. Tamed (12)
4. Seizing (6)
6. Singing voices (5)
7. Thoughtless (13)
8. Not discernible (12)
14. Multiplied threefold (7)
16. Plant with deep purple flowers (6)
18. Found agreeable (5)

CROSSWORD 260

ACROSS

1. Lacking seriousness (11)
9. Tight; taut (5)
10. Half of four (3)
11. Hurts (5)
12. Of definite shape (5)
13. Conclusions (8)
16. Fluent in the use of language (8)
18. Frenzied (5)
21. Steer (anag.) (5)
22. Exclamation of contempt (3)
23. Country in the Himalayas (5)
24. Attention-grabbing (3-8)

DOWN

2. Irreverence (7)
3. Active part of a fire (7)
4. Obtain through trickery (6)
5. Mental impressions (5)
6. Place providing accommodation (5)
7. Not exact (11)
8. Of a cheerful disposition (4-7)
14. Make a sucking sound (7)
15. Chain of flowers (7)
17. Marine gastropod (6)
19. Crazy (5)
20. Sceptic (5)

CROSSWORD 261

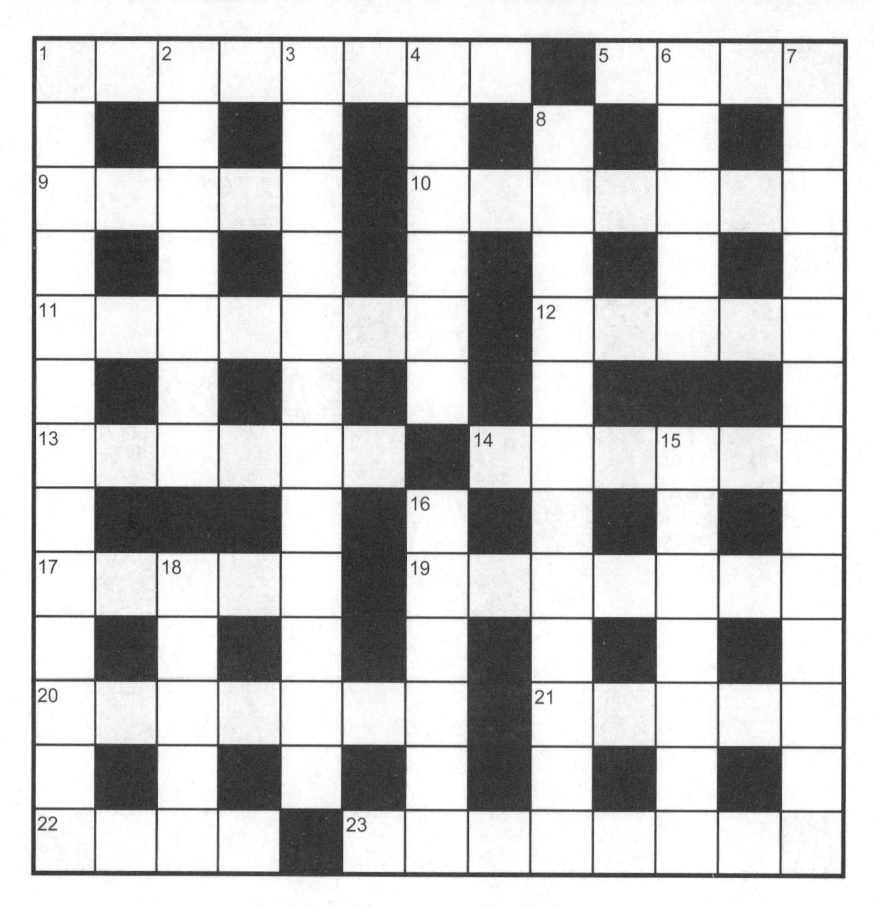

ACROSS

1. Fortress in Paris (8)
5. Push; poke (4)
9. Wide-awake (5)
10. Draws aimlessly (7)
11. Form of singing for entertainment (7)
12. Confusion (3-2)
13. Pokes gently (6)
14. False (6)
17. Earnings (5)
19. Imaginary line around the earth (7)
20. Freezing (3-4)
21. Horror film directed by Ridley Scott (5)
22. Trees of the genus Ulmus (4)
23. Love song (8)

DOWN

1. Type of traditional photography (5-3-5)
2. Slandered (7)
3. Shyness (12)
4. Climbing tool (6)
6. Loosen up (5)
7. Act of vanishing (13)
8. Corresponding; proportionate (12)
15. Greek white wine (7)
16. Hawk (6)
18. Shine brightly (5)

CROSSWORD 262

ACROSS

1. Make empty (6)
4. Sour to the taste (6)
9. Learned (7)
10. Clown (7)
11. Small house (5)
12. Rental agreement (5)
14. Skirmish (5)
17. Device used to connect to the internet (5)
19. Person acting as a deputy (5)
21. Drawout (anag.) (7)
23. Ordinary colloquial speech (7)
24. Enjoy greatly (6)
25. Plant with edible stalks (6)

DOWN

1. Oral (6)
2. Musical staff sign (4)
3. A general proposition (7)
5. Excessively mean (5)
6. Lessened (8)
7. Intelligent (6)
8. Temporary inability to remember something (6,5)
13. Unusual (8)
15. Passionate (7)
16. Arachnid (6)
18. Change (6)
20. Abominable snowmen (5)
22. Poker stake (4)

CROSSWORD 263

ACROSS

1. Tiny aquatic plant (4)
3. Vision (8)
9. Day trips (7)
10. Domestic cat (5)
11. Foreboding (12)
14. High ball in tennis (3)
16. Main artery (5)
17. That vessel (3)
18. Unkind; unsympathetic (12)
21. Moisten meat (5)
22. Stations at the ends of routes (7)
23. Refined (8)
24. Comedy sketch (4)

DOWN

1. Extremely lovable (8)
2. Rise to one's feet (3,2)
4. Opposite of no (3)
5. Adequate (12)
6. Small apes (7)
7. Playthings (4)
8. Perform below expectation (12)
12. Mistake (5)
13. In a very poor condition (8)
15. Payments in addition to wages (7)
19. Clay block (5)
20. Encourage in wrongdoing (4)
22. 19th Greek letter (3)

CROSSWORD 264

ACROSS

1. Insurgents (6)
7. Source of annoyance (8)
8. Item of furniture one sleeps on (3)
9. Regal (6)
10. Devastation (4)
11. Small (5)
13. Interiors (7)
15. Legal practitioners (7)
17. School of fish (5)
21. Drive away (4)
22. Flout (6)
23. Lipid (3)
24. Relating to office work (8)
25. Sedate (anag.) (6)

DOWN

1. Mocked (6)
2. Blunt thick needle (6)
3. E.g. performs karaoke (5)
4. Making a petition to God (7)
5. Echinoderm with a distinctive shape (8)
6. Machine that creates motion (6)
12. Musical instrument (8)
14. Aperture or hole (7)
16. For a short time (6)
18. Set of clothes (6)
19. Elevated off the ground (6)
20. Cries with grief (5)

CROSSWORD 265

ACROSS

1. Movement of water causing a small whirlpool (4)
3. Mocking (8)
9. Insubstantial (7)
10. Sequence (5)
11. Less common (5)
12. Shock physically (5-2)
13. Frightens; startles (6)
15. Unit of astronomical length (6)
17. Impartial (7)
18. State of the USA (5)
20. Feeling of boredom (5)
21. E.g. male and female (7)
22. Struggling (8)
23. Remain in the same place (4)

DOWN

1. Amusement (13)
2. Person who eats in a restaurant (5)
4. Birthplace of St Francis (6)
5. Formal announcements (12)
6. Tidies (7)
7. Prominently (13)
8. Military judicial body (5,7)
14. Former student (7)
16. Catchphrase (6)
19. Prevent (5)

CROSSWORD 266

ACROSS

1. Imitative work (8)
5. Exhaled hard (4)
9. Group of students; category (5)
10. Important church (7)
11. In a greedy manner (12)
14. Ancient (3)
15. Small cluster (5)
16. Possess (3)
17. Lexicons (12)
20. European country (7)
22. Uproarious party or fight (5)
23. 24-hour periods (4)
24. Recreational area for children (8)

DOWN

1. Agreement (4)
2. Deprived of food (7)
3. Directions (12)
4. Sewn edge (3)
6. Water lily (5)
7. Fretting (8)
8. Immeasurably (12)
12. Stir milk (5)
13. Consisting of fine particles (8)
16. Perennial herb (7)
18. Snug and nice to wear (5)
19. Dejected (4)
21. Every (3)

CROSSWORD 267

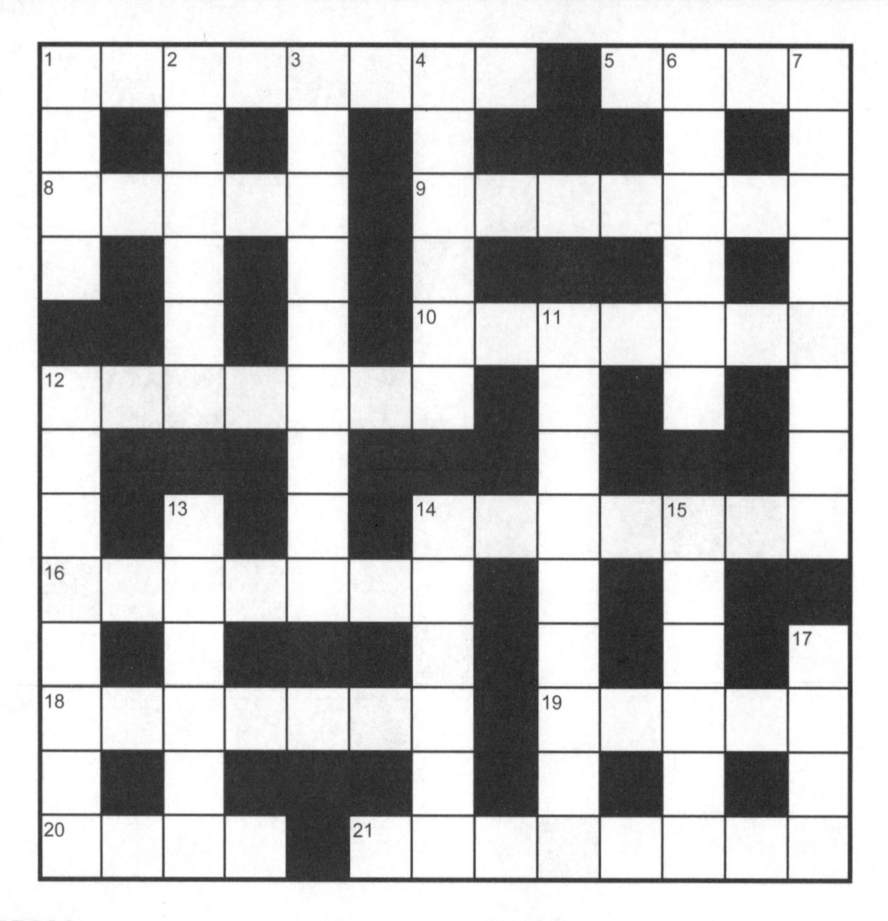

ACROSS

1. Subdue; vanquish (8)
5. Listening devices (4)
8. Small dust particles (5)
9. A particular item (7)
10. Someone who provides food (7)
12. Easily broken (7)
14. Nocturnal burrowing mammals (7)
16. Nuclear ___ : device that generates energy (7)
18. Occidental (7)
19. Stood up (5)
20. Valley (4)
21. White crested parrot (8)

DOWN

1. Unspecified in number (4)
2. Surface film; coating (6)
3. Readily recovering from shock (9)
4. Rarely encountered (6)
6. Straighten out (6)
7. Fortified wines (8)
11. Officially registered name (9)
12. Wrinkled; creased (8)
13. Maiden (6)
14. Wild horse (6)
15. Send for sale overseas (6)
17. Protest march (abbrev.) (4)

CROSSWORD 268

ACROSS

1. State of preoccupation (11)
9. Throat of a voracious animal (3)
10. Circular in shape (5)
11. Removes moisture (5)
12. Mournful poem (5)
13. Breadth (8)
16. Flying (8)
18. Apply pressure (5)
20. Representative; messenger (5)
21. Destroy (3,2)
22. Large vessel (3)
23. Lacking distinguishing characteristics (11)

DOWN

2. Single-edged hunting knife (5)
3. Delay or linger (5)
4. Graduates of an academic institution (6)
5. A child beginning to walk (7)
6. Policeman or woman (7)
7. Instantly (11)
8. Revive (11)
14. Stimulate a reaction (7)
15. Imitator (7)
17. Gender of nouns in some languages (6)
18. Kick out (5)
19. Sprites (5)

CROSSWORD 269

ACROSS

1. The actors in a show (4)
3. Large outbreak of a disease (8)
9. Workshop or studio (7)
10. Swagger (5)
11. Used a computer keyboard (5)
12. Relating to Flanders (7)
13. Mutter (6)
15. Shelter (6)
17. Country in western Africa (7)
18. Gains possession of (5)
20. Divide by two (5)
21. Proportionately (3,4)
22. Sunshades (8)
23. Unwanted wild plant (4)

DOWN

1. Artisanship (13)
2. Woolly ruminant animal (5)
4. Remove contaminants from (6)
5. Exemption from a rule (12)
6. Pertaining to warfare (7)
7. Reach the required standard (3,3,7)
8. Squint harder (anag.) (12)
14. Frequent customer (7)
16. Part of a flower (6)
19. Rogue; scoundrel (5)

CROSSWORD 270

ACROSS

1. Part of a house (8)
5. Support (4)
8. Large indefinite amount (5)
9. Hide (5-2)
10. Musical performance (7)
12. Suits; turns into (7)
14. Person devoted to love (7)
16. Chats (7)
18. Cause to absorb water (7)
19. Mythical monster (5)
20. Fixed costs (4)
21. Legendary island (8)

DOWN

1. Sculpture of the upper body (4)
2. Calamitous (6)
3. Test again (2-7)
4. Academy Awards (6)
6. Scarcity (6)
7. Intended to appeal to ordinary people (8)
11. Famous queen of Egypt (9)
12. Split into subdivisions (8)
13. Heavy food (6)
14. Agreement (6)
15. Bring into a country (6)
17. European mountain range (4)

CROSSWORD 271

ACROSS

1. Legacy (11)
9. Lacking interest (5)
10. Round bread roll (3)
11. Medium of exchange (5)
12. Move to music (5)
13. Scarceness (8)
16. Long-tailed parrot (8)
18. Survived (5)
21. Wander aimlessly (5)
22. A man's dinner jacket (abbrev.) (3)
23. Borders (5)
24. Having power (11)

DOWN

2. Convent (7)
3. Desiring what someone else has (7)
4. Contributes information (6)
5. Assisted (5)
6. Private room on a ship (5)
7. Unending life (11)
8. Restrained (11)
14. Mobile phone (7)
15. Mark written under a letter (7)
17. Point in an orbit furthest from earth (6)
19. Female fox (5)
20. Reside (5)

CROSSWORD 272

ACROSS

1. Trifling sum of money (5,6)
9. Deranged (3)
10. Heats up (5)
11. Small insect (5)
12. Way in (5)
13. Short joke (3-5)
16. Engraved inscription (8)
18. Woody-stemmed plant (5)
20. Moved by air (5)
21. Single piece of information (5)
22. Wander aimlessly (3)
23. Philosophical doctrine (11)

DOWN

2. In the middle of (5)
3. Humble (5)
4. Element with atomic number 6 (6)
5. Military attack or raid (7)
6. Flowing profusely (7)
7. Watertight (11)
8. Comprehends (11)
14. Retaliatory action (7)
15. Move slowly (7)
17. For the time being (3,3)
18. Country in the Arabian peninsula (5)
19. Animal enclosures (5)

CROSSWORD 273

ACROSS

1. Run-down and in poor condition (6)
4. Loves dearly (6)
9. Eight-sided polygon (7)
10. Feeling of vexation (7)
11. Pertaining to the sun (5)
12. Footwear (pl.) (5)
14. Tips (5)
17. Out of fashion (5)
19. Equipped (5)
21. Perfect happiness (7)
23. Made of clay hardened by heat (7)
24. From Denmark (6)
25. Mild or kind (6)

DOWN

1. Adheres to; fastens (6)
2. Surrounding glow (4)
3. Ill-mannered (7)
5. Stead (anag.) (5)
6. Frequent customers (8)
7. Soldier who keeps guard (6)
8. Utility (11)
13. Conjoining contradictory terms (8)
15. Shine brightly (7)
16. Moved rhythmically to music (6)
18. Make possible (6)
20. Ditches (5)
22. Adjoin (4)

CROSSWORD 274

ACROSS

1. Certain (8)
5. Tibetan Buddhist monk (4)
8. Remains of an old building (5)
9. Digit (7)
10. Give too much money (7)
12. Plotter (7)
14. Affably (7)
16. Postponed (7)
18. Small Arctic whale (7)
19. Become very hot (5)
20. Boring (4)
21. Space rock (8)

DOWN

1. Free from contamination (4)
2. Informer (6)
3. Formal written or spoken statement (9)
4. Seller (6)
6. Sudden (6)
7. Passageway (8)
11. Fair (9)
12. Made unhappy (8)
13. Not singular (6)
14. Grown-ups (6)
15. Pygmy chimpanzee (6)
17. Lids (anag.) (4)

CROSSWORD 275

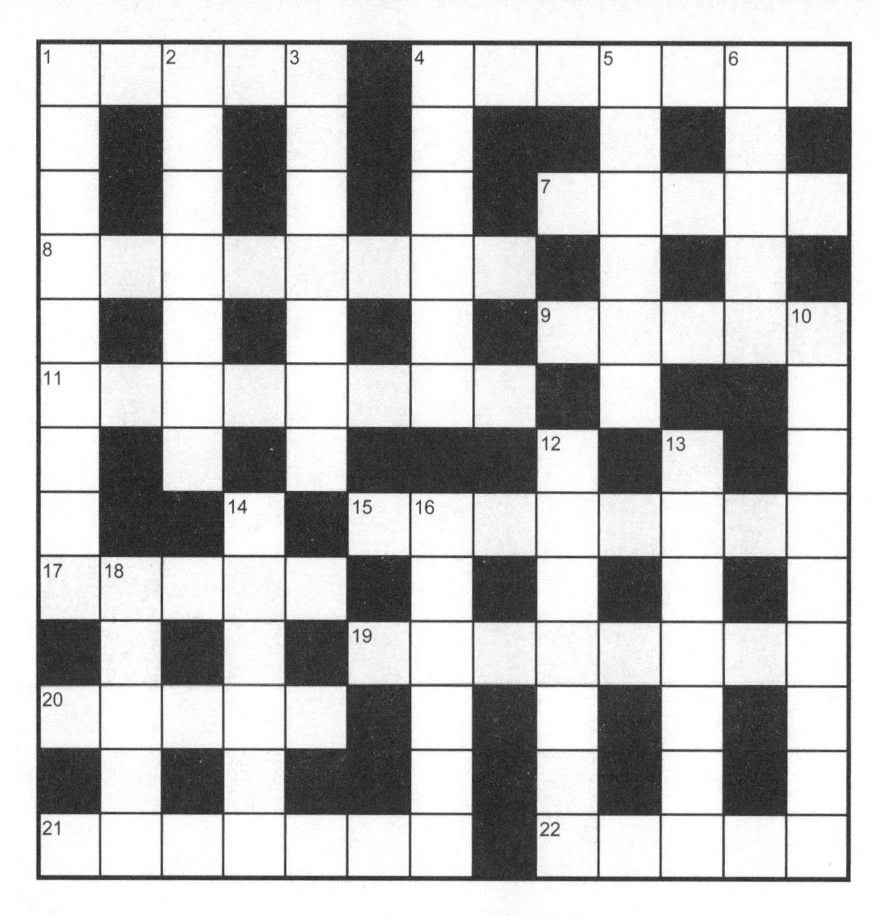

ACROSS

1. Brace (5)
4. Shackle (7)
7. Hat edges (5)
8. Crashes into (8)
9. Middle of the body (5)
11. Interrupt something (3,5)
15. Expression of praise (8)
17. Wards (anag.) (5)
19. Extremely happy (8)
20. Thaws (5)
21. Narrow strip of land (7)
22. Compact (5)

DOWN

1. Made by mixing ingredients (9)
2. Skilled sportsman (7)
3. Outcasts from society (7)
4. Extraterrestrial rock (6)
5. Pilot (6)
6. Unshapely masses; swellings (5)
10. Stargazing instrument (9)
12. Presage (7)
13. Restaurant in a workplace (7)
14. Sample of cloth (6)
16. Hidden storage places (6)
18. Rushes (5)

CROSSWORD 276

ACROSS

1. Fabricate (11)
9. Clumsy person (3)
10. Works one's trade steadily (5)
11. Suave (5)
12. Poison (5)
13. Piece for a soloist and orchestra (8)
16. Work outfits (8)
18. Form of identification (5)
20. Big (5)
21. Woodland spirit (5)
22. Toothed wheel (3)
23. Ancestors (11)

DOWN

2. Attach (5)
3. Unfasten a garment (5)
4. With hands on the hips (6)
5. Tuft of grass (7)
6. Mediterranean coastal region (7)
7. All the time (11)
8. Admit to be true (11)
14. Wavering vocal quality (7)
15. Envisage (7)
17. Sacred phrase (6)
18. Hard close-grained wood (5)
19. Furnishings of a room (5)

CROSSWORD 277

ACROSS

1. Seeping (6)
4. Changes (6)
9. Surplus or excess (7)
10. Extract (7)
11. Denim (anag.) (5)
12. Gets weary (5)
14. Rounded protuberances on camels (5)
17. Book leaves (5)
19. Active cause (5)
21. Precipitating (7)
23. Style of cooking (7)
24. Women (6)
25. Stupidity (6)

DOWN

1. Least young (6)
2. Silvery-white metallic element (4)
3. Sustain with food (7)
5. You usually do this whilst asleep (5)
6. Mapping out in advance (8)
7. Not moving or shaking (6)
8. Easily angered (3-8)
13. Containing less oxygen than usual (of air) (8)
15. Marred (7)
16. Package (6)
18. Sweet (6)
20. Social division in some societies (5)
22. After the beginning of (4)

CROSSWORD 278

ACROSS

1. Formidable; impressive (8)
5. Clothed (4)
9. Singing voice (5)
10. Prehistoric person (7)
11. Author of screenplays (12)
13. Hate (6)
14. Surround (6)
17. Bravely (12)
20. Flatter (7)
21. Large waterbirds (5)
22. Snake-like fish (4)
23. Official orders (8)

DOWN

1. Tiny amount (4)
2. Cure-all (7)
3. Immediately (12)
4. Subtle detail (6)
6. Threshold (5)
7. White flakes in the hair (8)
8. Ate excessively (12)
12. Obstruction (8)
15. Most unattractive (7)
16. Swiss city (6)
18. Customary (5)
19. Animal doctors (4)

CROSSWORD 279

ACROSS

1. Least clean (8)
5. Fling (4)
9. Intended (5)
10. Sounding a bell (7)
11. Motionless (5)
12. Nevertheless (3)
13. Good sense (5)
15. Stares with the mouth wide open (5)
17. Increase in amount (3)
19. Making a knot in (5)
20. Separated; remote (7)
21. Lesser (5)
22. Where a bird lays eggs (4)
23. Made (a noise) less intense (8)

DOWN

1. Process of taming an animal (13)
2. Harvesting (7)
3. Comprehensible (12)
4. Grunts (anag.) (6)
6. Bring together (5)
7. Prone to steal (5-8)
8. Not familiar with or used to (12)
14. Sophisticated hair style (7)
16. Penetrate (6)
18. Amounts of medication (5)

CROSSWORD 280

ACROSS

1. Showing utter resignation (6)
7. Leaving out (8)
8. Your (poetic) (3)
9. Make illegal (6)
10. Precious metal (4)
11. Having a stale smell (5)
13. Business matters (7)
15. Opening to a room (7)
17. Burns the surface of (5)
21. Labels (4)
22. Moon goddess in Greek mythology (6)
23. Piece of cloth (3)
24. Grammatical mistake (8)
25. Stopped temporarily (6)

DOWN

1. Song of devotion (6)
2. Jubilant (6)
3. Works hard (5)
4. Childbirth assistant (7)
5. Stop progressing (8)
6. Person who fishes (6)
12. Beat easily (8)
14. Civil action brought to court (7)
16. Public speaker (6)
18. Prevents (6)
19. Scorched (6)
20. Decline sharply (5)

CROSSWORD 281

ACROSS

1. Throb; dull pain (4)
3. Curved surface of a liquid in a tube (8)
9. Leading (anag.) (7)
10. Make law (5)
11. The management of a home (12)
14. Sort; kind (3)
16. Big cat (5)
17. Piece of pasture (3)
18. Deceiver (6-6)
21. Porcelain (5)
22. Conceals something from view (7)
23. Obstinately (8)
24. Symbol (4)

DOWN

1. E.g. a spider or scorpion (8)
2. Verse form (5)
4. Cease (3)
5. Lack of practical knowledge (12)
6. Water passage (7)
7. Hardens (4)
8. Not having a backbone (12)
12. Large bird of prey (5)
13. Military post (8)
15. Done in full awareness (7)
19. Sweet-scented shrub (5)
20. Bitter-tasting substance (4)
22. Nocturnal bird of prey (3)

CROSSWORD 282

ACROSS

1. Twist suddenly (6)
4. Cabers (anag.) (6)
9. Enunciate (7)
10. Marked by prosperity (of a past time) (7)
11. Acoustic detection system (5)
12. Concave roofs (5)
14. Ensnares (5)
17. Shows tiredness (5)
19. Stringed instruments (5)
21. Endanger (7)
23. Highest singing voice (7)
24. Swarmed (6)
25. Among (6)

DOWN

1. Cleaned using water (6)
2. Morally wicked (4)
3. Imitator (7)
5. Tree anchors (5)
6. Church rules (5,3)
7. Smiles contemptuously (6)
8. Charitable donation (11)
13. Having many parts (8)
15. Evidence of disease (7)
16. Enclosed recess (6)
18. Choose (6)
20. Empty area; gap (5)
22. Peruse (4)

CROSSWORD 283

ACROSS

1. Horse carts (5)
4. Piece of art made from various materials (7)
7. Criminal (5)
8. Defeated (8)
9. Vends (5)
11. Clattering (8)
15. Relating to love (8)
17. Stuck together (5)
19. More powerful (8)
20. Makes a garment from wool (5)
21. Assign (7)
22. Wet (5)

DOWN

1. Consuming quickly (9)
2. Swears (7)
3. Type of fetter (7)
4. Widespread (6)
5. Bigger (6)
6. Evil spirit (5)
10. Honesty; good faith (9)
12. Large monkeys (7)
13. Method of presenting a play (7)
14. Alphabetical character (6)
16. Interruption of service (6)
18. Narrow roads (5)

CROSSWORD 284

ACROSS

1. Show to be false (8)
5. Sailing vessel (4)
9. Pertaining to sound (5)
10. Fishing boat (7)
11. Proceeding from the pope (5)
12. Drink a little (3)
13. Intense light beam (5)
15. Sing softly (5)
17. Bite sharply (3)
19. Follow the position of (5)
20. Irreligious (7)
21. Lazes; does nothing (5)
22. Flow copiously (4)
23. Mammal with a sticky tongue (8)

DOWN

1. Not up to expectations (13)
2. Type of quarry (7)
3. Remembrance (12)
4. The electorate (6)
6. Grips (5)
7. Computer program for writing documents (4,9)
8. Intricate and confusing (12)
14. Promising young actress (7)
16. More likely than not (4-2)
18. Long tubes (5)

CROSSWORD 285

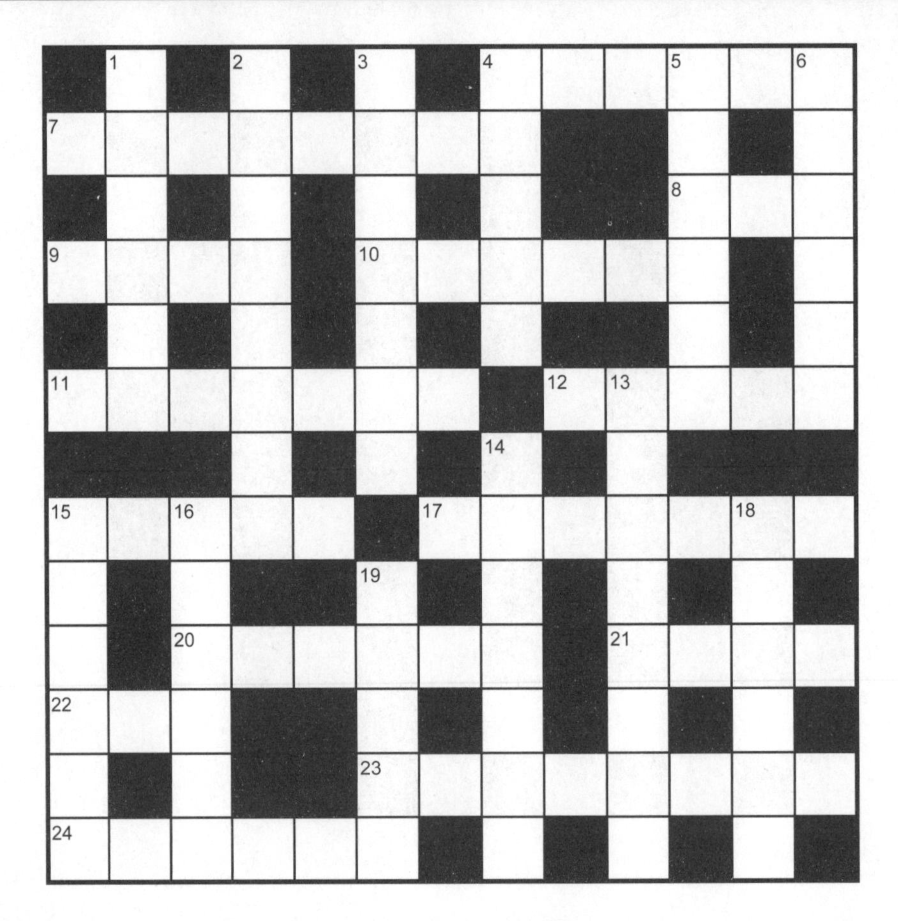

ACROSS

4. Increases a gap (6)
7. Coming from outside (8)
8. Flat-topped cap with a tassel (3)
9. What a cyclist rides (4)
10. Excessively ornate (of literature) (6)
11. Lively festivities (7)
12. Arbiter (5)
15. Waterslide (5)
17. Praise enthusiastically (7)
20. Enforce compliance with (6)
21. Brown seaweed (4)
22. Ease into a chair (3)
23. Moderate (8)
24. Makes spick and span (6)

DOWN

1. Stimulate (6)
2. Showing deep and solemn respect (8)
3. Public collection of books (7)
4. Ruin (5)
5. Envelop (6)
6. Crackle (6)
13. Improbable (8)
14. Long speeches (7)
15. Form-fitting garment (6)
16. Joined together (6)
18. Away from the coast (6)
19. Compositions in verse (5)

CROSSWORD 286

ACROSS

1. Sews (8)
5. Soothing remedy (4)
8. Acknowledged; assumed (5)
9. Large flat dish (7)
10. Religious ceremonies (7)
12. Salad vegetable (7)
14. Gadgets (7)
16. A parent's mother (7)
18. Country whose capital is Reykjavik (7)
19. Ruin (5)
20. Long deep cut (4)
21. Support at the top of a seat (8)

DOWN

1. Emit a breath of sadness (4)
2. Turn upside down (6)
3. Brought to an end (9)
4. Cease to be valid (6)
6. Real (6)
7. Bogs or marshes (8)
11. Crossed (9)
12. Chuckling (8)
13. Dampens (6)
14. Move slowly (6)
15. Coax into doing something (6)
17. Small ink stain (4)

CROSSWORD 287

ACROSS

1. Extend beyond a surface (8)
5. Mocks (4)
9. Loves uncritically (5)
10. Exceptionally good (7)
11. Lacking tolerance or flexibility (6-6)
13. Had a strong smell (6)
14. Believer in God (6)
17. Inadequately manned (12)
20. Actually; in reality (2,5)
21. Machine for shaping wood or metal (5)
22. Mud (4)
23. Listen to again (4,4)

DOWN

1. Fleshes out unnecessarily (4)
2. Go faster than (7)
3. Minimum purchase cost at auction (7,5)
4. Repudiate (6)
6. Worked steadily at a trade (5)
7. Firmness (8)
8. Charmingly (12)
12. Focused and level-headed (8)
15. Resistance to change (7)
16. Walk casually (6)
18. Postpone (5)
19. Accidental hole that lets liquid escape (4)

CROSSWORD 288

ACROSS

1. Very dirty (6)
4. Lived by (6)
9. Imitate (7)
10. Large Israeli city (3,4)
11. Heroic tales (5)
12. Path or road (5)
14. Judged; ranked (5)
17. Correct (5)
19. Basic units of chemical elements (5)
21. Encroach (7)
23. Reduced in scope or length (3-4)
24. Attempting (6)
25. Loan shark (6)

DOWN

1. Encourage the development of (6)
2. Quieten down; send to sleep (4)
3. Weighing more (7)
5. Boxing contests (5)
6. Pulling against resistance (8)
7. Showy (6)
8. Highly destructive (11)
13. Undeserving (8)
15. Sparred (anag.) (7)
16. Thing that brings good luck (6)
18. Move unsteadily (6)
20. Exhibited (5)
22. Close by (4)

CROSSWORD 289

ACROSS

1. Public and formal (8)
5. Slanting; crooked (4)
9. Tiny (5)
10. Given; bequeathed (7)
11. Food shop (12)
14. Tear (3)
15. Send money (5)
16. Disallow (3)
17. State of being in disrepair (12)
20. Perennial plant with fleshy roots (7)
22. Lubricated (5)
23. Give temporarily (4)
24. A large spar (8)

DOWN

1. Expel; drive out (4)
2. Sudden outburst of something (5-2)
3. Someone skilled in penmanship (12)
4. Large primate (3)
6. Flightless birds (5)
7. Broadening (8)
8. Coming from outside (12)
12. Targeted (5)
13. Extravagant (8)
16. Young chicken (7)
18. Cloth woven from flax (5)
19. Modify (4)
21. Sticky substance (3)

CROSSWORD 290

ACROSS

1. A flat float (4)
3. Deny (8)
9. Take a seat (3,4)
10. Highways (5)
11. Made in bulk (4-8)
14. Long narrow inlet (3)
16. Gets through merit (5)
17. Hurried (3)
18. Limitless (12)
21. Spirit in a bottle (5)
22. Anniversary of an event (7)
23. Redeploy (8)
24. Stringed instrument (4)

DOWN

1. Culinary herb (8)
2. Outdoor fundraising events (5)
4. Charged particle (3)
5. Restrict within limits (12)
6. Non-professional (7)
7. Opposite of least (4)
8. Entirety (12)
12. Unpleasant giants (5)
13. Come before in time (8)
15. Pungent gas (7)
19. Stomach (5)
20. Jelly or culture medium (4)
22. Run steadily (3)

CROSSWORD 291

ACROSS

1. Unit of time (6)
7. Inventive; creative (8)
8. Of a low standard (3)
9. Grouchy (6)
10. Zest; liveliness (4)
11. Agree or correspond (5)
13. Looking at fiercely (7)
15. Scarcity (7)
17. Rescued (5)
21. Area of mown grass (4)
22. Country (6)
23. Performed an action (3)
24. Plot (8)
25. Pastiness (6)

DOWN

1. Surrender (6)
2. Club (6)
3. Moods (anag.) (5)
4. Two-wheeled vehicle (7)
5. Type of restaurant (8)
6. Substance found in wine (6)
12. Famous Scottish lake (4,4)
14. Template (7)
16. River in South America (6)
18. One who wantonly destroys property (6)
19. Totter or tremble (6)
20. Sharply inclined (5)

CROSSWORD 292

ACROSS

1. Transfer responsibility elsewhere (4,3,4)
9. Slow down (5)
10. Thee (3)
11. Gives as a reference (5)
12. Recipient of money (5)
13. Deceptive (8)
16. Sentence sung before a psalm (8)
18. Misplaces (5)
21. Stop (5)
22. Performance by a musician (3)
23. Similar (5)
24. Very steep (11)

DOWN

2. Sharply (7)
3. Remain alive (7)
4. Listener (6)
5. Short high-pitched tone (5)
6. Shyly (5)
7. Group of islands (11)
8. Oversee (11)
14. Perceive with the senses (7)
15. Massage technique (7)
17. Christening (6)
19. Smooth transition (5)
20. Stem of an arrow (5)

CROSSWORD 293

ACROSS

1. Steep in liquid (6)
4. Sudden fear (6)
9. Written language for blind people (7)
10. Hears (7)
11. Removes water from a boat (5)
12. Relieved of an illness (5)
14. Desolate (5)
15. Semiconductor (5)
17. Add coal to a fire (5)
18. Small dissenting group (7)
20. Assemble; gather (7)
21. Bog (6)
22. Very difficult or complex (6)

DOWN

1. Drink (6)
2. Pink wading bird (8)
3. Bottoms of shoes (5)
5. Plunder (7)
6. Departed (4)
7. Flipped a coin (6)
8. Action of being rescued (11)
13. Fragrant (8)
14. Firm opinions (7)
15. Put out of shape (6)
16. Tidily (6)
17. Art gallery (5)
19. Singe (4)

CROSSWORD 294

ACROSS

4. Opposite of faster (6)
7. Intellectual (8)
8. Introverted (3)
9. Fail totally (4)
10. Develop (6)
11. Terribly (7)
12. E.g. arms and legs (5)
15. Sticky (5)
17. Bodies of writing (7)
20. Sad pot (anag.) (6)
21. Eurasian crow (4)
22. Vessel; jolt (3)
23. Overcame (8)
24. Indigenous (6)

DOWN

1. Cushion for the head (6)
2. Small American squirrel (8)
3. Distress (7)
4. Fast (5)
5. Sagacity (6)
6. Poems; sounds alike (6)
13. Brought into a country (8)
14. Have (7)
15. Inhabitant of Troy (6)
16. Red wine (6)
18. Firmly established (6)
19. Foam or froth (5)

CROSSWORD 295

ACROSS

1. Optimistic (4)
3. Remote; cut off (8)
9. Assistant; follower (7)
10. Dispose of (5)
11. Written in pictorial symbols (12)
13. Equine sounds (6)
15. Part of the eye (6)
17. Unofficially (3,3,6)
20. Agreeable sound or tune (5)
21. Outer layer of a hair (7)
22. Holding close (8)
23. Neat in appearance (4)

DOWN

1. Arriving at a destination (8)
2. Reproductive unit of fungi (5)
4. Decorous; proper (6)
5. Repository for misplaced items (4,8)
6. State of being twisted (7)
7. Swindle (4)
8. Conjectural (12)
12. Reverie (8)
14. Steeps in liquid (7)
16. Ordained minister (6)
18. Happen (5)
19. Superhero film based on comic characters (1-3)

CROSSWORD 296

ACROSS

4. Ride a horse at pace (6)
7. In the adjacent residence (4,4)
8. Domestic bovine animal (3)
9. Insect stage (4)
10. Next after third (6)
11. Biggest (7)
12. Benefactor (5)
15. Tends (anag.) (5)
17. Remains of living things (7)
20. Read with care (6)
21. Smallest pig of the litter (4)
22. Remove branches (3)
23. Woody (8)
24. Lectern (6)

DOWN

1. Source of caviar (6)
2. Not curly (of hair) (8)
3. Small shark (7)
4. Thin mortar (5)
5. Composite fungus and alga (6)
6. Tin alloy (6)
13. Notes; sees (8)
14. Not native (7)
15. Lump or blob (6)
16. Bit sharply (6)
18. Batting order (4-2)
19. Misgiving (5)

CROSSWORD 297

ACROSS

1. A cargo (6)
7. Extremely happy (8)
8. Long bench (3)
9. Deny of food (6)
10. Tear down (4)
11. Pierced by a bull's horn (5)
13. Pertaining to a river (7)
15. Devise beforehand (7)
17. Trims (5)
21. Greek spirit (4)
22. Characteristically French (6)
23. Head covering (3)
24. University teacher (8)
25. Scrap (6)

DOWN

1. Small pet canine (6)
2. Water diviner (6)
3. Toothed wheels (5)
4. Calls for (7)
5. Capital of Liberia (8)
6. Public square in Italy (6)
12. Daring feats (8)
14. Person who dawdles (7)
16. Awakened (6)
18. Material wealth (6)
19. Sculptured figure (6)
20. Utter impulsively (5)

CROSSWORD 298

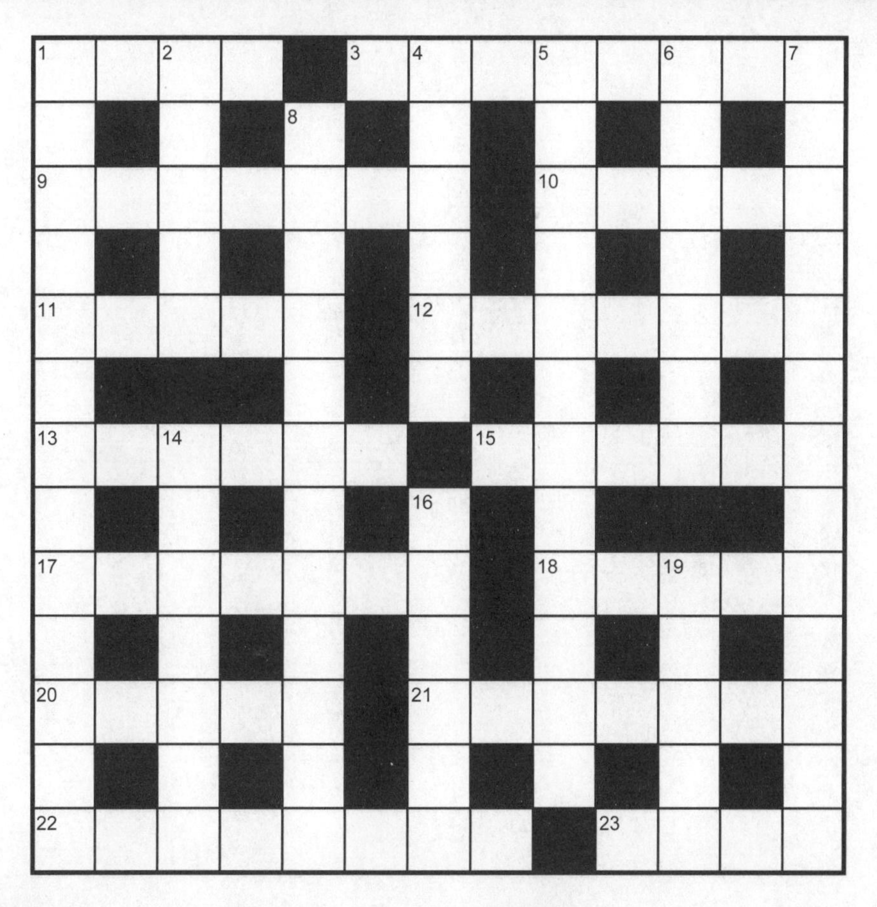

ACROSS

1. Wine container (4)
3. Devilry (8)
9. Objects that indicate position (7)
10. Belonging to them (5)
11. Extreme displeasure (5)
12. Set aside for a purpose (7)
13. Cast doubt upon (6)
15. Fierce woman (6)
17. Saunter (anag.) (7)
18. Allowed by official rules (5)
20. Raise up (5)
21. Hasty (7)
22. Fatherly (8)
23. Merriment (4)

DOWN

1. Friendship (13)
2. Show indifference with the shoulders (5)
4. Arch of the foot (6)
5. Butterfly larvae (12)
6. Japanese flower arranging (7)
7. Prescience (13)
8. Cooling device (12)
14. Nationalist (7)
16. Respiratory condition (6)
19. Question intensely (5)

CROSSWORD 299

ACROSS

1. Grow in number (8)
5. Domesticated ox (4)
9. Solid blow (5)
10. Magnified view (5-2)
11. Not artificial (7)
12. Manner of speaking (5)
13. Money received (6)
14. Tips and instruction (6)
17. Certain to end in failure (2-3)
19. Juicy soft fruit (7)
20. Back pain (7)
21. Stringed instrument (5)
22. Pull abruptly (4)
23. Tardiness (8)

DOWN

1. Deliberately (13)
2. Harsh; corrosive (7)
3. Based on untested ideas (12)
4. Farming tool (6)
6. All (5)
7. Not ostentatious (13)
8. Significant (12)
15. Fragrant gum or spice (7)
16. Eastern temple (6)
18. Ladies (5)

CROSSWORD 300

ACROSS

4. Very fine substance (6)
7. Feud (8)
8. Adult males (3)
9. Cow meat (4)
10. Support (6)
11. Unfasten (7)
12. Small motor-racing vehicles (5)
15. Baby carriage (5)
17. Period of conflict (7)
20. Culpable (6)
21. Electrically charged particles (4)
22. Fall behind (3)
23. Responded (8)
24. Abrupt (6)

DOWN

1. Within this context (6)
2. Improving the mind; enlightening (8)
3. Steadfast (7)
4. Large public gardens (5)
5. More moist (6)
6. Spans (6)
13. Achieved (8)
14. Infantile (7)
15. Constructs (6)
16. Silenced (6)
18. Way of doing something (6)
19. Obtain information from various sources (5)

CROSSWORD 301

ACROSS

1. Pain in a person's belly (7,4)
9. Be in debt (3)
10. Scorch (5)
11. Floor of a building (5)
12. Impudent (5)
13. Reverse somersault (8)
16. Withers (8)
18. Pastime (5)
20. Logical and easy to understand (5)
21. Rescuer (5)
22. Fish appendage (3)
23. Mimic (11)

DOWN

2. People aged 13-19 (5)
3. Untidy (5)
4. Where one finds Quebec (6)
5. Simian (7)
6. Ponderously (7)
7. Meaningless (11)
8. Acting out a part (4,7)
14. Liberty (7)
15. Supervise (7)
17. Departs (6)
18. Wading bird (5)
19. Suit (5)

CROSSWORD 302

ACROSS

1. Woody plants (6)
4. Country in northern Europe (6)
9. Trying experiences (7)
10. Experienced serviceman (7)
11. Climb (5)
12. Fully prepared (5)
14. Wise men (5)
17. Overly self-confident (5)
19. Clear and easy to understand (5)
21. Flexible (7)
23. Have a moderating effect on (7)
24. Mistakes (6)
25. Doglike mammals (6)

DOWN

1. Precious metal (6)
2. Engrossed (4)
3. Acts in a disloyal manner (7)
5. Walks through water (5)
6. Theatrical (8)
7. Tensed (anag.) (6)
8. Shipment (11)
13. Comfy seat (8)
15. Fragmentary (7)
16. Trite remark (6)
18. Sailing vessels (6)
20. Discourage (5)
22. Settlement smaller than a city (4)

CROSSWORD 303

ACROSS

1. People who shape horseshoes (8)
5. Creative disciplines (4)
9. Decal (anag.) (5)
10. Ship worker (7)
11. Traversed (7)
12. Concerning (5)
13. Frozen plain (6)
14. Sense of musical time (6)
17. Entice to do something (5)
19. Pancreatic hormone (7)
20. Evident (7)
21. Capital of Egypt (5)
22. Team (4)
23. Educational institutions (8)

DOWN

1. Congratulations (13)
2. Nocturnal carnivorous mammal (7)
3. Imprudence (12)
4. Withdraw (6)
6. Lover of Juliet (5)
7. Holier-than-thou (13)
8. Highly abstract (12)
15. Effective; having a striking effect (7)
16. Complete failure (6)
18. Relocated (5)

CROSSWORD 304

ACROSS

1. Compose a dance routine (11)
9. Financial resources (5)
10. Relations (3)
11. Camel-like animal (5)
12. Remove paint from a wall (5)
13. Borough of New York City (8)
16. Device that regulates water flow (8)
18. Absorbent cloth (5)
21. Promotional wording (5)
22. Material from which a metal is extracted (3)
23. Small firework (5)
24. Administrative assistants (11)

DOWN

2. Six-sided shape (7)
3. Comments (7)
4. By word of mouth (6)
5. Takes a break (5)
6. Card game (5)
7. Joyful occasion (11)
8. Indescribable (11)
14. Talk foolishly (7)
15. Capable of being dissolved (7)
17. Alter or adapt (6)
19. In what place (5)
20. Not a winner (5)

CROSSWORD 305

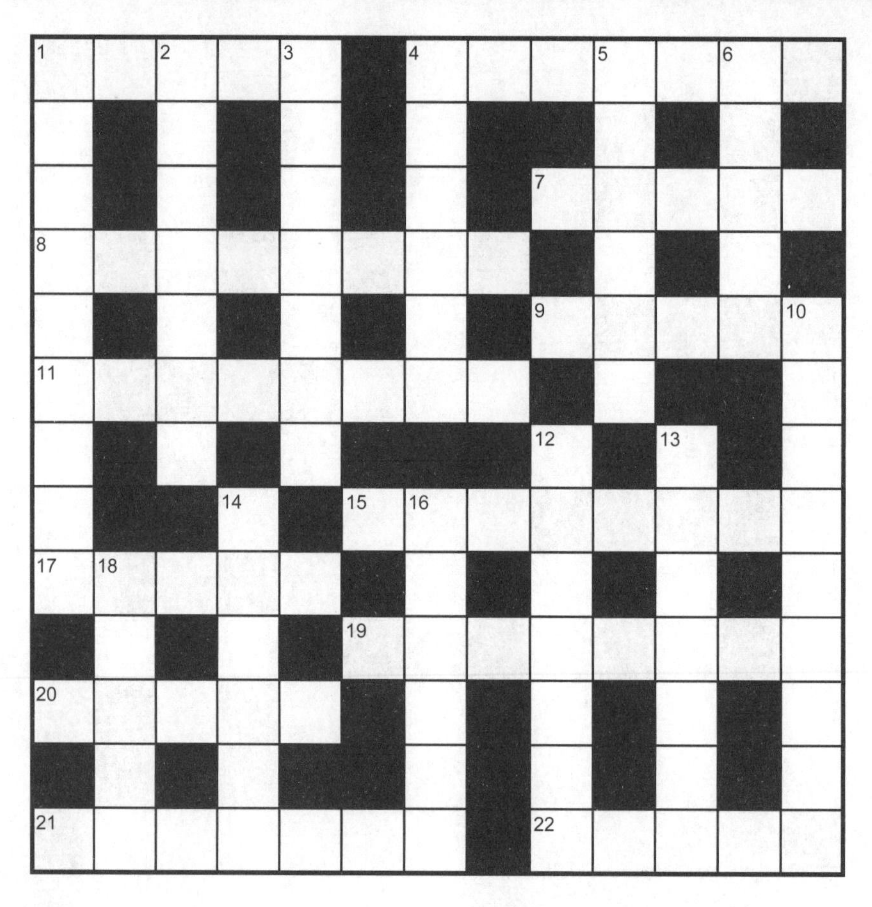

ACROSS

1. Consecrate (5)
4. Permits to travel (7)
7. Hit hard (5)
8. Bathing costume (8)
9. Small sales stand (5)
11. Familiar description for a person (8)
15. Cabbage salad (8)
17. Faint (5)
19. Disparage (8)
20. Quick meal (5)
21. Diffusion of molecules through a membrane (7)
22. Military blockade (5)

DOWN

1. Tasteless showiness (9)
2. No longer in existence (7)
3. E.g. spring and winter (7)
4. Belief in a god (6)
5. SI unit of thermodynamic temperature (6)
6. Timber framework (5)
10. General erudition (9)
12. Ways of doing things (7)
13. Unsurpassed (3-4)
14. Mexican cloak (6)
16. Large bodies of water (6)
18. Birds use these to fly (5)

CROSSWORD 306

ACROSS

1. Enthusiastic approval (11)
9. Gang (3)
10. Remedies (5)
11. Lance (5)
12. Metallic compound (5)
13. Secondary personality (5,3)
16. Tank for keeping fish (8)
18. Shady spot under trees (5)
20. Hank of wool (5)
21. Less moist (5)
22. Deep hole in the ground (3)
23. Money spent (11)

DOWN

2. Inner circle (5)
3. Fortunate (5)
4. Subject to death (6)
5. Thin paper products used for wiping (7)
6. Commanded (7)
7. Abashed (11)
8. Confirm (11)
14. Music player (7)
15. Person of high rank (7)
17. Undone (6)
18. Round cap (5)
19. Car windscreen cleaner (5)

CROSSWORD 307

ACROSS

1. Absence of passion (6)
4. Not sinking (6)
9. Disparaging remarks (7)
10. Rabbit holes (7)
11. E.g. taste or touch (5)
12. Manages (5)
14. Ponders (5)
17. Stinging insects (5)
19. Alcoholic beverage (5)
21. Forbidden by law (7)
23. Quick musical tempo (7)
24. Entangle (6)
25. Venomous snakes (6)

DOWN

1. Language (6)
2. Affirm with confidence (4)
3. Great courage (7)
5. Clenched hands (5)
6. Greasiness (8)
7. Throws a coin in the air (6)
8. Mood (11)
13. Clock timing device (8)
15. Rinsed around (7)
16. Series of eight notes (6)
18. Dishes of leafy greens (6)
20. Fits of violent anger (5)
22. Stare (4)

CROSSWORD 308

ACROSS

1. Freedom from difficulty (4)
3. Assimilate again (8)
9. Floating (7)
10. Ellipses (5)
11. Money (5)
12. Instruction (7)
13. Topics for debate (6)
15. Strong ringing sounds (6)
17. Gossip (7)
18. U-shaped curve in a river (5)
20. Join together; merge (5)
21. One of the platinum metals (7)
22. Metallic element used in light bulbs (8)
23. Biblical garden (4)

DOWN

1. Ornamentation (13)
2. Indifferent to emotions (5)
4. Distinct being (6)
5. Style of playing blues (6-6)
6. Enthusiastic reception (7)
7. Female professional (13)
8. Failure to act with prudence (12)
14. Stopping place for a train (7)
16. Piece of text that names the writer of an article (6)
19. Impossible to see round (of a bend) (5)

CROSSWORD 309

ACROSS

4. Dock for small yachts (6)
7. Soldier (8)
8. Note down (3)
9. Platform leading out to sea (4)
10. Slight prickling sensation (6)
11. Symbolic objects (7)
12. Ways or tracks (5)
15. Interruption (5)
17. Quick departure (7)
20. Underground railway systems (6)
21. System of contemplation (4)
22. Space or interval (3)
23. Third in order (8)
24. Swollen edible root (6)

DOWN

1. Reactive metal (6)
2. Portable device to keep rain out (8)
3. Whenever (7)
4. Complains (5)
5. Force fluid into (6)
6. Thespians (6)
13. Cyan tail (anag.) (8)
14. Ascertain dimensions (7)
15. Sharp knife (6)
16. Walked awkwardly (6)
18. Long-haired variety of cat (6)
19. Foam (5)

CROSSWORD 310

ACROSS

1. Popular holiday destination (6)
4. Musical works (6)
9. Protective location (7)
10. Not connected to the internet (7)
11. Courageous (5)
12. Sycophant (5)
14. Religious groups (5)
15. Reduce prices substantially (5)
17. Supplied by tube (5)
18. Open-minded; given freely (7)
20. Building (7)
21. Resistant to something (6)
22. Imperfection (6)

DOWN

1. Step down from a job (6)
2. Flowering plant (5,3)
3. Irritable (5)
5. Financial gains (7)
6. Indian dress (4)
7. Certainly (6)
8. Missiles (11)
13. Able to adjust (8)
14. Heighten (7)
15. Highly seasoned type of sausage (6)
16. Strangest (6)
17. Item won in a competition (5)
19. Smile broadly (4)

CROSSWORD 311

ACROSS

4. Beat as if with a flail (6)
7. Worker (8)
8. Leap on one foot (3)
9. Tolled (4)
10. Lively Spanish dance (6)
11. Light beard (7)
12. Danes (anag.) (5)
15. Eats a main meal (5)
17. Road or roofing material (7)
20. Red salad fruit (6)
21. Deep affection (4)
22. Damp (3)
23. Person who studies plants (8)
24. Surrenders (6)

DOWN

1. Deposit knowledge (6)
2. Qualified for entry (8)
3. Look something over closely (7)
4. Informs (5)
5. Reverberated (6)
6. Occur (6)
13. Ranks in society (8)
14. Bodyguards (7)
15. Lethargic; sleepy (6)
16. Stinging weed (6)
18. Sumptuously rich (6)
19. Wounding remarks (5)

CROSSWORD 312

ACROSS

1. Model figures used as toys (5)
4. Sells abroad (7)
7. Pile (5)
8. Events that hinder progress (8)
9. Assumed appearance (5)
11. Money given generously (8)
15. Say mean things about another (8)
17. Burn (5)
19. Computer programs (8)
20. Pledge (5)
21. Lost grip (7)
22. Iron alloy (5)

DOWN

1. Passes into a solution (9)
2. Portable lamp (7)
3. Bundles of grain stalks (7)
4. Calls forth (6)
5. Move faster than (6)
6. Mexican tortilla wraps (5)
10. Transitory (9)
12. Streaks (anag.) (7)
13. Very odd (7)
14. Positioned (6)
16. Declared (6)
18. Hoarse sound made by a frog (5)

CROSSWORD 313

ACROSS

1. Special ___ : film illusion (6)
4. Symbolic (6)
9. Tax imposed on ships (7)
10. Pieces of correspondence sent through the post (7)
11. Garners (5)
12. Ten more than forty (5)
14. Factual evidence (5)
15. Keep (5)
17. Fall heavily (5)
18. Division of a book (7)
20. Silhouette (7)
21. Failing to win (6)
22. Large snake (6)

DOWN

1. Complete (6)
2. Spanish dance (8)
3. Protective garments (5)
5. Set a boat free from her moorings (4,3)
6. Give a particular title to (4)
7. Dry and brittle (of food) (6)
8. Restraint (4-7)
13. Grow in a vigorous way (8)
14. Painter (anag.) (7)
15. Companionable (6)
16. Abdominal organ (6)
17. Oily; greasy (5)
19. Seabirds (4)

CROSSWORD 314

ACROSS

1. Word used by magicians (11)
9. Currently in progress (5)
10. Protective cover (3)
11. Bolt for fastening metal plates (5)
12. Christmas song (5)
13. Last (8)
16. Person who repairs cars (8)
18. Jewel from an oyster shell (5)
21. Children's entertainer (5)
22. Sound of a dove (3)
23. Make inoperative (5)
24. Quality of being timeless (11)

DOWN

2. Briefness (7)
3. Study of the body (7)
4. Quantity (6)
5. Loft (5)
6. Measuring stick (5)
7. Cautious (11)
8. Youth (11)
14. Register at a hotel (5,2)
15. Not outside (7)
17. Senior members of a tribe (6)
19. With a forward motion (5)
20. Name applied to something (5)

CROSSWORD 315

ACROSS

4. Harsh (6)
7. Short film (8)
8. Nocturnal mammal (3)
9. Particles around a comet (4)
10. Pertaining to the mind (6)
11. Mends (7)
12. Arrives (5)
15. Lacking enthusiasm; weary (5)
17. Having joined characters (of writing) (7)
20. Determine (6)
21. Set of playing cards (4)
22. Large (3)
23. Imitator (8)
24. Simpler (6)

DOWN

1. Reduce to a lower grade (6)
2. Wild prank (8)
3. European country (7)
4. Creep (5)
5. Symbol or representation (6)
6. Teaser (anag.) (6)
13. Glass-like volcanic rock (8)
14. Melodious (7)
15. Mix up (6)
16. Evades (6)
18. Winner (6)
19. Person who goes underwater (5)

CROSSWORD 316

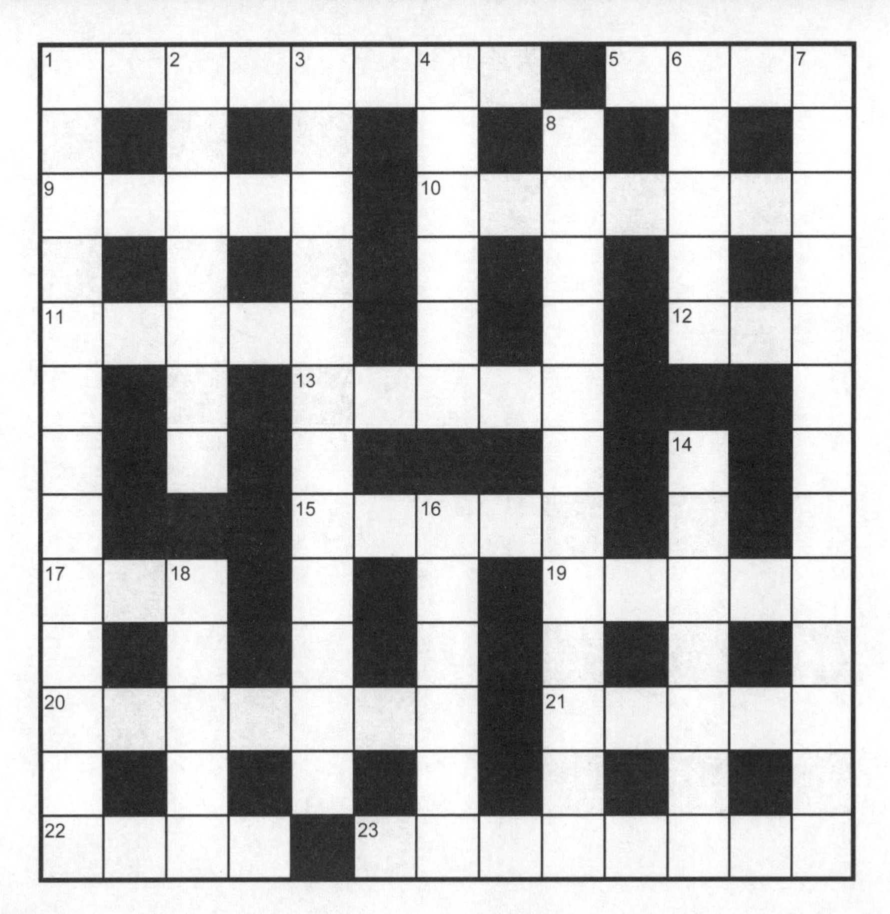

ACROSS

1. Unfaithful (8)
5. Performs in a play (4)
9. Edge or border (5)
10. E.g. biology (7)
11. Passenger ship (5)
12. Cheek (slang) (3)
13. Remnant of a dying fire (5)
15. Hard and brittle (5)
17. Seventh Greek letter (3)
19. Hurts (5)
20. Larval frog (7)
21. Coarse twilled cotton fabric (5)
22. Endure (4)
23. Thoroughly cooked (of meat) (4-4)

DOWN

1. Relating to growth (13)
2. Squeeze into a compact mass (7)
3. Excessive response (12)
4. Boards (anag.) (6)
6. Artificial waterway (5)
7. Any means of advancement (8,5)
8. Pertaining to a person's life (12)
14. Colonnade (7)
16. Hinder (6)
18. Mountain range in South America (5)

CROSSWORD 317

ACROSS

1. Fellows (5)
4. Flowers (7)
7. Holy chalice (5)
8. The face above the eyebrows (8)
9. Muscular contraction (5)
11. Abstract ideas (8)
15. Relating to sound (8)
17. Vibrated (5)
19. Dowdiness (8)
20. Ring (5)
21. Bewilder (7)
22. Estimate (5)

DOWN

1. Chinese philosopher (9)
2. Offend the modesty of (7)
3. Capable of seeing (of a person) (7)
4. Navigational instrument (6)
5. Capital of Zimbabwe (6)
6. Belief in a god or gods (5)
10. Procedures (9)
12. Massaging (7)
13. Tall tower (7)
14. Move with a bounding motion (6)
16. Outer layer of the cerebrum (6)
18. Door hanger (5)

CROSSWORD 318

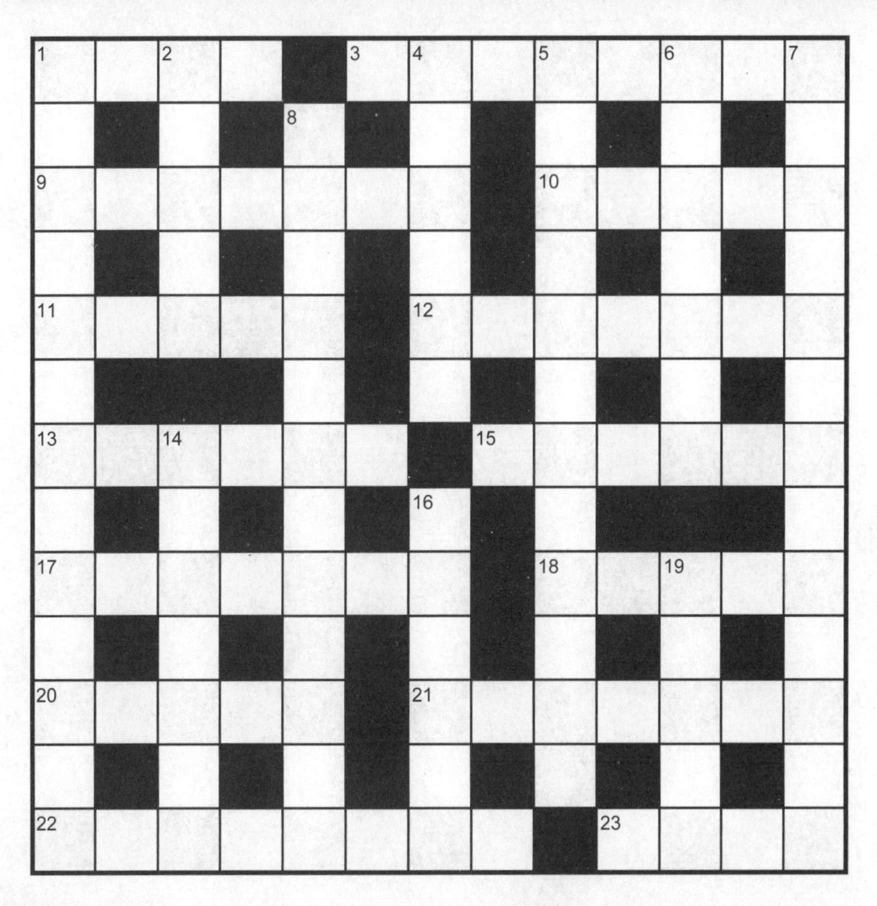

ACROSS

1. Lock lips (4)
3. Overly anxious and sensitive (8)
9. Foreboding (7)
10. Supply with food (5)
11. Not heavy (5)
12. Quell (7)
13. Judged (6)
15. Jail (6)
17. Frees from an obligation (7)
18. Household garbage (5)
20. Organ situated in the skull (5)
21. Selfishness (7)
22. The whole of something (8)
23. Sewing join (4)

DOWN

1. Intelligent and informed (13)
2. Move back and forth (5)
4. Make certain of (6)
5. Convalescence (12)
6. Rags (7)
7. Plant with bright flowers (13)
8. Metal device for removing tops (6,6)
14. Graceful in form (7)
16. Upward slope (6)
19. Media (anag.) (5)

CROSSWORD 319

ACROSS

7. Pursuit of pleasure (8)
8. Noes (anag.) (4)
9. Direct one's gaze at (4)
10. 12th month (8)
11. Fled from captivity (7)
12. Outer layer of bread (5)
15. Makes well (5)
17. Prickles (7)
20. Musical wind instruments (8)
22. Move about aimlessly (4)
23. Clock face (4)
24. Debilitated (8)

DOWN

1. Wading birds (6)
2. Alcoholic drink with several ingredients (8)
3. Enigmas (7)
4. Hit hard (5)
5. Literary composition (4)
6. Precious stones (6)
13. Took into account (8)
14. Blood relation (7)
16. Greek mathematician (6)
18. Overjoyed (6)
19. Understood with certainty (5)
21. Anger or irritate (4)

CROSSWORD 320

ACROSS

1. Microorganisms (5)
4. Sets free or releases (7)
7. Biblical king (5)
8. Atmospheric gas (8)
9. Type of bottle (5)
11. Evading (8)
15. Using the minimum necessary (8)
17. Big (5)
19. Looked for (8)
20. Rushes along (5)
21. Bewilder (7)
22. Small particle (5)

DOWN

1. Domesticated cavy (6,3)
2. Disturbance; commotion (7)
3. Disguises or covers (7)
4. Not noticed (6)
5. Excessively (6)
6. Speed in nautical miles per hour (5)
10. Very low (of a price) (5-4)
12. Catching (7)
13. Ancient large storage jar (7)
14. Outlaw (6)
16. Weird (6)
18. Unsteady (5)

CROSSWORD 321

ACROSS

1. Gambles (6)
4. Token (6)
9. Played out (7)
10. Become less intense (4,3)
11. View; picture (5)
12. Satisfy a thirst (5)
14. Royal (5)
17. Summed together (5)
19. Brilliant successes (5)
21. Feeling guilty (7)
23. Beg (7)
24. Relatively limited (of an amount) (6)
25. Pay no attention to (6)

DOWN

1. Becomes alert after sleep (6)
2. Precious stones (4)
3. Regain strength (7)
5. Resay (anag.) (5)
6. Took the trouble to do something (8)
7. Book of accounts (6)
8. Keep cold (11)
13. Amended (8)
15. Whipping (7)
16. Howl (6)
18. Work out logically (6)
20. Prophets (5)
22. Not stereo (4)

CROSSWORD 322

ACROSS

1. Spiritually symbolic (8)
5. Box (4)
9. Smallest quantity (5)
10. Working extremely hard (7)
11. Suspend; prevent (5)
12. Floor covering (3)
13. Section of a long poem (5)
15. Birds do this to clean their feathers (5)
17. Very cold (3)
19. Seven (anag.) (5)
20. Quivering singing effect (7)
21. Subject of a talk (5)
22. Fishing sticks (4)
23. Careless (8)

DOWN

1. Manage badly (13)
2. Platform (7)
3. Act of seizing something en route (12)
4. Reach (6)
6. Device that splits light (5)
7. Virtuousness (13)
8. Unplugged (12)
14. Go before (7)
16. Continent (6)
18. Give up (5)

CROSSWORD 323

ACROSS

1. Act gloomily (anag.) (11)
9. Put a question to (3)
10. Very loud (5)
11. Collection of maps (5)
12. Flowers (5)
13. Pertaining to the chest (8)
16. Personal magnetism (8)
18. Goes through carefully (5)
20. Balance (5)
21. Snake (5)
22. Came first in a race (3)
23. Freedom from dirt (11)

DOWN

2. Finds agreeable (5)
3. Below zero (of temperature) (5)
4. Multiply by three (6)
5. Faithfulness (7)
6. Building where art is displayed (7)
7. Visible to the naked eye (11)
8. Annoying (11)
14. Far-reaching; thorough (7)
15. Difficult choice (7)
17. E.g. monkey or whale (6)
18. Sully or blemish (5)
19. Young deer (pl.) (5)

CROSSWORD 324

ACROSS

1. Not real or genuine (6)
4. Shallow dish (6)
9. Plot (7)
10. Capable of relieving pain (7)
11. Water droplets (5)
12. Puff up (5)
14. Financial institutions (5)
15. Aromatic spice (5)
17. Fragile (5)
18. Female spirit (7)
20. Riding the waves (7)
21. Portions of a play (6)
22. Quantum of electromagnetic radiation (6)

DOWN

1. Encrypt (6)
2. Capital of Chile (8)
3. Two children born at the same time (5)
5. Takes in (7)
6. Guinea pig (4)
7. Happen again (6)
8. Unintelligible (11)
13. Church musician (8)
14. Apiary (7)
15. Private rooms on ships (6)
16. Large bottle for wine (6)
17. Estuary (5)
19. Back of the neck (4)

CROSSWORD 325

ACROSS

1. Makes available for sale (6)
7. Amount (8)
8. Healthy (3)
9. Effect; force (6)
10. Child's bed (4)
11. Songs for two people (5)
13. Wild (of an animal) (7)
15. Rebuttal (7)
17. Non-flowering plants (5)
21. Mud grooves (4)
22. Personal attendants (6)
23. Container for a drink (3)
24. Cosmetic product for the skin (8)
25. Garment maker (6)

DOWN

1. Cause to feel upset (6)
2. Pointless (6)
3. Crouch (5)
4. Lacking (7)
5. Enclosure formed from upright stakes (8)
6. Clothing (6)
12. Day of the week (8)
14. Solicit votes from (7)
16. Matches (6)
18. Scoundrel (6)
19. Smile affectedly (6)
20. Behave amorously (5)

CROSSWORD 326

ACROSS

1. Huge three-horned dinosaur (11)
9. Triangular river mouth (5)
10. Signal for action (3)
11. Monotonous hum (5)
12. Suggest (5)
13. Be overcome with laughter (8)
16. Intelligentsia (8)
18. Embarrass (5)
21. Latin American dance (5)
22. Consume food (3)
23. Research deeply (5)
24. Company that transmits TV shows (11)

DOWN

2. Bellowing (7)
3. Silvery-white metal (7)
4. Measuring sticks (6)
5. Walk heavily and firmly (5)
6. Chooses (5)
7. Expects to happen (11)
8. Document confirming an achievement (11)
14. Ferocious small mammals (7)
15. Lack of success (7)
17. Sloping (of a typeface) (6)
19. Stage performer (5)
20. Many-headed snake (5)

CROSSWORD 327

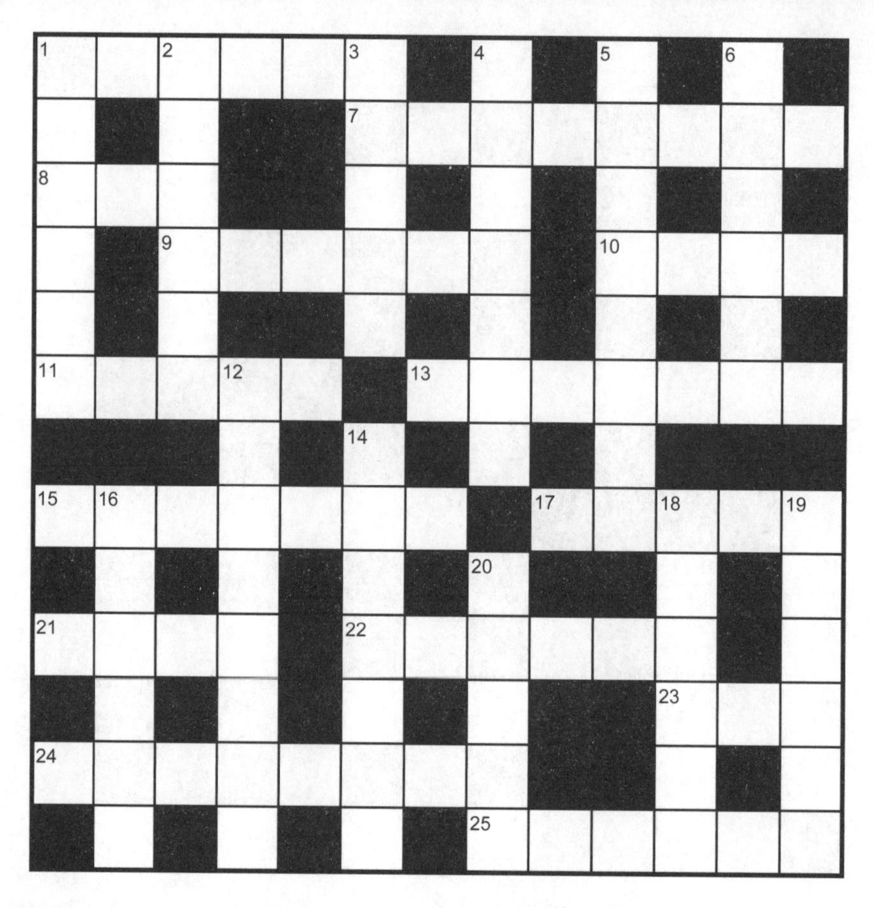

ACROSS

1. Wishing for (6)
7. Lift (8)
8. Young male (3)
9. Ursine (anag.) (6)
10. Highly excited (4)
11. Watery; marshy (5)
13. Belief that there is no God (7)
15. Fugitive (7)
17. Vaulted (5)
21. A brief piece of film (4)
22. Deeply recessed (of someone's eyes) (6)
23. Enjoyable (3)
24. Assume control of (4,4)
25. Soup spoons (6)

DOWN

1. Mix socially (6)
2. Working steadily with a tool (6)
3. Class (5)
4. Returns to a former state (7)
5. Hot pepper (8)
6. Benefactors (6)
12. Wrestled (8)
14. Huge (7)
16. Remove goods from a van (6)
18. Resolute or brave (6)
19. Imbibes (6)
20. Knotty protuberance on a tree (5)

CROSSWORD 328

ACROSS

1. Remaining; surplus (8)
5. Ooze or leak slowly (4)
8. Reject with disdain (5)
9. Licentious (7)
10. Painting medium (7)
12. Groups together (7)
14. Inflexible and unyielding (7)
16. Estimates (7)
18. Copy; mimic (7)
19. Eat steadily (5)
20. Very strong wind (4)
21. Adjoining (8)

DOWN

1. In case (4)
2. Articulate; eloquent (6)
3. Medicinal creams (9)
4. Has objective reality (6)
6. Breadwinner (6)
7. Pattern of circular spots (5,3)
11. Tree known for the nut it produces (9)
12. Burbling (8)
13. Cordial (6)
14. Climb (6)
15. Street (6)
17. Close (4)

CROSSWORD 329

ACROSS

1. Make more concentrated (8)
5. Eager; keen (4)
9. Type of coffee drink (5)
10. Organic solvent (7)
11. Person studying after a first degree (12)
13. Compact group of mountains (6)
14. Flexible (6)
17. Feeling depressed (5-7)
20. Derided (7)
21. Do really well at (5)
22. Perceives (4)
23. Campaigner (8)

DOWN

1. Room in a jail (4)
2. Concepts (7)
3. Very exciting (12)
4. Set of steps (6)
6. Flowering plant (5)
7. Intensified (8)
8. Main premises of a company (12)
12. Importance; stress (8)
15. Penetrated (7)
16. Showing gentleness (6)
18. Worship; venerate (5)
19. Smudge (4)

CROSSWORD 330

ACROSS

1. Removes errors (8)
5. Strip of leather worn round the waist (4)
9. Damp (5)
10. Short moral story (7)
11. Protective layers (7)
12. Strength (5)
13. Average; moderate (6)
14. Whole (6)
17. Facial protuberances (5)
19. Sterile (7)
20. Learning institution (7)
21. A satellite of Uranus (5)
22. Ox-like mammals (4)
23. Viciously (8)

DOWN

1. Harmonious; compatible (13)
2. Ruled (7)
3. Device for putting out fires (12)
4. Computer keyboard user (6)
6. Arm joint (5)
7. Conceptually (13)
8. Surpassing in influence (12)
15. Mound made by insects (7)
16. Legal practitioner (6)
18. Main plant stem (5)

CROSSWORD 331

ACROSS

1. Mend with rows of stitches (4)
3. Maritime (8)
9. Outline of a natural feature (7)
10. Brusque (5)
11. Act of influencing someone deviously (12)
14. Haul (3)
16. Number in a trilogy (5)
17. Cry of disapproval (3)
18. Impossible to achieve (12)
21. Doctrine; system of beliefs (5)
22. European country (7)
23. Completely preoccupied with (8)
24. Ring (4)

DOWN

1. Destroy in large numbers (8)
2. Angry dispute (3-2)
4. Mixture of gases we breathe (3)
5. Fellowship (12)
6. SI unit of electric charge (7)
7. Raise up (4)
8. Contests (12)
12. Insect grub (5)
13. Fit together easily (8)
15. Is curious about (7)
19. Flat-bottomed boat (5)
20. Reflection of sound (4)
22. Era (anag.) (3)

CROSSWORD 332

ACROSS

1. Of like kind (4)
3. Chord played in rapid succession (8)
9. Moaned (7)
10. Laborious task (5)
11. Resolutely (12)
13. Stomach crunches (3-3)
15. Poser; enigma (6)
17. Discreditable (12)
20. Pollex (5)
21. Children's carers (7)
22. Feigns (8)
23. Matured (4)

DOWN

1. Roadside board showing directions (8)
2. Group of singers (5)
4. Steering mechanism of a boat (6)
5. Intensely painful (12)
6. Grumbled (7)
7. Augury (4)
8. Without equal (12)
12. Freed from captivity (8)
14. Commendation (7)
16. Thought; supposed (6)
18. Existing (5)
19. Pace (4)

CROSSWORD 333

ACROSS

1. Have an impact on (6)
4. Sharp cutting implements (6)
9. Coming from the south (7)
10. Natural environment (7)
11. Microscopic fungus (5)
12. Inferior to (5)
14. Yellow citrus fruit (5)
17. Alter (5)
19. Brings up (5)
21. Turns upside down (7)
23. Certificate (7)
24. Lived with as a guest (6)
25. Mineral used to make plaster of Paris (6)

DOWN

1. In a careless manner (6)
2. Body fat (4)
3. Personal possession (7)
5. Beastly (5)
6. Quality of being different (8)
7. Military greeting (6)
8. Pertaining to marriage (11)
13. Renovated (8)
15. Innocently (7)
16. Relating to a wedding (6)
18. Remove weapons (6)
20. Jostle and push (5)
22. Mocks (4)

CROSSWORD 334

ACROSS

1. Rebound (8)
5. Move rapidly (4)
9. Stringed instrument (5)
10. Intrusions (7)
11. Acrid (7)
12. Recently made (5)
13. Ice homes (6)
14. The spirit or soul (6)
17. Eject lava (5)
19. River in South America (7)
20. A curse; wicked look (4,3)
21. Approaches (5)
22. Indication (4)
23. Fanaticism (8)

DOWN

1. Open-mindedness (13)
2. Rank in the forces (7)
3. Reticent; secretive (12)
4. Official proclamations (6)
6. Egg-shaped (5)
7. Naughtily (13)
8. Opposite of amateur (12)
15. Substance used to remove heat (7)
16. Hold fast (6)
18. Exploiting unfairly (5)

CROSSWORD 335

ACROSS

1. Adequacy (11)
9. Ancient harps (5)
10. Before the present (of time) (3)
11. Rides the waves (5)
12. Go away from quickly (5)
13. Habitually lazy (8)
16. Choosing from various sources (8)
18. Tries out (5)
21. Brazilian dance (5)
22. Single in number (3)
23. Outdoor shelters (5)
24. Creating an evocative mood (11)

DOWN

2. Improve equipment (7)
3. Incorrectly (7)
4. Opera by Bizet (6)
5. Gets less difficult (5)
6. Seat of authority (5)
7. Endpoint of a journey (11)
8. Advertisements (11)
14. Print anew (7)
15. Things that evoke reactions (7)
17. Doze (6)
19. Snow and rain mix (5)
20. Fight (3-2)

CROSSWORD 336

ACROSS

1. Hideousness (8)
5. Sixth Greek letter (4)
9. Kind of wheat (5)
10. Mass of flowers (7)
11. Competed in a speed contest (5)
12. Japanese monetary unit (3)
13. Refute by evidence (5)
15. A written document (5)
17. Word expressing negation (3)
19. Type of tree (5)
20. Aims or purposes (7)
21. Expect to happen (5)
22. Men (4)
23. Cartoon artist (8)

DOWN

1. Comprehension (13)
2. Expressive (of music) (7)
3. Practice of mentioning famous people one knows (4-8)
4. Residential district (6)
6. Piece of writing (5)
7. Person who manages the affairs of an insolvent company (13)
8. Comical tuner (anag.) (12)
14. Shining (7)
16. Toxin (6)
18. Tawdry (5)

CROSSWORD 337

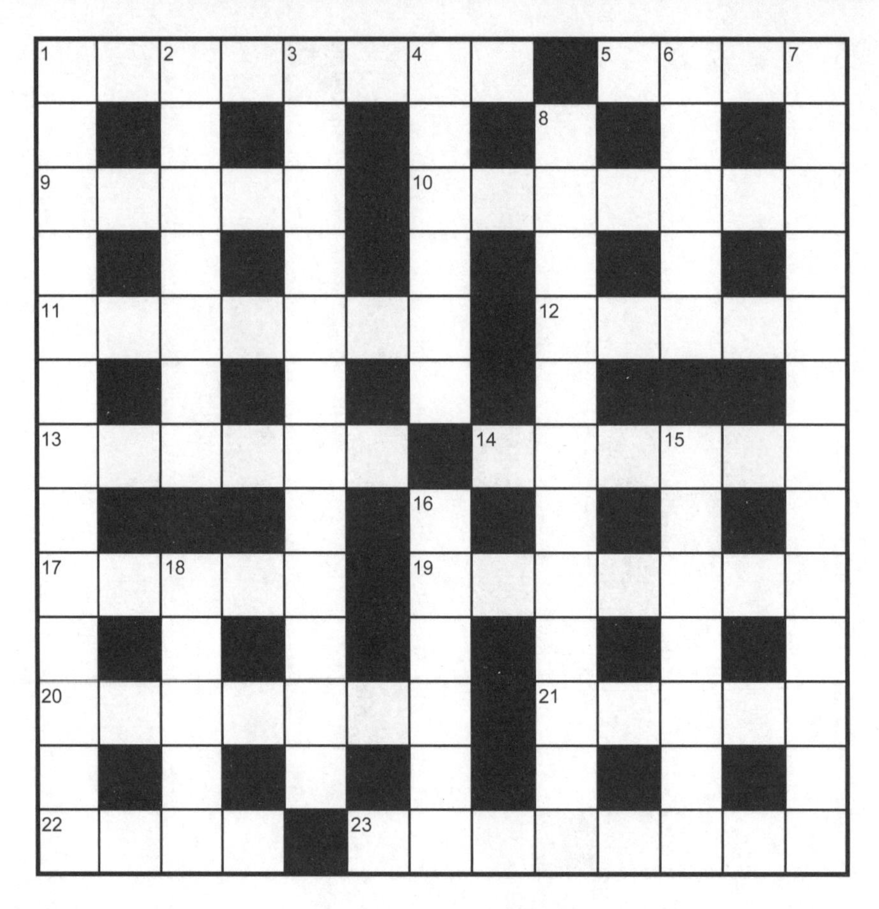

ACROSS

1. Opposition to war (8)
5. At what time (4)
9. Extent or limit (5)
10. Atomic particle (7)
11. Republic in South America (7)
12. Crawl (5)
13. Passage to the lungs and stomach (6)
14. Exist permanently in (6)
17. Stares at in a lecherous way (5)
19. Varnish (7)
20. Meaninglessness (7)
21. The Hunter (constellation) (5)
22. Check; exam (4)
23. Impressive manner of a person (8)

DOWN

1. One with extremely high standards (13)
2. Vanquish (7)
3. A type of error in speech (8,4)
4. Assorted; various (6)
6. Vast multitude (5)
7. Absence (13)
8. Part of the mind (12)
15. Act of avoiding capture (7)
16. Participant in a game (6)
18. Large indefinite quantities (5)

CROSSWORD 338

ACROSS

1. Refill (6)
7. Argued logically (8)
8. Cry of a cat (3)
9. Small insect (6)
10. Boxing match (4)
11. Trench (5)
13. Not crying (3-4)
15. Seems (7)
17. Brag (5)
21. Sheet of floating ice (4)
22. Capital of the Philippines (6)
23. Prevent (3)
24. Summon to return (4,4)
25. Unless (6)

DOWN

1. Cause to remember (6)
2. Opposite of highest (6)
3. Speak in a slow manner (5)
4. Cattle troughs (7)
5. Straw hat (8)
6. Continue (6)
12. Intelligently (8)
14. Branch of linguistics (7)
16. Post (6)
18. Fit for cultivation (of land) (6)
19. Desire for water (6)
20. Slithering animal (5)

CROSSWORD 339

ACROSS

1. Quick reply (8)
5. Plant stalk (4)
9. Juicy fruit (5)
10. Yellow fruits (7)
11. More irate (7)
12. Type of coffee drink (5)
13. Pictorial representations (6)
14. Complex carbohydrate (6)
17. Standards (5)
19. Momentum (7)
20. Cast a spell on (7)
21. Show triumphant joy (5)
22. Hearing organs (4)
23. Spatters with liquid (8)

DOWN

1. Friendly (13)
2. Capital of Nicaragua (7)
3. Variety of wildlife in an area (12)
4. Being with organic and cybernetic parts (6)
6. Cloak (5)
7. State of the USA (13)
8. Use of words that mimic sounds (12)
15. Enhance a photo (7)
16. Chess piece (6)
18. Oarsman (5)

CROSSWORD 340

ACROSS

1. Soften; become less severe (6)
7. Repudiate (8)
8. Fruit preserve (3)
9. Make something new (6)
10. Pay attention to (4)
11. Shallow food containers (5)
13. Breathing aid in water (7)
15. Slander (7)
17. Sleeveless cloaks (5)
21. Opposite of short (4)
22. Summon to serve in the armed forces (4-2)
23. Young dog (3)
24. Shape of the waxing moon (8)
25. Multiples of twenty (6)

DOWN

1. Turn down (6)
2. Thin layer of sedimentary rock (6)
3. Large woody plants (5)
4. A precise point in time (7)
5. Elation (8)
6. Plan of action (6)
12. Least old (8)
14. Bumped into (7)
16. On a ship or train (6)
18. Pungent condiment (6)
19. Ear bone (6)
20. Lists (anag.) (5)

CROSSWORD 341

ACROSS

1. Full development (8)
5. First man (4)
9. Type of diagram (5)
10. Single-handed (7)
11. Restrain (7)
12. Bird sound; chirp (5)
13. Stifle (anag.) (6)
14. Make worse (6)
17. Confess to (5)
19. Type of diving (4-3)
20. Catches fire (7)
21. Spiny yellow plant (5)
22. Ark builder (4)
23. Very loyal (8)

DOWN

1. Enlargement (13)
2. Instructs (7)
3. Restore to good condition (12)
4. Very reliable (6)
6. Evade (5)
7. Large sea (13)
8. Boxing class (12)
15. Takes a firm stand (7)
16. Ukrainian port (6)
18. Spiritual nourishment (5)

CROSSWORD 342

ACROSS

1. Soaked thoroughly (8)
5. Boyfriend or male admirer (4)
9. Plants of a region (5)
10. Accelerate (5,2)
11. Wanderer (5)
12. Female kangaroo (3)
13. Stanza of a poem (5)
15. Sailing vessel (5)
17. Ancient boat (3)
19. Entertain (5)
20. Brought forth (7)
21. Happening (5)
22. Prying; overly curious (4)
23. Gave prominence to (8)

DOWN

1. Removal of trees from an area (13)
2. Changes gradually (7)
3. Ability to see the future (12)
4. Christian festival (6)
6. Finished (5)
7. Unparalleled (13)
8. Second part of the Bible (3,9)
14. Arrogance; loftiness (7)
16. Hold gently and carefully (6)
18. Renown (5)

CROSSWORD 343

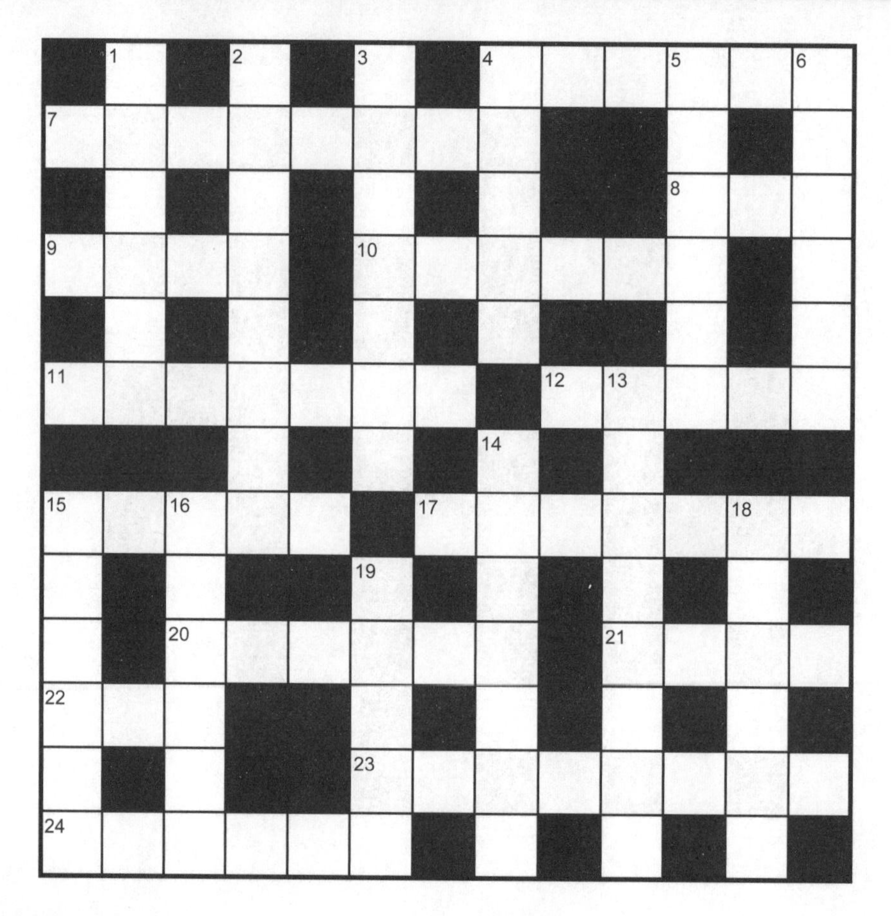

ACROSS

4. Terminate a telephone call (4,2)
7. Green vegetable (8)
8. Mammal with a bushy tail (3)
9. Dark cloud of smoke (4)
10. Approval; recognition (6)
11. If (7)
12. Seasons (5)
15. Striped animal (5)
17. Climbing tools (7)
20. Expose as being false (6)
21. Invalid (4)
22. Listening device (3)
23. Rocked (8)
24. Advance evidence for (6)

DOWN

1. Raise for discussion (6)
2. Person who shapes stone (8)
3. Instructs (7)
4. Gave a job to (5)
5. Talented (6)
6. Tiny dots making up an image (6)
13. Set in from the margin (8)
14. Containers (7)
15. Country whose capital is Lusaka (6)
16. Moved (6)
18. Respite (6)
19. Completely; really (5)

CROSSWORD 344

ACROSS

1. Make fun of (8)
5. Heroic tale (4)
9. Track of an animal (5)
10. Nasal opening (7)
11. Vehemently (12)
13. Disturb the smoothness of (6)
14. Stringed instrument (6)
17. Data about a population (12)
20. Flowed (of liquid) (7)
21. Draw or bring out (5)
22. Look for (4)
23. Appendages on a bird's skin (8)

DOWN

1. Reckless; hasty (4)
2. Decline gradually (4-3)
3. Heart specialist (12)
4. Sudden forward thrusts (6)
6. Land measures (5)
7. Lessening; diminishing (8)
8. Amazement (12)
12. Manufactures (8)
15. Discourse (7)
16. Oar (6)
18. Electronic device (5)
19. Barrels (4)

CROSSWORD 345

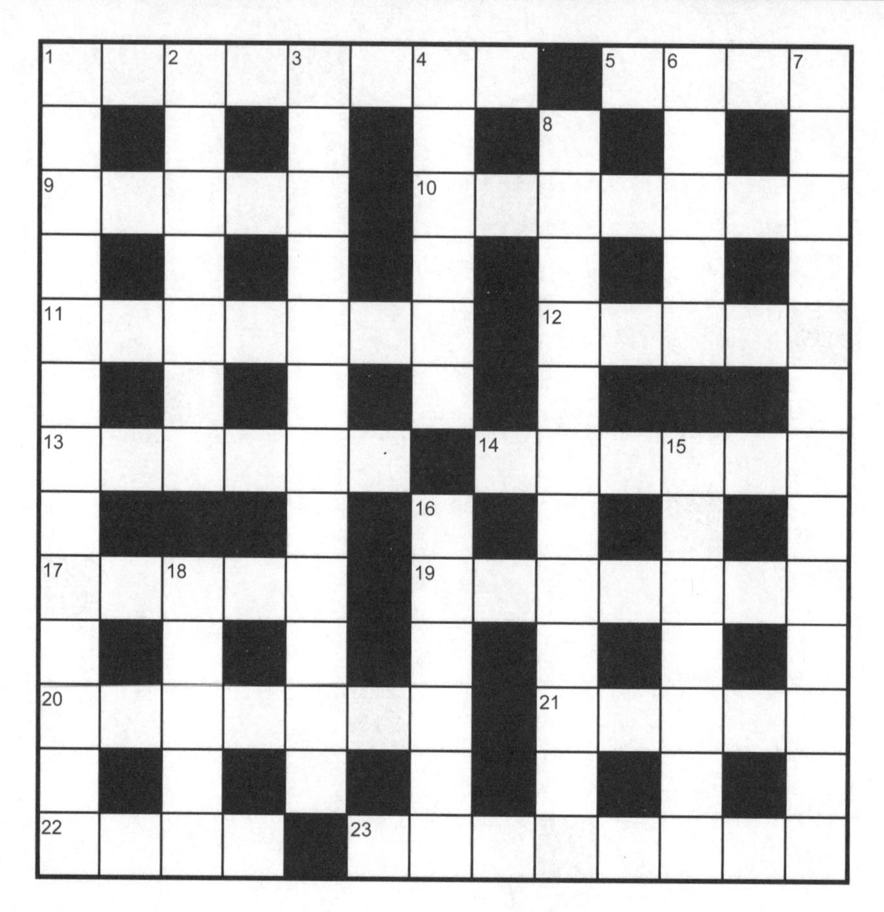

ACROSS

1. Formed a mental concept of (8)
5. Of similar character (4)
9. Frozen dew (5)
10. Sheikdom in the Persian Gulf (7)
11. Novice driver (7)
12. Respond to (5)
13. Humorously sarcastic (6)
14. Action of making use of something (6)
17. Embed; type of filling (5)
19. Not carrying weapons (7)
20. Chanted (7)
21. Plant spike (5)
22. Three feet length (4)
23. Fetch (8)

DOWN

1. State of being unable to err (13)
2. Pear-shaped fruit native to Mexico (7)
3. Growing stronger (12)
4. Set out on a journey (6)
6. Australian marsupial (5)
7. Absence (13)
8. Carport choir (anag.) (12)
15. One of two gaps in a shirt (7)
16. Quash; tame (6)
18. Coming after (5)

CROSSWORD 346

ACROSS

1. Anxious uncertainty (8)
5. Familiar name for a potato (4)
8. Trite (5)
9. Platform (7)
10. Beating (7)
12. Exceptionally large (7)
14. Undoing a knot (7)
16. Addresses boldly (7)
18. Opposite of morning (7)
19. Tremble (5)
20. Army vehicle (4)
21. Marriage ceremony (8)

DOWN

1. Garment for the foot (4)
2. Text of a play (6)
3. E.g. residents of Cairo (9)
4. Flashing light (6)
6. Allow (6)
7. Harmful (8)
11. Current state of affairs (6,3)
12. Decorate; adorn (8)
13. Television surface (6)
14. Customary practices (6)
15. Fillings (6)
17. Cut down a tree (4)

CROSSWORD 347

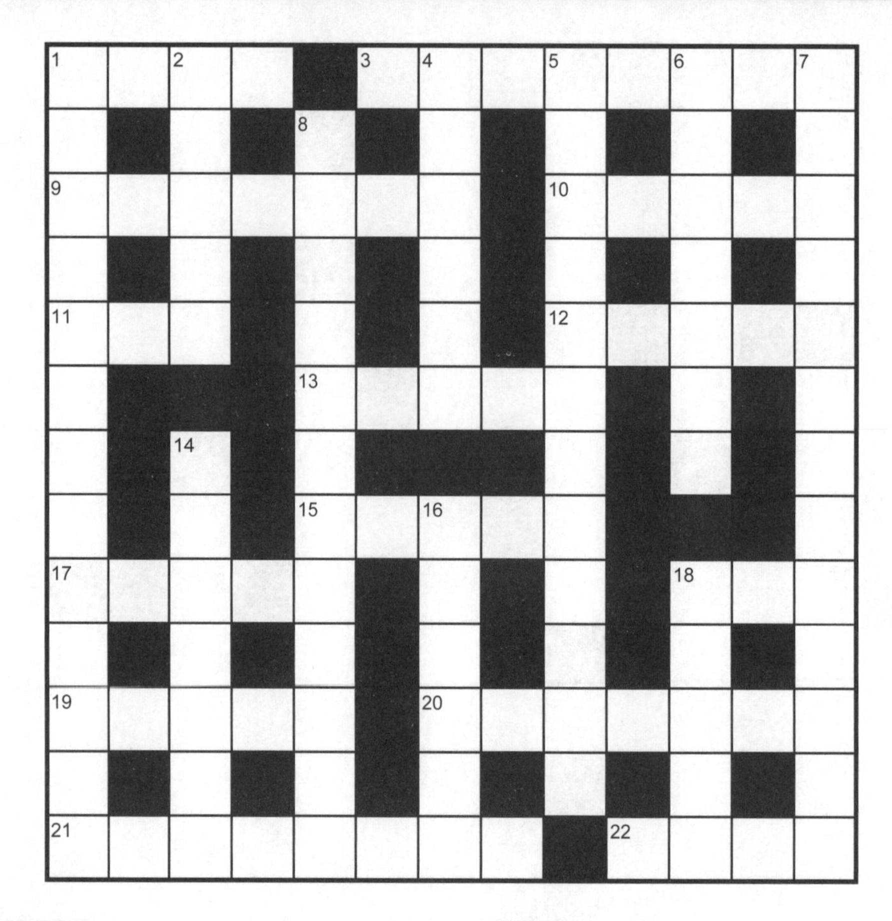

ACROSS

1. Cease (4)
3. Cowards (8)
9. Examine (7)
10. A central point (5)
11. Clothing needed for an activity (3)
12. Call forth (5)
13. More mature (5)
15. Faint southern constellation (5)
17. Lively Bohemian dance (5)
18. Additionally (3)
19. Ancient object (5)
20. Drink containing vermouth (7)
21. Sleepily (8)
22. Obstacle (4)

DOWN

1. Easily angered (5-8)
2. Tines (anag.) (5)
4. Intense dislike (6)
5. Room attached to a house (12)
6. Jealous (7)
7. 25th anniversary of marriage (6,7)
8. Renditions (12)
14. Famous astronomer (7)
16. Standard; usual (6)
18. Pertaining to bees (5)

CROSSWORD 348

ACROSS

1. Prominent (4,7)
9. Scottish lakes (5)
10. Compete (3)
11. Artifice (5)
12. Thick sweet liquid (5)
13. Conversation between two people (3-2-3)
16. Microorganisms (8)
18. Green citrus fruits (5)
21. Makes less dense (5)
22. One more than five (3)
23. Operatic songs (5)
24. Petty (5-6)

DOWN

2. Asked to come along (7)
3. Very large; clumsy (7)
4. Calculate; think that (6)
5. Combines (5)
6. Crowbar (5)
7. Person with strong patriotic feelings (11)
8. Re-evaluation (11)
14. Hat with a wide brim (7)
15. Walk aimlessly (7)
17. Chamber of the heart (6)
19. Principle of conduct (5)
20. Will (5)

CROSSWORD 349

ACROSS

1. Brief (4)
3. Progresses (8)
9. Sovereign (7)
10. Shout of appreciation (5)
11. Self-esteem (3)
12. A sum owed (5)
13. Avoid (5)
15. Take part in combat (5)
17. Go over again (5)
18. Touch gently (3)
19. Former name of Myanmar (5)
20. Noisy confusion (7)
21. Opposite of westerly (8)
22. Lump of earth (4)

DOWN

1. Measurable by a common standard (13)
2. Musical form with a recurrent theme (5)
4. Garden flowering plant (6)
5. Able to use both hands well (12)
6. Large room (7)
7. Easily angered (5-8)
8. Most prominent position (5,2,5)
14. Notes down (7)
16. Small pet rodent (6)
18. Absolute (5)

CROSSWORD 350

ACROSS

1. Female sheep (pl.) (4)
3. Great difficulty (8)
9. Tribune (anag.) (7)
10. Strange and mysterious (5)
11. Greek writer of fables (5)
12. Install (7)
13. Habitual practice (6)
15. Place inside something else (6)
17. Fatuously (7)
18. Mark of repetition (5)
20. Humiliate (5)
21. Anarchic (7)
22. Christmas season (8)
23. Catch sight of (4)

DOWN

1. Noteworthy and rare (13)
2. Peers (5)
4. Pertaining to vinegar (6)
5. Scolding (8-4)
6. Green vegetation (7)
7. Affectedly (13)
8. Action of moving a thing from its position (12)
14. Burdensome work (7)
16. Rode a bike (6)
19. Lock of hair (5)

CROSSWORD 351

ACROSS

1. Oscillates (8)
5. Upper front part of a boot (4)
8. Smells strongly (5)
9. Mexican spirit (7)
10. Fix (7)
12. Show to be reasonable (7)
14. Has an impact on (7)
16. Enslave (anag.) (7)
18. Reveal (7)
19. Type of large deer (5)
20. Part of an egg (4)
21. Lengthen (8)

DOWN

1. Action word (4)
2. Brief intervals (6)
3. Link (9)
4. Restaurant (6)
6. Excuses of any kind (6)
7. Egg-laying mammal (8)
11. Artisans (9)
12. Envy (8)
13. Annul (6)
14. Relating to stars (6)
15. Domed roof (6)
17. Give up one's rights (4)

CROSSWORD 352

1		2		■	3	4		5		6		7
	■		■	8	■		■		■		■	
9							■	10				
	■		■		■		■		■		■	
11					■	12						
	■	■	■		■		■		■		■	
13		14				■	15					
	■		■		■	16	■		■	■	■	
17							■	18		19		
	■		■		■		■		■		■	
20					■	21						
	■		■		■		■		■		■	
22								■	23			

ACROSS

1. Deities (4)
3. Impartial parties (8)
9. Block (7)
10. Visual representation (5)
11. Network points where lines intersect (5)
12. Pledged to marry (7)
13. System of ideas to explain something (6)
15. Black Sea peninsula (6)
17. Repeats from memory (7)
18. Select; formally approve (5)
20. Extent (5)
21. Get better (7)
22. Submissive (8)
23. Potential applications (4)

DOWN

1. Amiably (4-9)
2. Chopped finely (5)
4. Small hole (6)
5. Reckless; ready to react violently (7-5)
6. Mercury alloy (7)
7. Loyalty in the face of trouble (13)
8. Fully extended (12)
14. Fugitive (7)
16. Allocate (6)
19. Woodwind instruments (5)

CROSSWORD 353

ACROSS

1. Touches gently (4)
3. New York (3,5)
9. Feeling of aversion (7)
10. Spear (5)
11. Dark towering cloud (12)
14. Unwell (3)
16. External (5)
17. And not (3)
18. Explanatory section of a book (12)
21. Donald ___ : US President (5)
22. Drinking vessel (7)
23. Our galaxy (5,3)
24. Optical device (4)

DOWN

1. Intended to teach (8)
2. Broom (5)
4. Deep anger (3)
5. Comprehensive (3-9)
6. Flightless seabird (7)
7. Days before major events (4)
8. List of books referred to (12)
12. Observed (5)
13. Explosive shells (8)
15. Pertaining to the tongue (7)
19. Senseless (5)
20. Basic unit of matter (4)
22. Popular beverage (3)

CROSSWORD 354

ACROSS

1. Sing like a bird (5)
4. Residential areas (7)
7. Small loose stones (5)
8. Migratory birds (8)
9. Period of time consisting of 28 - 31 days (5)
11. Pleasantness (8)
15. Far on in development (8)
17. Part of a church tower (5)
19. Itch silk (anag.) (8)
20. Area of open land (5)
21. Planet (7)
22. Boxes lightly (5)

DOWN

1. Harmony (9)
2. Early childhood (7)
3. Body of troops (7)
4. Lays eggs (6)
5. Remove an obstruction from a sink (6)
6. Sheep's sound (5)
10. Difficulties (9)
12. Promotes commercially (7)
13. Spiny anteater (7)
14. Gambol (6)
16. Of delicate beauty (6)
18. Self-respect (5)

CROSSWORD 355

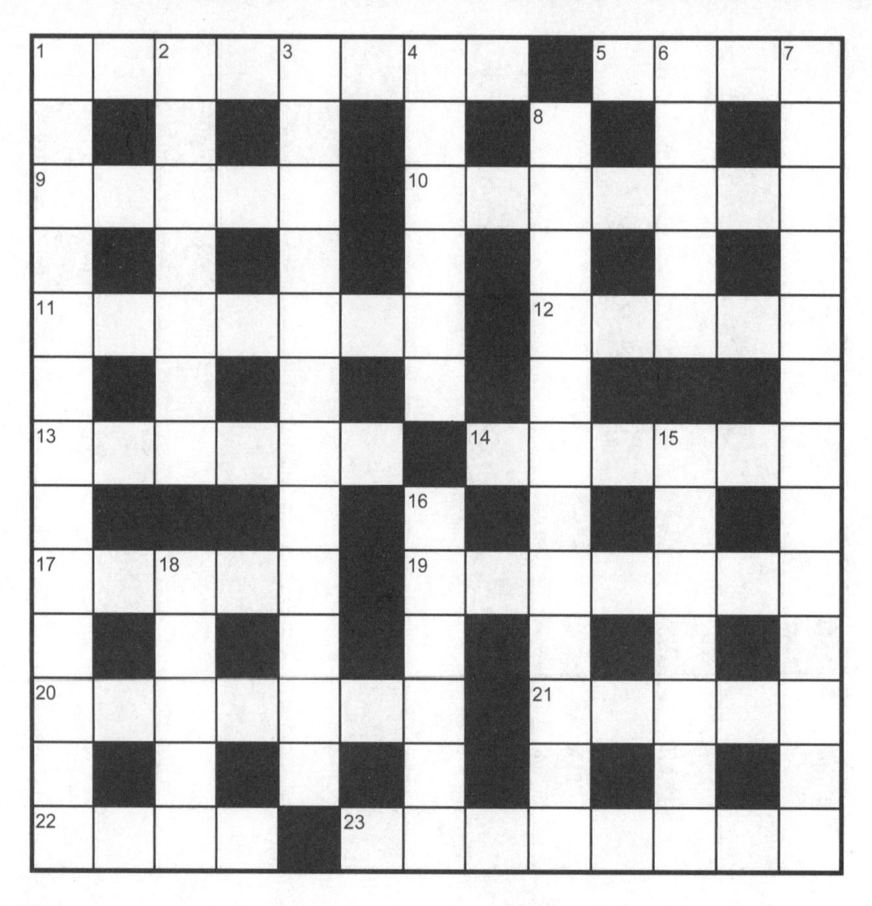

ACROSS

1. Corrosive precipitation (4,4)
5. ___ Kournikova: former tennis star (4)
9. Models for a photograph (5)
10. Program for viewing web pages (7)
11. Swell with fluid (7)
12. A leaf of paper (5)
13. Respect and admire (6)
14. Floor covering (6)
17. Viewpoint (5)
19. Japanese warriors (7)
20. Extinguish a candle (4,3)
21. Ruined; rendered inoperable (5)
22. At any time (4)
23. Ex-servicemen (8)

DOWN

1. Understandable (13)
2. Clear perception (7)
3. Revival of something (12)
4. Saturated (6)
6. Of the nose (5)
7. Fitness to fly (13)
8. Not catching fire easily (3-9)
15. No pears (anag.) (7)
16. Insect that transmits sleeping sickness (6)
18. Make right (5)

CROSSWORD 356

ACROSS

1. Rural scenery (11)
9. Implant (5)
10. Court (3)
11. Governed (5)
12. Clean with a brush (5)
13. Reflective thinker (8)
16. Person who campaigns for political change (8)
18. Not illuminated (5)
21. Entrance barriers (5)
22. Rocky hill (3)
23. Gestured at (5)
24. Stargazers (11)

DOWN

2. Affluent (7)
3. Provoked or teased (7)
4. Refund (6)
5. Teams (5)
6. Sowed (anag.) (5)
7. Lucidity (11)
8. Neutral (11)
14. Domain (7)
15. Wine merchant (7)
17. Cowardly (6)
19. Lingers furtively (5)
20. Tall structure on a castle (5)

CROSSWORD 357

ACROSS

1. Hair-cleansing preparations (8)
5. Grows old (4)
9. Barrier (5)
10. Data input devices (7)
11. Exorbitant (12)
14. Saw (anag.) (3)
15. Come into contact with (5)
16. Superhuman being (3)
17. Shockingly (12)
20. Seize and take legal custody of (7)
22. Increment (5)
23. Core meaning (4)
24. Not injured (8)

DOWN

1. Strain (4)
2. Incorporates into (7)
3. Absurd (12)
4. Tree that bears acorns (3)
6. Tropical fruit (5)
7. Stops temporarily (8)
8. Abnormal anxiety about health (12)
12. Solicits custom (5)
13. Winding strands about each other (8)
16. Element with atomic number 31 (7)
18. Strong cords (5)
19. Glass ornament; small ball (4)
21. Animal lair (3)

CROSSWORD 358

ACROSS

1. Someone who writes the words for a song (8)
5. Fill to capacity; stuff (4)
9. Essential (5)
10. Equilateral parallelogram (7)
11. Not intoxicating (of a drink) (12)
13. Universe (6)
14. Irrelevant pieces of information (6)
17. Antique; not modern (3-9)
20. Fire-breathing creatures (7)
21. Objection (5)
22. Rode (anag.) (4)
23. Substance causing a reaction (8)

DOWN

1. Molten matter (4)
2. Allocations (7)
3. Fellow plotter (12)
4. Hit (6)
6. Insurgent (5)
7. E.g. a trumpeter or pianist (8)
8. First language (6,6)
12. Agreed (8)
15. Watching (7)
16. Long-bladed hand tool (6)
18. Hang with cloth (5)
19. Restrain (4)

CROSSWORD 359

ACROSS

1. Views (8)
5. Second Greek letter (4)
8. Bronze medal position (5)
9. Provider of financial cover (7)
10. Hurries (7)
12. Arrogant person (7)
14. Strong verbal attack (7)
16. Rod used in weightlifting (7)
18. Lattice (7)
19. Vacillate (5)
20. Mammal with antlers (4)
21. Stringed musical instrument (8)

DOWN

1. Cereal grains (4)
2. Ploys (6)
3. Authoritative order (9)
4. Chess piece (6)
6. Creepier (6)
7. Type of word puzzle (8)
11. Believed (a lie) (9)
12. With undiminished force (8)
13. Mourn the loss of (6)
14. State of matter (6)
15. Wonder at (6)
17. Smile broadly (4)

CROSSWORD 360

ACROSS

1. State of the USA (4)
3. Recollected (8)
9. Newtlike salamander (7)
10. Kingdom (5)
11. Unit of heat (5)
12. Reserved and shy (7)
13. Trigonometric function (6)
15. Overrun in large numbers (6)
17. Inactive pill (7)
18. Amide (anag.) (5)
20. Diacritical mark (5)
21. Bathing tub with bubbles (7)
22. Period when a machine is out of action (8)
23. Verge (4)

DOWN

1. Unexpected (13)
2. Positive electrode (5)
4. Cream pastry (6)
5. Physics of movement through air (12)
6. Foliage (7)
7. Serving to show (13)
8. Beginning (12)
14. Lacking depth (7)
16. Situation that appears irresolvable (6)
19. Bewildered (5)

CROSSWORD 361

ACROSS

1. Half-conscious state (6)
4. Move in haste (6)
9. Finery (7)
10. Large crustacean (7)
11. Knocks into (5)
12. Looks good on (5)
14. Haggard (5)
15. Hear a court case anew (5)
17. Small seat (5)
18. Progress (7)
20. Turns around (on a chair) (7)
21. Hustle (anag.) (6)
22. Upper classes (6)

DOWN

1. Pulsates (6)
2. Heated exchange of views (8)
3. Telephones (5)
5. Consume by fire (7)
6. Speak in a wild way (4)
7. Hankers after (6)
8. Insensitivity (11)
13. Not guilty (8)
14. Flexible athlete (7)
15. Responds to (6)
16. Stylish; high quality (6)
17. Chute (5)
19. Bad habit (4)

CROSSWORD 362

ACROSS

1. Pollutes (6)
4. Reach a destination (6)
9. Caused to burn (7)
10. Skill or expertise in a field (7)
11. Gamble (5)
12. Personnel at work (5)
14. Dubious (5)
17. Thermosetting resin (5)
19. Captivates (5)
21. Substance such as a gel or emulsion (7)
23. War carriage (7)
24. Bubble violently (6)
25. Egyptian god (6)

DOWN

1. Entices to do something (6)
2. Knowledge (abbrev.) (4)
3. Become airborne (4,3)
5. Rejuvenate (5)
6. An engraved design (8)
7. Undergo a hardship (6)
8. Insults (11)
13. Annul or abolish (8)
15. E.g. primrose and lemon (7)
16. Amazes (6)
18. Songlike cries (6)
20. Metal worker (5)
22. Finished; complete (4)

CROSSWORD 363

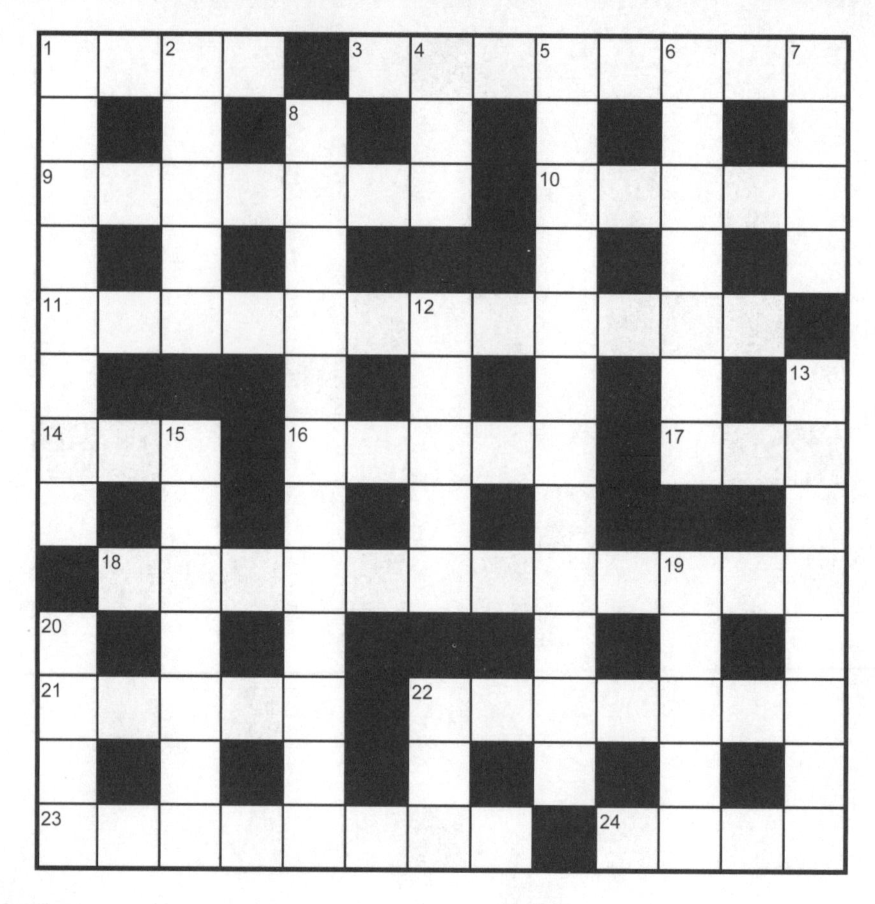

ACROSS

1. Make fun of (4)
3. Unbarred (8)
9. Give in to temptation (7)
10. Spy (5)
11. Laudatory (12)
14. Religious sister (3)
16. Smell (5)
17. How (anag.) (3)
18. What p.m. stands for (4,8)
21. Roman country house (5)
22. Respectable; refined (7)
23. Prodigal (8)
24. Pottery material (4)

DOWN

1. Squander money (8)
2. Chocolate powder (5)
4. Pen point (3)
5. Perceptions (12)
6. Technical knowledge (4-3)
7. Depressions (4)
8. Strengthen; confirm (12)
12. Complete (5)
13. Usually (8)
15. Pasta strips (7)
19. Perfect (5)
20. Affirm solemnly (4)
22. Antelope (3)

CROSSWORD 364

ACROSS

1. Breathe out (6)
4. Not moving (6)
9. Catchphrase (7)
10. Mutters (7)
11. Thin roofing slabs (5)
12. Attacks without warning (5)
14. Cleans (5)
15. Long-legged bird (5)
17. Packs of cards (5)
18. Aerial (7)
20. Earthenware container (7)
21. Meal (6)
22. Cuts off (6)

DOWN

1. Large property with land; holding (6)
2. Mountainous region (8)
3. Dens (5)
5. Slight earthquakes (7)
6. Useful implement (4)
7. Stops (6)
8. Show (11)
13. Passive (8)
14. Aridity (7)
15. Type of craftsman (6)
16. Rhesus (anag.) (6)
17. Mournful song (5)
19. Snare (4)

CROSSWORD 365

ACROSS

1. Reduction in worth (11)
9. About (5)
10. Bustle (3)
11. A number between an eighth and a tenth (5)
12. Employer (5)
13. Bookish (8)
16. Made subject to (8)
18. Maladroit (5)
21. Interior (5)
22. Female pronoun (3)
23. Bands worn around the waist (5)
24. Energetically (11)

DOWN

2. Issue forth (7)
3. Sport with arrows (7)
4. Raise up (6)
5. Instruct (5)
6. Opposite one of two (5)
7. Weak form of illumination (11)
8. Needleworker (11)
14. Country in northern Africa (7)
15. Decorative altar cloth (7)
17. Central parts of cells (6)
19. Ahead of time (5)
20. Leg bone (5)

SOLUTIONS

SOLUTIONS

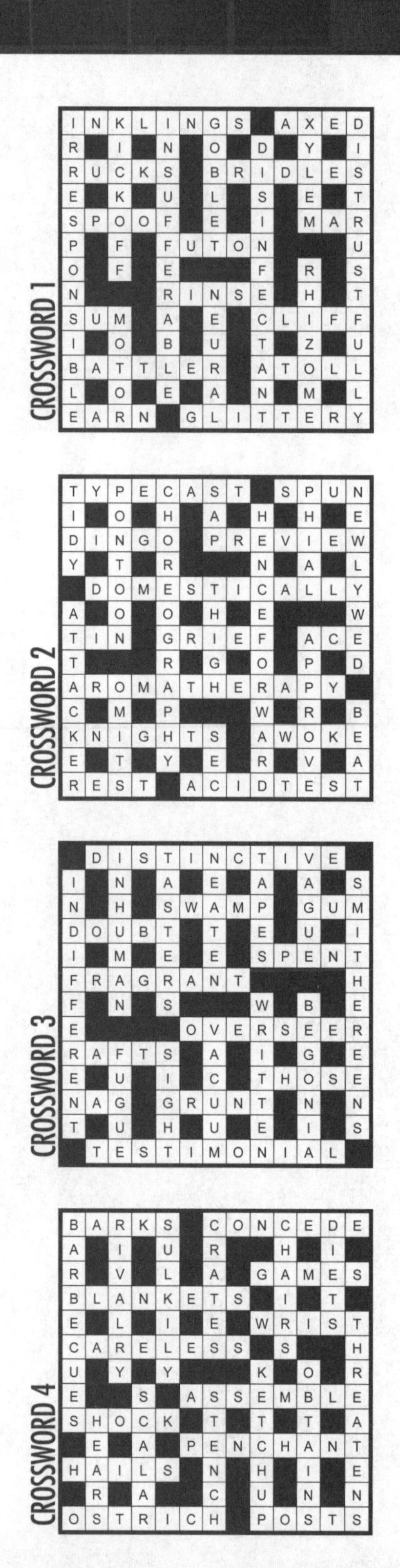

CROSSWORD 5

M	A	R	M	O	S	E	T		S	P	O	T
I		O		T		N		A		I		R
S	Y	L	P	H		Z	A	M	B	E	Z	I
C		L		E		Y		A		T		A
E	P	I	G	R	A	M		L	O	Y	A	L
L		N		W		E		G				A
L	A	G	O	O	N		R	A	T	I	O	N
A				R		S		M		M		D
N	A	T	A	L		E	X	A	M	P	L	E
E		H		D		N		T		U		R
O	R	A	C	L	E	S		I	D	L	E	R
U		N		Y		O		O		S		O
S	A	K	E		G	R	A	N	D	E	U	R

CROSSWORD 6

S	C	H	O	O	L		A	C	T	I	N	G
O		A		V		R		A		N		N
R		F		E		E	X	P	A	N	S	E
R	E	T	O	R	T	S		E		U		I
O				A		E		D	O	E	R	S
W	H	I	R	L		M				N		S
		N		L	O	B	B	Y		D		
S		S				L		T	O	O	T	H
T	R	I	M	S		A		T				U
U		G		E		N	U	R	S	I	N	G
F	A	N	A	T	I	C		I		N		G
F		I		U		E		U		N		E
S	T	A	M	P	S		A	M	U	S	E	D

CROSSWORD 7

G	A	R	A	G	E		S	W	E	L	L	S
A		E		I		T		A		O		L
D	E	C	O	D	E	R		R		L		U
F		L		D		A	L	L	E	L	E	S
L	A	I	T	Y		N		O				H
Y		N				S		R	A	S	P	Y
		E		H	O	P	E	D		C		
F	O	R	T	E		A				A		H
I				R		R		H	E	N	C	E
C	O	T	E	R	I	E		A		S		I
K		O		I		N	I	P	P	I	N	G
L		L		N		T		P		O		H
E	U	L	O	G	Y		C	Y	G	N	E	T

CROSSWORD 8

B	R	A	N	D	N	E	W		G	N	U	S
I		B		A		N				O		C
D	A	L	L	Y		S	U	M	A	T	R	A
E		O		D		U				A		L
		O		R		E	X	A	C	T	E	D
D	A	M	P	E	N	S		N		E		I
I				A				N				N
R		S		M		A	M	A	Z	I	N	G
E	X	P	O	S	E	D		P		N		
C		R				O		U		D		K
T	O	A	S	T	E	R		R	E	U	S	E
O		I				N		N		C		Y
R	U	N	G		E	S	C	A	P	E	E	S

SOLUTIONS

CROSSWORD 9

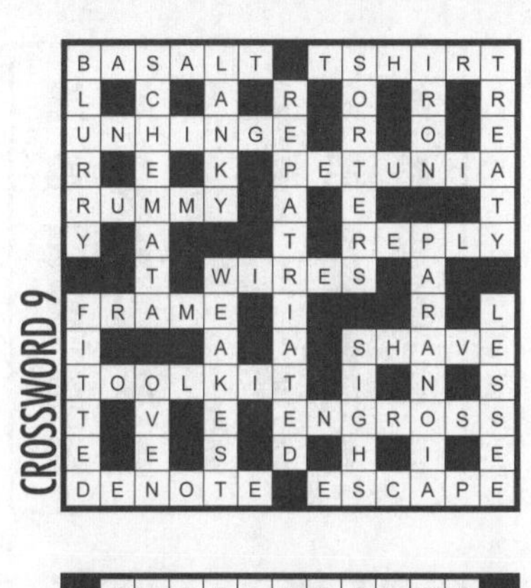

B	A	S	A	L	T		T	S	H	I	R	T
L		C		A		R		O		R		R
U	N	H	I	N	G	E		R		O		E
R		E		K		P	E	T	U	N	I	A
R	U	M	M	Y		A		E				T
Y		A				T		R	E	P	L	Y
		T		W	I	R	E	S		A		
F	R	A	M	E		I				R		L
I				A		A		S	H	A	V	E
T	O	O	L	K	I	T		I		N		S
T		V		E		E	N	G	R	O	S	S
E		E		S		D		H		I		E
D	E	N	O	T	E		E	S	C	A	P	E

CROSSWORD 10

	C	U	T	T	I	N	G	E	D	G	E	
D		N		E		O		A		A		O
E		D		S	T	U	N	G		Z	A	P
T	A	R	O	T		G		E		E		E
E		E		I		A		R	A	D	O	N
R	E	S	O	N	A	T	E					A
M		S		G				G		S		N
I					O	P	E	R	A	T	E	D
N	E	C	K	S		E		A		O		S
A		A		U		L		N	E	I	G	H
T	A	R		I	D	L	E	D		C		U
E		P		T		E		P		A		T
	E	S	S	E	N	T	I	A	L	L	Y	

CROSSWORD 11

C	A	P	A	C	I	T	Y		O	M	I	T
A		R		H		O		D		I		A
G	L	O	V	E		T	H	E	R	M	A	L
E		L		E				T		I		I
	C	O	N	S	E	Q	U	E	N	C	E	S
O		N		E		U		R				M
F	O	G		B	R	O	O	M		V	I	A
F				U		T		I		I		N
E	N	T	E	R	T	A	I	N	I	N	G	
N		O		G				A		E		F
D	U	D	G	E	O	N		B	A	G	E	L
E		A		R		A		L		A		E
R	A	Y	S		A	P	P	E	A	R	E	D

CROSSWORD 12

C	O	S	M	E	T	I	C		A	R	I	A
U		Y		C		N		C		E		L
L	I	N	G	O		G	L	O	W	E	R	S
L		O		N		E		N		V		A
	I	N	C	O	N	S	E	Q	U	E	N	T
E		Y		M		T		U				I
S	U	M	M	I	T		F	I	B	U	L	A
T				C		P		S		N		N
R	E	S	T	A	U	R	A	T	E	U	R	
A		I		L		E		A		S		L
N	O	D	U	L	E	S		D	O	U	S	E
G		L		Y		E		O		A		A
E	K	E	S		S	T	A	R	T	L	E	D

CROSSWORD 13

S	U	M	M	E	D		A		S		G	
A		A			U	N	C	O	M	M	O	N
V	E	X			K		I		O		B	
I		I	M	P	E	N	D		O	I	L	S
N		M			S		I		T		I	
G	A	S	E	S		E	T	C	H	I	N	G
			N		A		Y		I			
A	B	S	C	O	N	D		J	E	R	K	S
	R		L		Y		S			E		N
H	E	R	O		B	A	T	M	A	N		I
	A		S		O		E			D	I	P
A	D	D	E	N	D	U	M			E		E
	S		S		Y		S	C	A	R	E	S

CROSSWORD 14

R	W	A	N	D	A		S	P	O	U	T	S
E		C		I		F		L		N		P
T		M		S		O	V	E	R	D	U	E
O	P	E	N	A	I	R		A		E		N
O				V		T		T	I	R	E	D
K	A	Z	O	O		N				C		S
		I		W	R	I	T	E		U		
C		M				G		M	A	T	C	H
L	O	B	E	S		H		B				U
O		A		T		T	H	R	E	A	D	S
S	U	B	S	O	I	L		O		P		T
E		W		A		Y		I		E		L
S	M	E	L	T	S		P	L	E	D	G	E

CROSSWORD 15

E	X	A	M		U	N	C	O	R	K	E	D
S		G		M		I		B		I		A
C	U	R	E	A	L	L		S	O	B	E	R
A		E		N				C		B		K
P	R	E	S	U	M	P	T	U	O	U	S	
I				F		E		R		T		F
S	I	R		A	C	C	R	A		Z	O	O
T		A		C		A		N				R
	D	I	S	T	I	N	C	T	N	E	S	S
G		S		U				I		L		W
O	S	I	E	R		D	E	S	P	I	T	E
L		N		E		O		M		T		A
F	I	G	U	R	I	N	E		B	E	A	R

CROSSWORD 16

	S		B		S		S	A	C	H	E	T
S	T	A	R	D	U	S	T			U		O
	O		U		B		R			M	E	T
O	W	L	S		V	I	E	N	N	A		T
	E		H		E		W			N		E
A	D	J	O	U	R	N		S	H	E	A	R
			F		T		O		A			
D	A	F	F	Y		B	U	R	Y	I	N	G
R		L			S		T		M		U	
I		O	R	A	T	E	S		A	R	M	Y
V	O	W			O		I		K		B	
E		E			R	E	D	D	E	N	E	D
N	O	R	W	A	Y		E		R		R	

SOLUTIONS

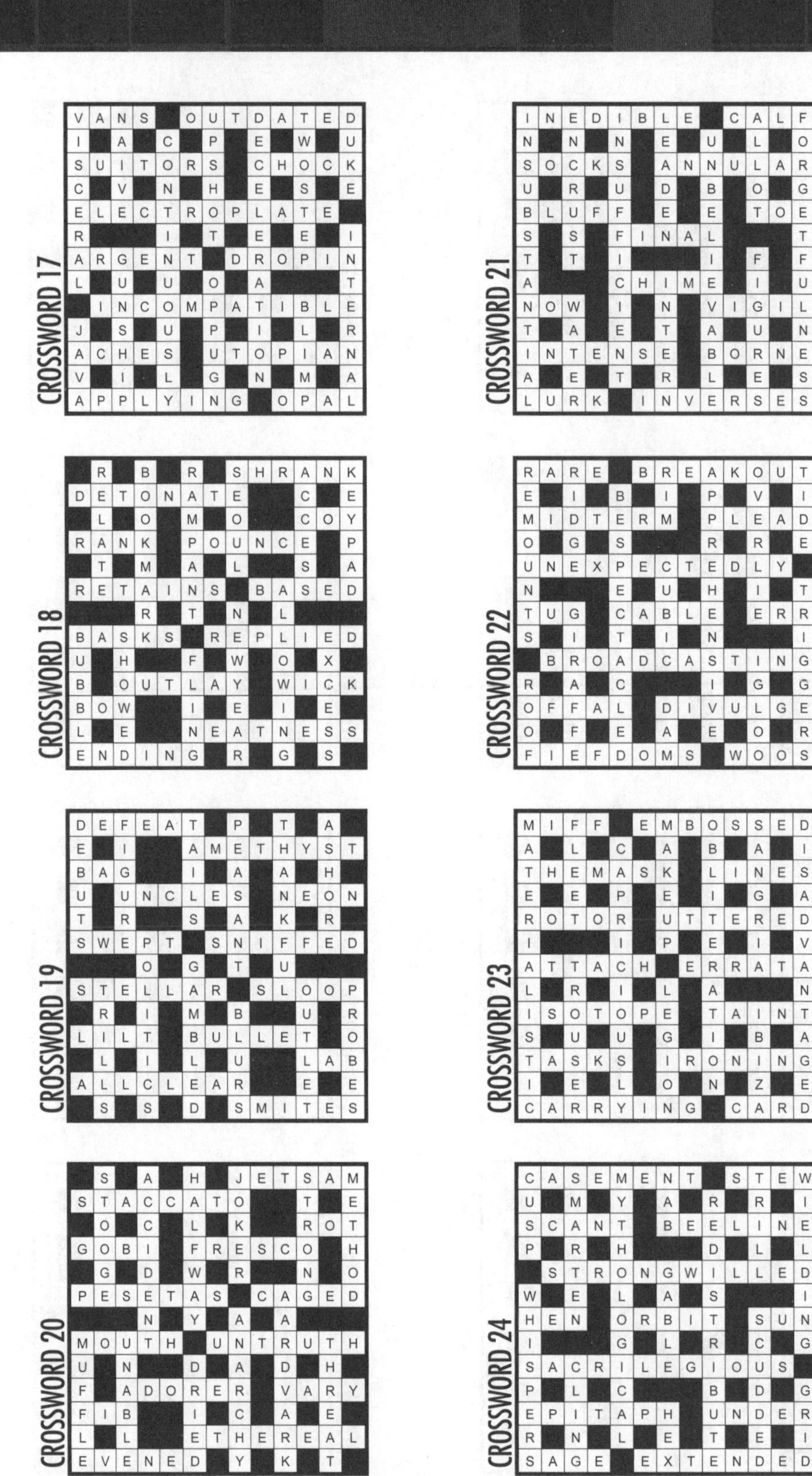

SOLUTIONS

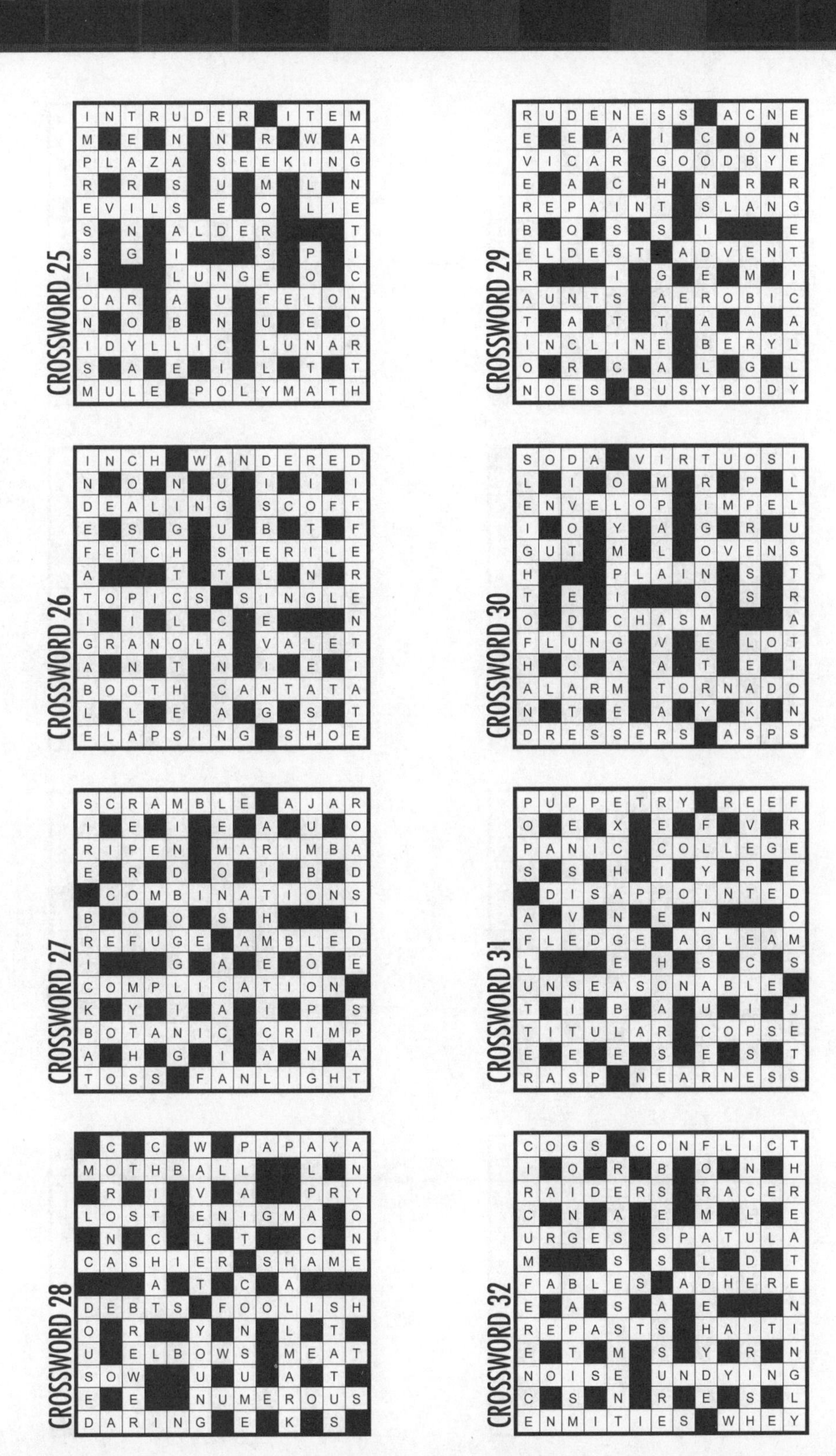

CROSSWORD 25
CROSSWORD 26
CROSSWORD 27
CROSSWORD 28
CROSSWORD 29
CROSSWORD 30
CROSSWORD 31
CROSSWORD 32

SOLUTIONS

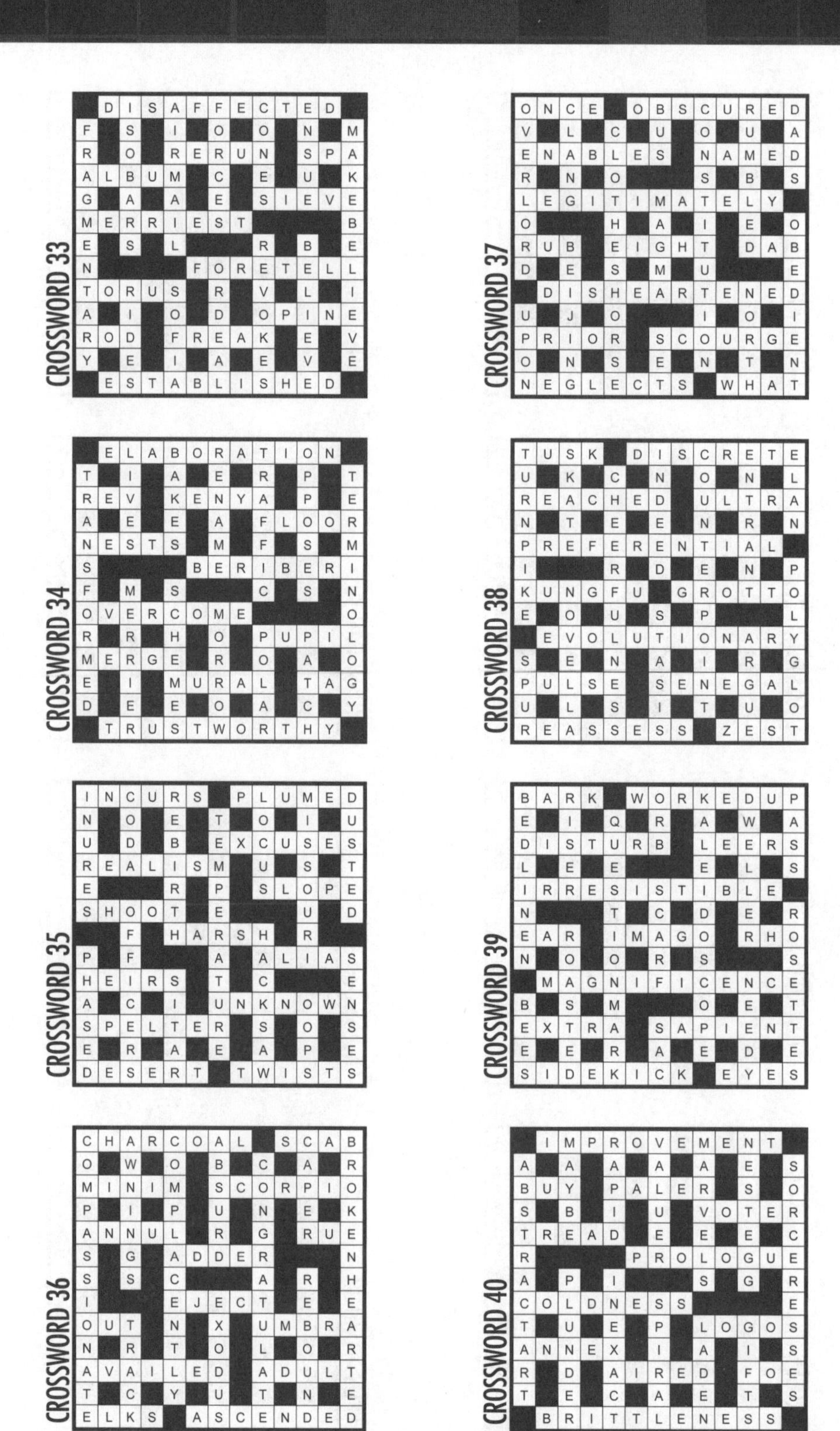

SOLUTIONS

CROSSWORD 45

R	I	T	E		W	O	N	D	E	R	E	D
E		O		D		I		I		O		O
C	O	N	C	E	A	L		S	C	O	W	L
E		E		S				I		F		L
I	N	D	O	C	T	R	I	N	A	T	E	
V				R		E		F		O		N
E	B	B		I	R	A	T	E		P	H	I
R		R		P		R		C				N
	C	O	N	T	E	M	P	T	I	B	L	E
S		W		I				I		E		T
T	A	N	G	O		P	H	O	N	E	M	E
O		I		N		U		N		F		E
P	R	E	S	S	I	N	G		H	Y	M	N

CROSSWORD 46

P	E	R	S	P	I	R	E		P	O	N	D
A		O		E		E				B		I
L	O	V	E	R		N	E	T	T	L	E	S
M		I		I		E				I		P
		N		M		W	R	I	G	G	L	E
D	I	G	G	E	R	S		N		E		N
A				T				A				S
M		S		E		B	R	U	S	Q	U	E
A	P	P	A	R	E	L		G		U		
S		H				O		U		A		C
C	H	E	R	O	O	T		R	I	V	A	L
U		R				C		A		E		A
S	U	E	T		C	H	I	L	D	R	E	N

CROSSWORD 47

	M		D		S		S	T	U	C	C	O
G	I	G	A	N	T	I	C			Y		R
	N		R		I		O			C	U	B
B	U	N	K		L	A	U	R	E	L		I
	E		R		L		T			E		T
S	T	R	O	K	E	D		T	U	S	K	S
			O		D		D		P			
B	A	L	M	Y		P	E	N	C	I	L	S
U		E			B		S		O		I	
M		A	L	L	E	G	E		M	I	N	X
P	A	R			L		R		I		G	
E		N			I	N	V	E	N	T	E	D
D	E	S	I	R	E		E		G		R	

CROSSWORD 48

	D	I	S	H	O	N	E	S	T	L	Y	
R		N		A		U		T		A		I
O		V		P	U	R	E	E		P	E	N
C	H	E	A	P		S		E		A		C
K		S		E		E		R	A	Z	O	R
A	S	T	O	N	I	S	H					E
N		S		S				M		M		M
D					C	R	E	A	T	I	V	E
R	A	M	P	S		E		R		R		N
O		O		O		B		C	H	A	N	T
L	A	W		L	A	U	G	H		C		A
L		E		V		F		E		L		L
	A	R	M	E	D	F	O	R	C	E	S	

SOLUTIONS

CROSSWORD 53

SERENDIPITY
C X F R U E A
O C FRILL PIN
SWIPE V L I O
M T C E SUDAN
OVERTURN Y
L S S F S M
O STILETTO
GAVEL A O I U
I I I C TILTS
SOP NOTES T L
T E E I A O Y
PREDICAMENT

CROSSWORD 55

VISITS CHURCH
I U R O E A O
SOPHISM R G R
A P P NUMBERS
GULFS I I E
E I S TERMS
E TUCKS E
GUSTY I D S
A R E SLEEP
REFRAIN H S O
N U N CHEMIST
E L N E L G T
RELAYS PLENTY

CROSSWORD 56

APPLICATION
S R U A A R C
USA RECUR G O
S W C K DRAIN
CINCH L I N T
E MEALTIME
P S S Y C M
TACITURN P
I H O E DOWEL
BREAM T O I A
L R ABUZZ PUT
E Z C R E E E
NOTHINGNESS

SOLUTIONS

	K	I	L	I	M	A	N	J	A	R	O	
D		N		T		D		A		I		G
E		H		A	D	D	O	N		F	I	R
S	N	A	R	L		L		U		L		A
I		B		I		E		S	P	E	C	S
C	O	I	N	C	I	D	E					S
C		T		S				A		B		H
A					S	C	E	N	A	R	I	O
T	O	W	N	S		H		I		O		P
I		I		L		O		S	T	A	M	P
O	D	D		U	N	I	T	E		D		E
N		T		R		C		E		E		R
	S	H	E	P	H	E	R	D	I	N	G	

CROSSWORD 57

I	N	C	H	E	S		S		F		I	
M		O			A	L	T	E	R	I	N	G
P	A	W			V		A		U		V	
I		E	X	P	E	R	T		C	O	A	X
S		R			S		E		T		D	
H	U	S	K	Y		A	L	L	O	W	E	D
			A		D		Y		S			
M	E	R	M	A	I	D		H	E	L	I	X
	E		I		T		Q			U		E
T	R	E	K		T	R	U	I	S	M		R
	I		A		I		A			B	O	X
G	L	A	Z	I	E	R	S			A		E
	Y		E		S		H	O	A	R	D	S

CROSSWORD 58

R	E	A	P	P	E	A	R		L	A	T	H
I		N		E		C				T		U
F	L	O	U	R		C	O	N	F	O	R	M
E		I		S		U				N		I
		N		U		S	T	E	W	A	R	D
S	A	T	I	A	T	E		X		L		I
U				D				P				T
R		Q		E		E	A	R	T	H	L	Y
F	O	U	N	D	E	D		E		E		
A		A				I		S		L		H
C	O	R	R	E	C	T		S	L	I	M	E
E		T				O		E		U		L
S	L	O	W		P	R	E	S	U	M	E	D

CROSSWORD 59

I	F	F	Y		S	T	R	E	N	G	T	H
N		L		S		R		L		R		Y
S	C	A	P	U	L	A		E	Q	U	I	P
I		I		P		D		C		B		E
G	E	L		E		E		T	U	B	E	R
N				R	A	D	A	R		E		C
I		Q		N				O		D		R
F		U		A	V	A	I	L				I
I	N	A	P	T		D		Y		A	R	T
C		R		U		R		S		C		I
A	S	T	E	R		I	D	I	O	T	I	C
N		E		A		F		S		E		A
T	O	T	A	L	I	T	Y		I	D	O	L

CROSSWORD 60

E	M	P	E	R	O	R	S		O	W	E	D
N		L		E		E		C		H		I
C	H	I	M	P		V	I	O	L	I	N	S
O		A		E		A		N		F		G
U	M	B	E	R		M		V		F	U	R
R		L		C	O	P	R	A				A
A		E		U				L		C		C
G				S	A	U	C	E		O		E
E	L	F		S		N		S	C	U	F	F
M		A		I		R		C		T		U
E	N	C	L	O	S	E		E	Q	U	A	L
N		E		N		A		N		R		L
T	O	T	S		F	L	A	T	T	E	R	Y

CROSSWORD 61

S	U	D	S		S	U	N	B	E	A	M	S
O		O		S		R		U		B		I
P	S	Y	C	H	I	C		R	U	R	A	L
H		E		A		H		G		I		V
I	N	N		R		I		L	A	D	L	E
S				P	A	N	D	A		G		R
T		C		S				R		E		J
I		O		H	Y	E	N	A				U
C	O	N	G	O		L		L		W	E	B
A		S		O		A		A		A		I
T	A	U	N	T		P	A	R	A	S	O	L
E		L		E		S		M		T		E
D	E	T	E	R	R	E	D		G	E	N	E

CROSSWORD 62

	A	C	C	E	L	E	R	A	T	O	R	
S		O		M		D		R		U		P
T	O	P		P	R	I	N	T		T		R
O		E		T		B		W	E	D	G	E
R	U	D	D	Y		L		O		O		R
Y					F	E	A	R	S	O	M	E
T		B		B				K		R		C
E	M	U	L	A	T	E	S					O
L		F		B		U		S	E	V	E	R
L	O	F	T	Y		R		W		I		D
E		A		S	M	O	K	E		E	W	E
R		L		I		P		E		W		D
	P	O	R	T	R	A	I	T	I	S	T	

CROSSWORD 63

	U		C		E		E	I	G	H	T	H
O	N	T	H	E	J	O	B			I		I
	B		L		E		B			P	A	D
M	E	M	O		C	L	E	N	C	H		D
	N		R		T		D			O		E
A	D	M	I	R	E	D		J	A	P	A	N
			N		D		C		D			
P	I	L	E	D		C	O	N	D	U	I	T
U		Y			D		P		I		N	
F		N	A	M	E	L	Y		C	O	D	E
F	A	X			I		I		T		I	
E		E			G	U	N	M	E	T	A	L
D	E	S	I	G	N		G		D		N	

CROSSWORD 64

SOLUTIONS

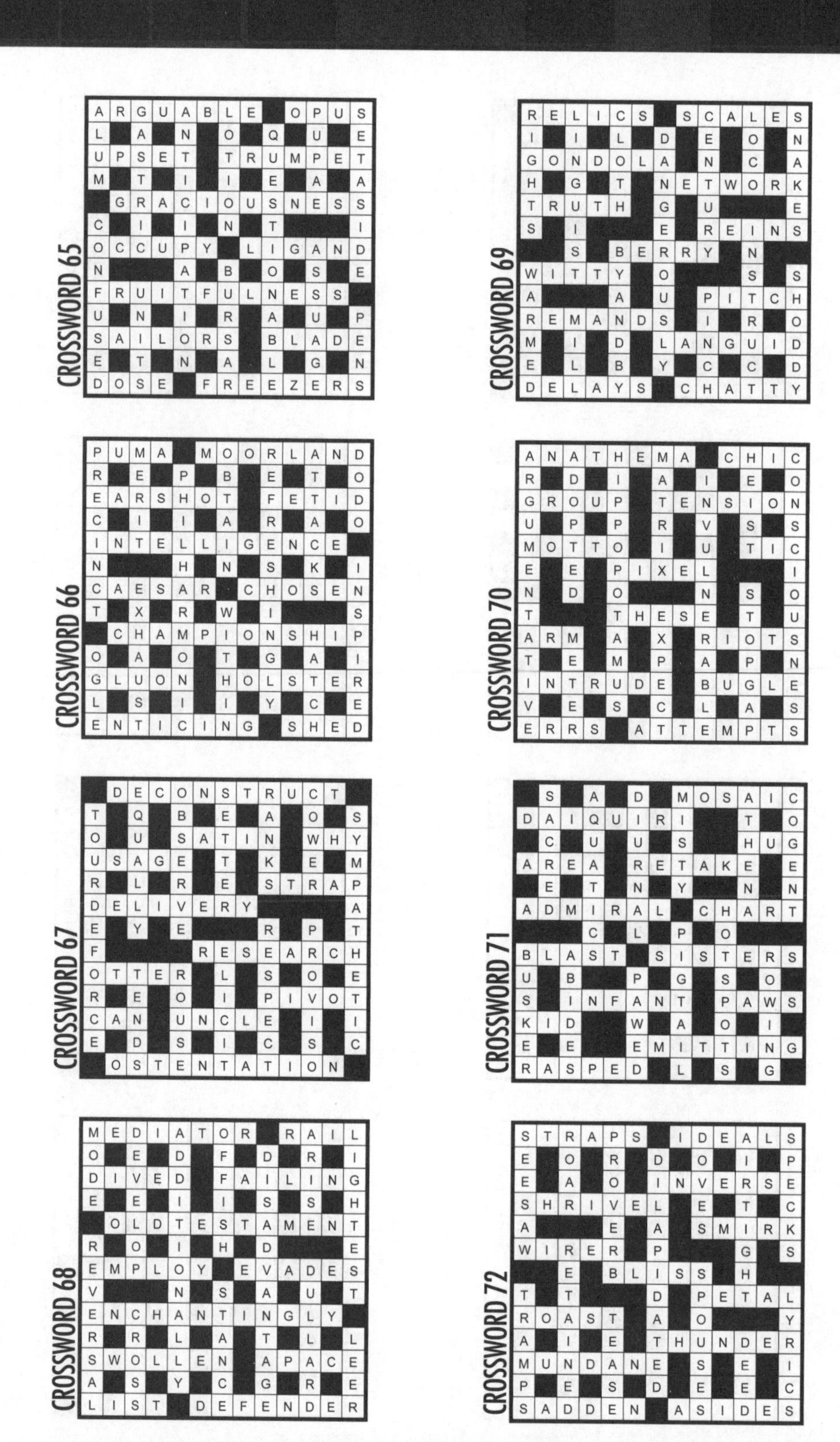

CROSSWORD 65
CROSSWORD 66
CROSSWORD 67
CROSSWORD 68
CROSSWORD 69
CROSSWORD 70
CROSSWORD 71
CROSSWORD 72

SOLUTIONS

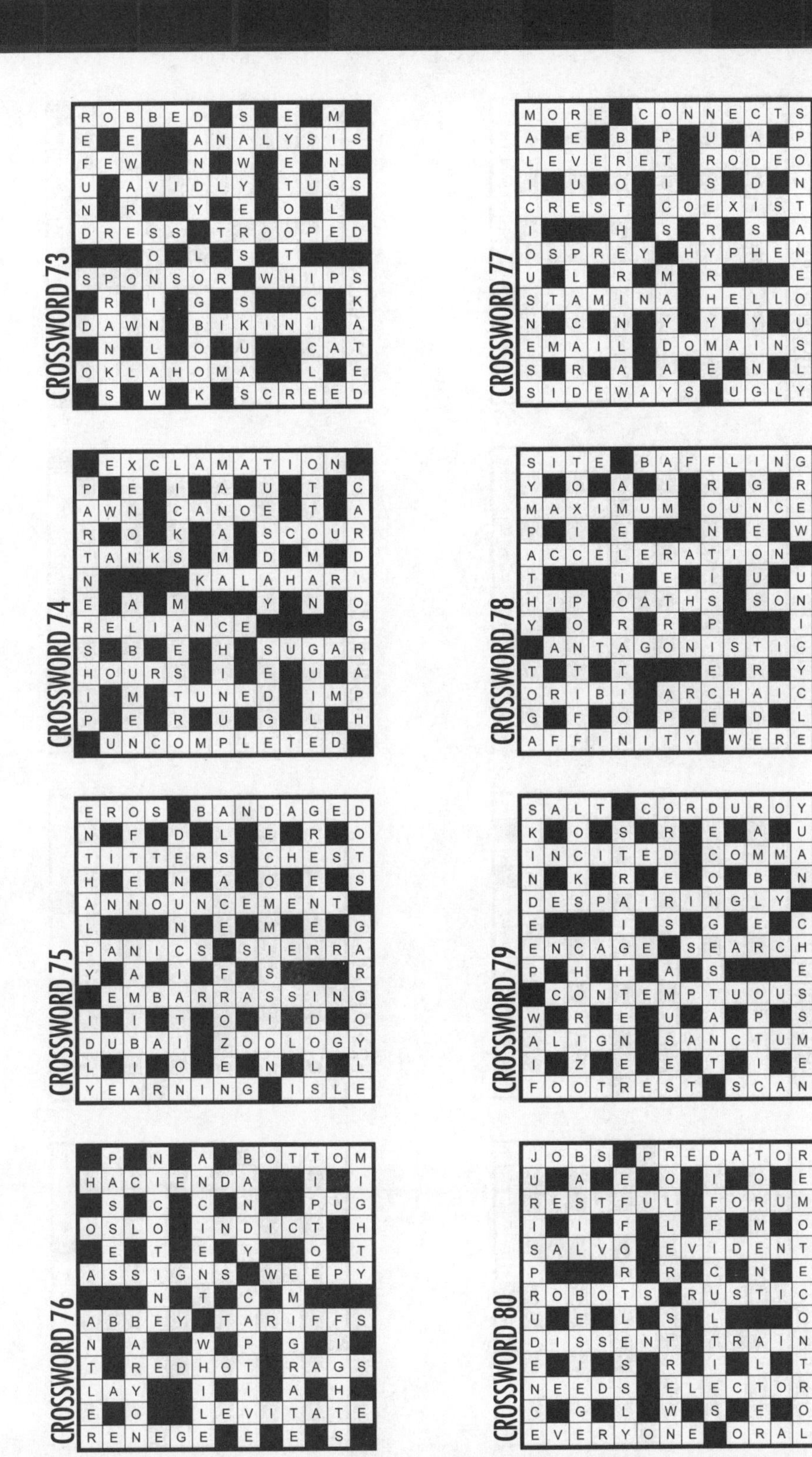
CROSSWORD 73
CROSSWORD 77
CROSSWORD 74
CROSSWORD 78
CROSSWORD 75
CROSSWORD 79
CROSSWORD 76
CROSSWORD 80

SOLUTIONS

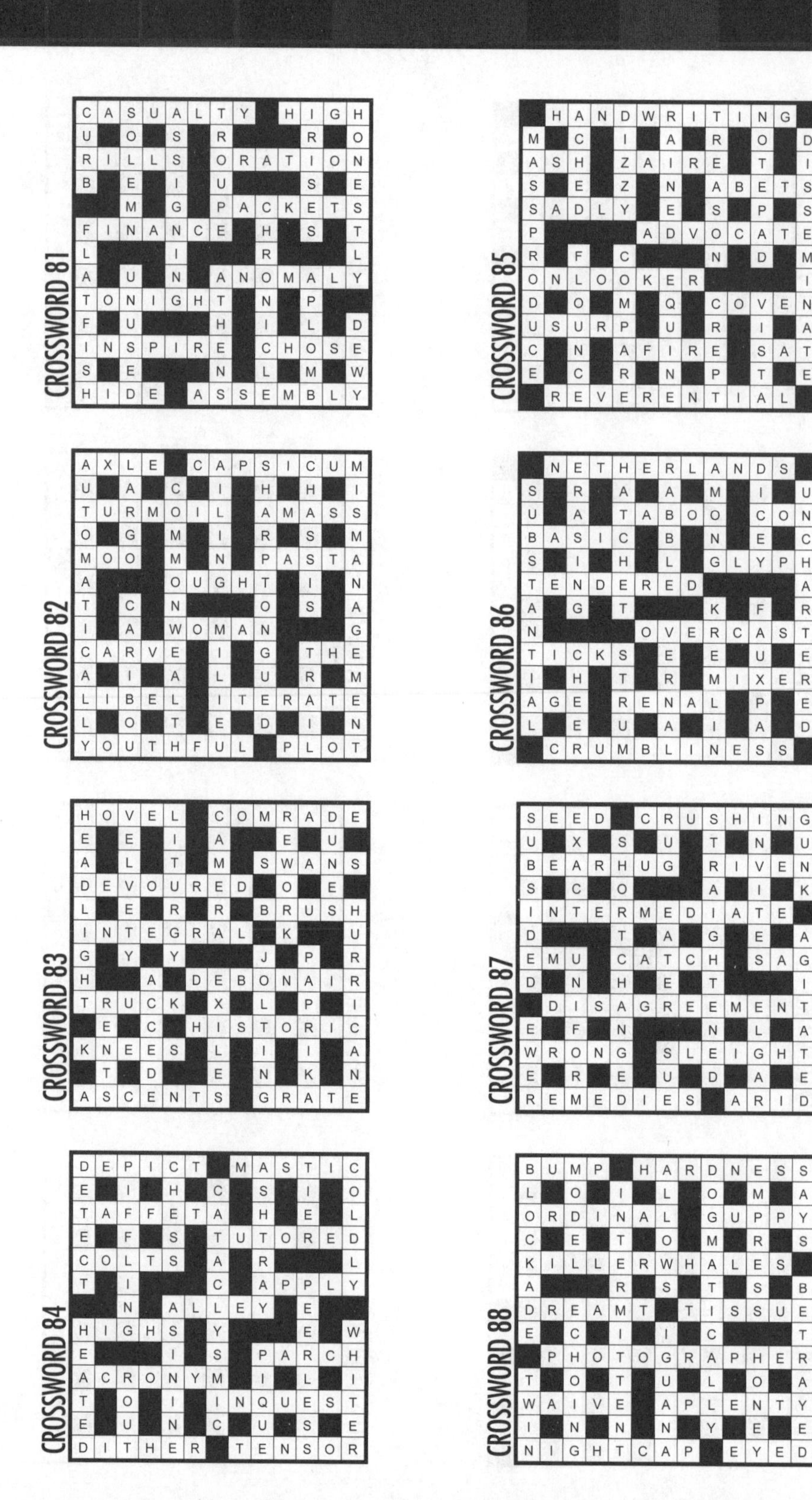

SOLUTIONS

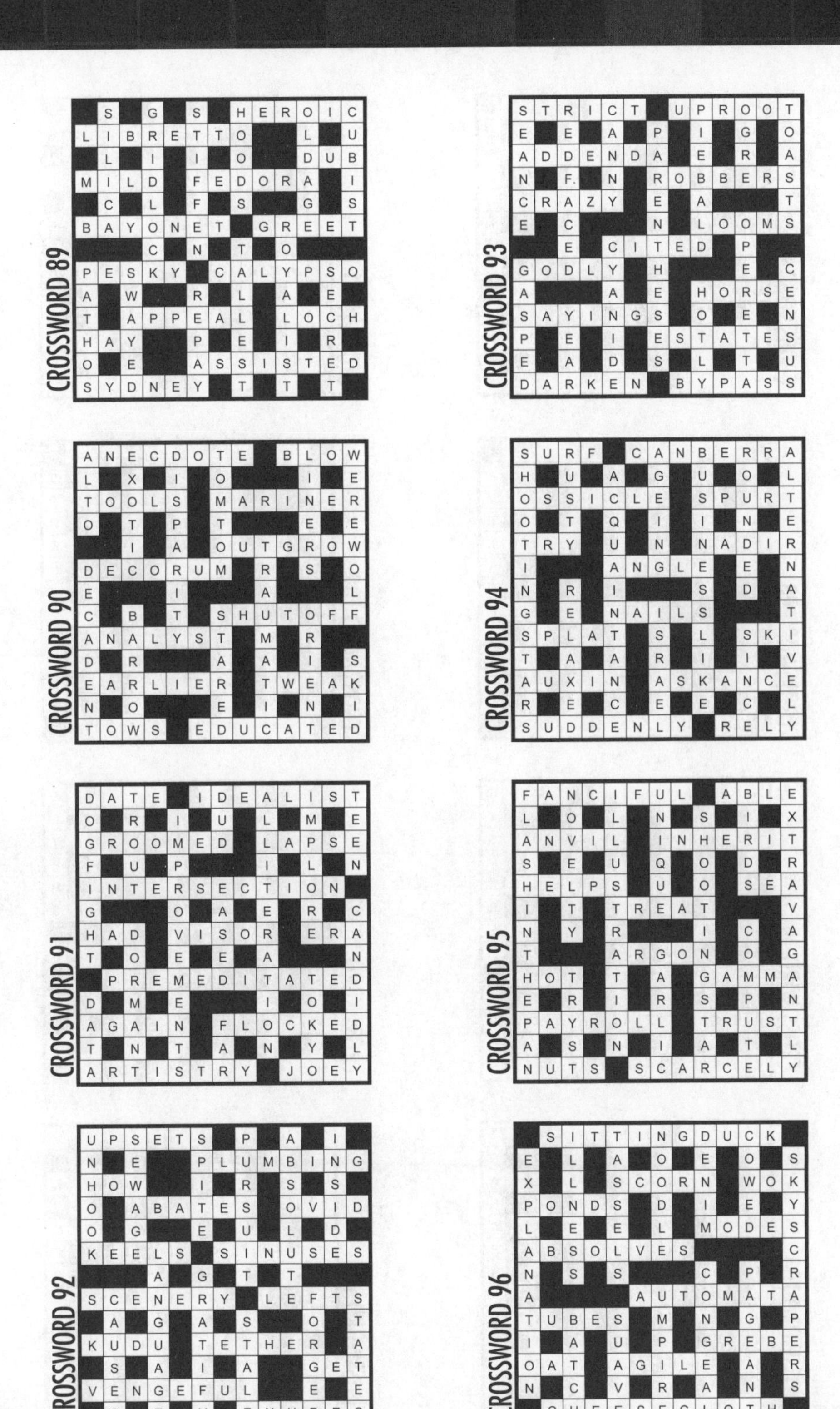
CROSSWORD 89
CROSSWORD 90
CROSSWORD 91
CROSSWORD 92
CROSSWORD 93
CROSSWORD 94
CROSSWORD 95
CROSSWORD 96

SOLUTIONS

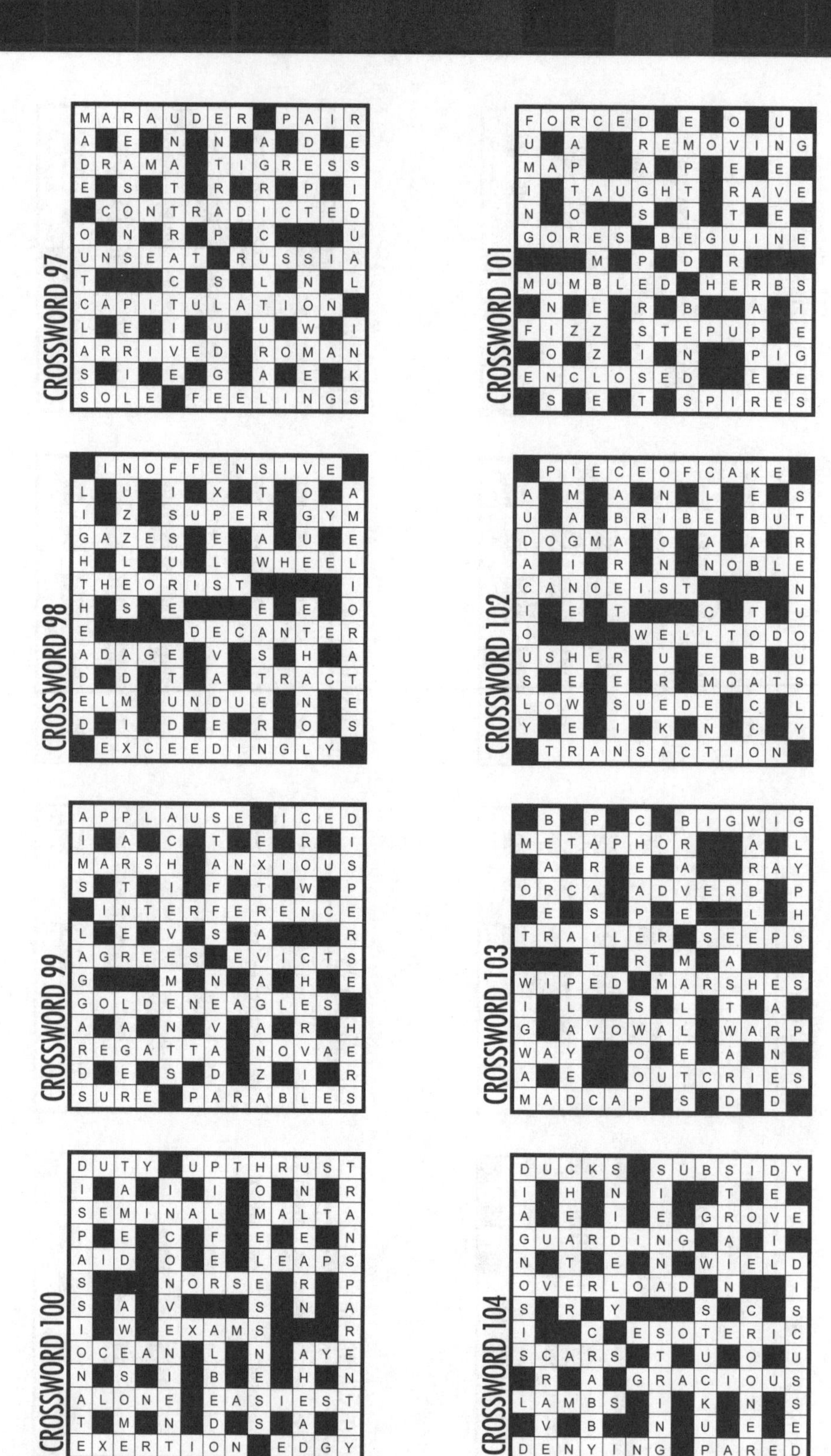

CROSSWORD 97
CROSSWORD 98
CROSSWORD 99
CROSSWORD 100
CROSSWORD 101
CROSSWORD 102
CROSSWORD 103
CROSSWORD 104

SOLUTIONS

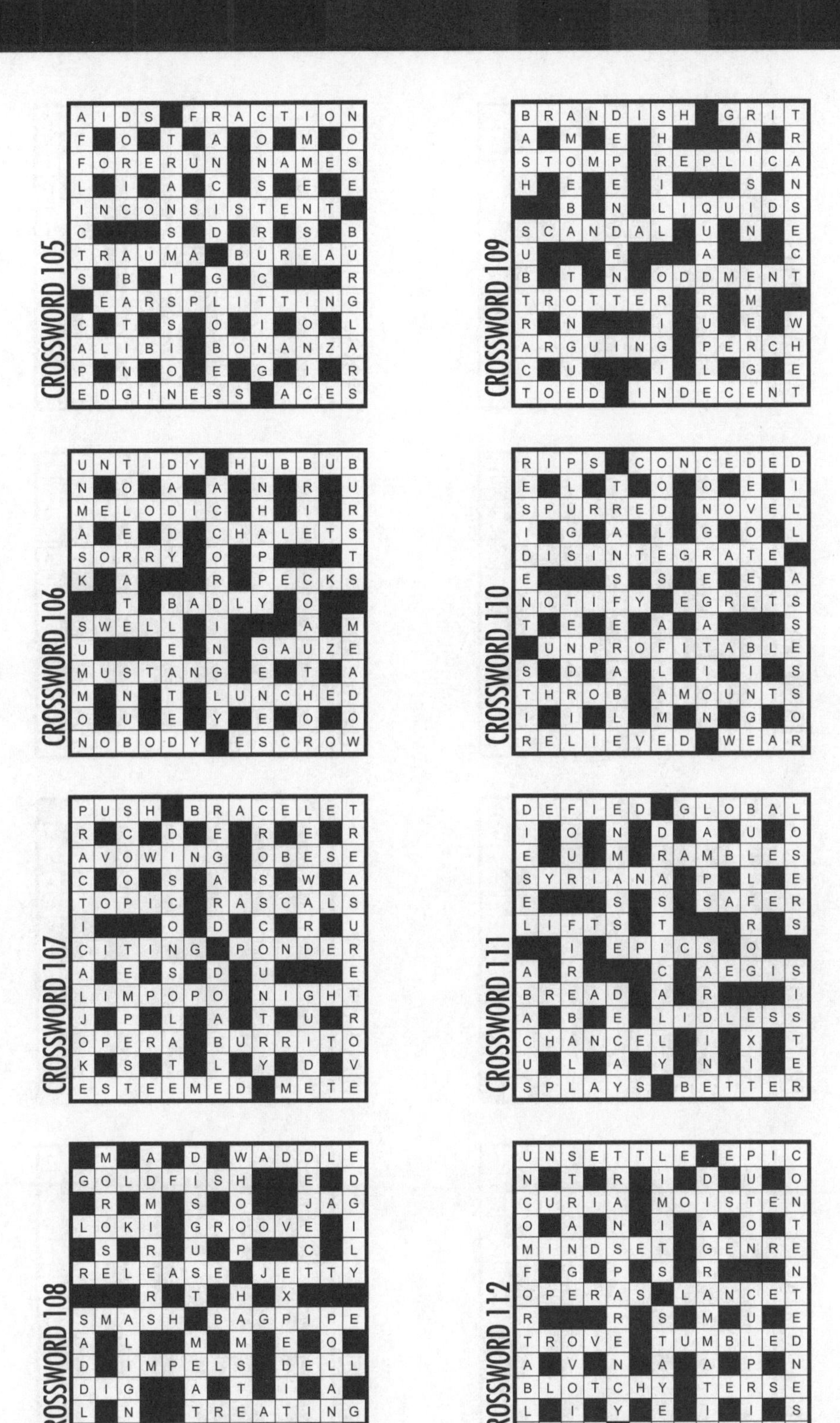
CROSSWORD 105
CROSSWORD 109
CROSSWORD 106
CROSSWORD 110
CROSSWORD 107
CROSSWORD 111
CROSSWORD 108
CROSSWORD 112

SOLUTIONS

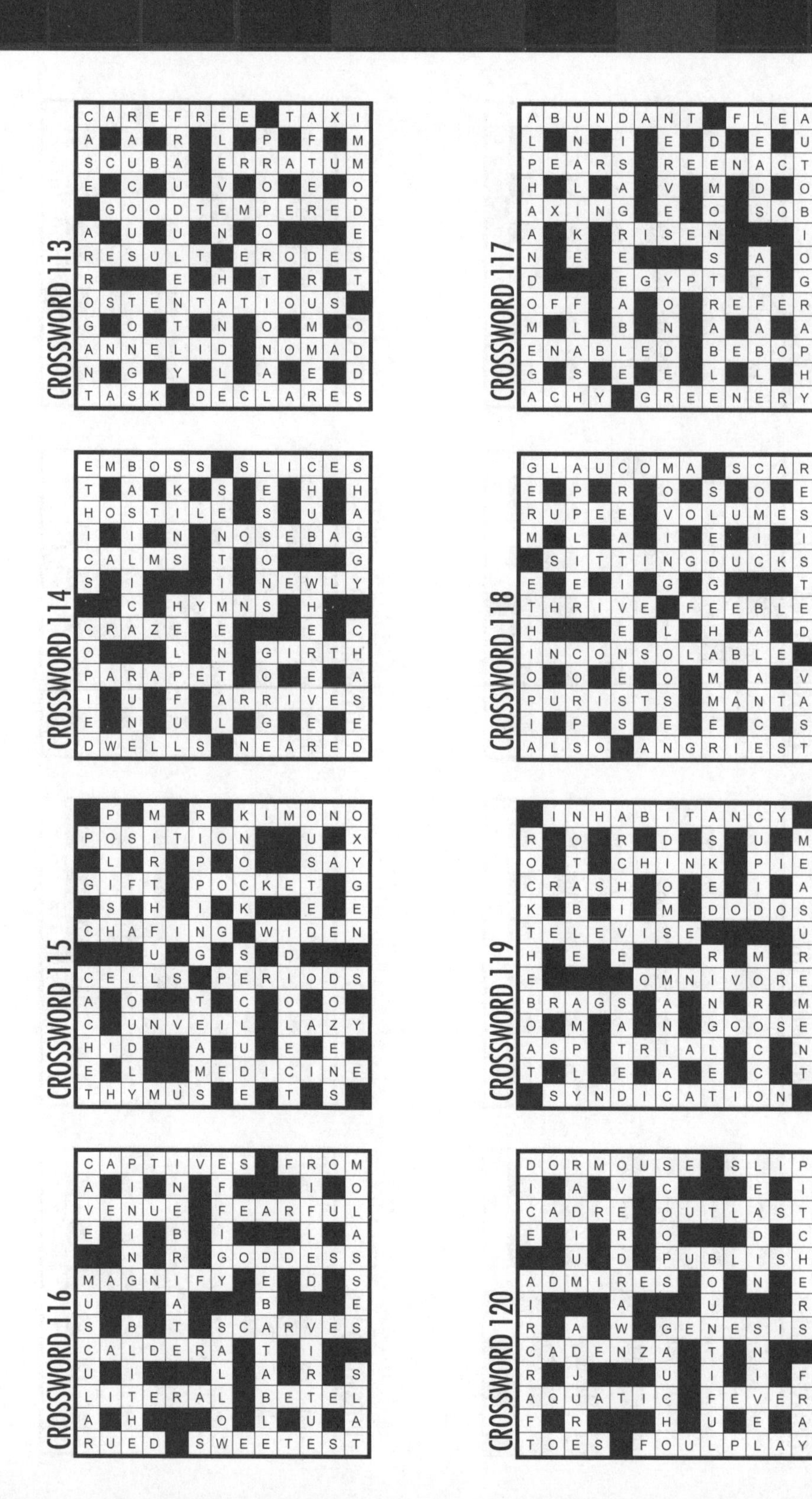

SOLUTIONS

CROSSWORD 125

B	R	A	N	D	Y		B	A	M	B	O	O
E		Q		R		D		N		O		B
S	H	U	T	E	Y	E		N		L		E
E		I		G		L	A	U	N	D	R	Y
T	A	L	E	S		I		A				E
S		I				C		L	I	V	I	D
		N		S	K	I	P	S		A		
T	E	E	T	H		O				U		R
R				I		U		B	U	L	G	E
O	C	T	O	P	U	S		E		T		G
O		O		P		L	O	D	G	I	N	G
P		N		E		Y		I		N		A
S	P	E	E	D	Y		E	M	I	G	R	E

CROSSWORD 126

	L		B		P		H	U	S	H	U	P
P	A	N	O	R	A	M	A			A		O
	C		O		R		B			V	E	T
M	U	R	K		S	T	I	G	M	A		E
	N		C		N		T			N		N
M	A	L	A	R	I	A		A	D	A	P	T
			S		P		P		I			
B	E	S	E	T		W	A	Y	S	I	D	E
L		L			P		S		T		I	
U		O	S	I	E	R	S		U	L	N	A
R	O	W			E		A		R		I	
B		L			V	A	G	A	B	O	N	D
S	C	Y	T	H	E		E		S		G	

CROSSWORD 127

A	P	P	E	N	D		S		T		M	
L		E			R	A	T	I	O	N	A	L
M	U	D			O		A		R		L	
O		A	T	O	N	E	S		T	O	I	L
N		L			E		H		I		G	
D	U	S	T	Y		D	E	C	L	I	N	E
			A		T		D		L			
S	T	A	R	C	H	Y		P	A	C	E	S
	O		T		E		G			O		E
S	W	A	N		R	A	N	D	O	M		D
	E		E		E		A			M	A	G
C	R	O	S	S	B	O	W			I		E
	S		S		Y		S	U	I	T	E	S

CROSSWORD 128

E	M	U	L	S	I	O	N		G	U	R	U
X		P		I		T		A		N		N
T	I	T	A	N		I	M	P	U	T	E	D
R		I		G		O		P		I		I
A	N	G	E	L	U	S		R	O	L	L	S
P		H		E		E		O				C
O	P	T	I	M	A		H	A	W	A	I	I
L				I		M		C		C		P
A	S	P	E	N		E	T	H	I	C	A	L
T		O		D		D		A		U		I
I	N	S	T	E	A	D		B	I	S	O	N
O		E		D		L		L		E		E
N	E	R	D		D	E	P	E	N	D	E	D

SOLUTIONS

CROSSWORD 129

F	E	S	T	I	V	A	L		M	Y	T	H
A		U		N		L		I		E		E
M	A	N	I	A		L	A	M	B	A	D	A
E		B		D		U		P		R		V
	C	U	R	M	U	D	G	E	O	N	L	Y
C		R		I		E		R				S
H	O	N	E	S	T		U	S	A	B	L	E
I				S		A		O		U		T
C	O	N	S	I	S	T	E	N	T	L	Y	
K		O		B		O		A		L		A
P	R	O	B	L	E	M		T	W	I	R	L
E		K		E		I		O		S		A
A	P	S	E		S	C	O	R	C	H	E	S

CROSSWORD 130

M	U	S	T		R	A	D	I	A	T	O	R
E		A		O		I		N		O		O
A	L	L	O	V	E	R		C	A	R	G	O
S		A		E		W		O		O		T
U	N	D	E	R	G	A	R	M	E	N	T	
R				C		Y		P		T		P
E	N	D	E	A	R		B	E	F	O	U	L
S		E		U		A		T				A
	C	A	N	T	A	N	K	E	R	O	U	S
O		D		I		I		N		D		T
D	I	S	C	O		M	A	C	H	I	N	E
E		E		U		A		E		U		R
S	P	A	R	S	E	L	Y		E	M	U	S

CROSSWORD 131

	A	F	T	E	R	B	U	R	N	E	R	
S		O		B		A		E		X		A
W	A	X		O	O	Z	E	D		C		S
I		E		N		A		W	A	L	L	S
T	E	D	D	Y		A		O		A		I
Z					D	R	O	O	P	I	N	G
E		O		P				D		M		N
R	E	B	E	L	L	E	D					M
L		L		A		N		B	U	D	G	E
A	M	I	T	Y		C		A		R		N
N		Q		F	O	O	D	S		A	N	T
D		U		U		R		I		W		S
	W	E	L	L	M	E	A	N	I	N	G	

CROSSWORD 132

B	R	O	O	M	S		S	H	A	P	E	D
E		P		A		O		O		I		E
C	H	E	C	K	U	P		T		L		B
O		R		E		I	N	H	A	L	E	R
M	E	A	T	S		N		E				I
E		T				I		A	C	I	D	S
		E		A	V	O	I	D		N		
V	E	S	T	S		N				F		M
E				T		A		B	R	E	V	E
R	A	P	P	O	R	T		A		R		A
S		O		U		E	N	G	I	N	E	S
U		K		N		D		G		A		L
S	T	E	E	D	S		B	Y	P	L	A	Y

CROSSWORD 133

S	A	S	H		C	L	E	M	A	T	I	S
U		L		D		A		U		O		E
R	O	O	M	I	E	R		L	O	C	A	L
R		T		S		V		T		C		F
E	T	H	I	C		A	N	I	M	A	T	E
P				O		L		P		T		V
T	Y	P	I	N	G		A	L	K	A	L	I
I		A		T		N		I				D
T	O	R	P	E	D	O		C	L	O	N	E
I		V		N		S		I		M		N
O	V	E	R	T		H	O	T	T	E	S	T
U		N		E		O		Y		G		L
S	H	U	T	D	O	W	N		Z	A	N	Y

CROSSWORD 134

H	U	F	F		R	E	Q	U	I	R	E	D
E		O		I		N		S		E		U
S	P	R	I	N	G	S		E	X	T	O	L
I		G		H		I		R		U		Y
T	H	O	R	O	U	G	H	F	A	R	E	
A				S		N		R		N		P
T	R	U	M	P	S		F	I	E	S	T	A
E		S		I		S		E				R
	M	U	L	T	I	L	I	N	G	U	A	L
G		A		A		I		D		T		A
A	D	L	I	B		G	E	L	A	T	I	N
S		L		L		H		Y		E		C
P	A	Y	M	E	N	T	S		E	R	N	E

CROSSWORD 135

A	W	E	D		S	A	T	I	A	B	L	E
P		G		W		S		R		O		X
P	A	R	S	E	C	S		R	I	O	J	A
R		E		L		E		E		K		G
O	C	T	E	T		R	A	S	P	I	N	G
X				E		T		P		N		E
I	N	B	O	R	N		M	E	R	G	E	R
M		A		W		M		C				A
A	U	S	T	E	R	E		T	O	A	S	T
T		S		I		R		I		N		E
I	C	I	N	G		I	N	V	O	K	E	D
O		S		H		N		E		L		L
N	O	T	A	T	I	O	N		D	E	N	Y

CROSSWORD 136

K	N	O	T		S	C	O	U	R	G	E	D
I		U		C		O		N		R		O
N	A	T	I	O	N	S		A	P	A	R	T
G		D		N		M		C		N		E
S	H	O	R	T	C	I	R	C	U	I	T	
I				E		C		E		T		G
Z	E	U	G	M	A		A	P	P	E	A	R
E		N		P		C		T				A
	E	C	H	O	L	O	C	A	T	I	O	N
E		L		R		L		B		N		D
T	H	E	T	A		U	M	L	A	U	T	S
C		A		R		M		E		R		O
H	U	R	R	Y	I	N	G		M	E	A	N

SOLUTIONS

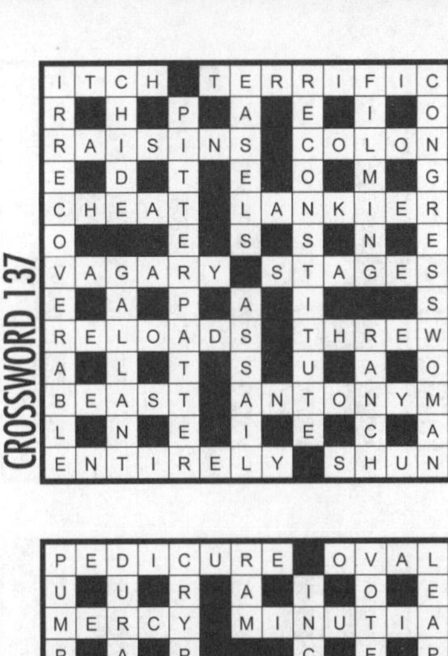

CROSSWORD 137

I	T	C	H		T	E	R	R	I	F	I	C
R		H		P		A		E		I		O
R	A	I	S	I	N	S		C	O	L	O	N
E		D		T		E		O		M		G
C	H	E	A	T		L	A	N	K	I	E	R
O				E		S		S		N		E
V	A	G	A	R	Y		S	T	A	G	E	S
E		A		P		A		I				S
R	E	L	O	A	D	S		T	H	R	E	W
A		L		T		S		U		A		O
B	E	A	S	T		A	N	T	O	N	Y	M
L		N		E		I		E		C		A
E	N	T	I	R	E	L	Y		S	H	U	N

CROSSWORD 138

P	E	D	I	C	U	R	E		O	V	A	L
U		U		R		A		I		O		E
M	E	R	C	Y		M	I	N	U	T	I	A
P		A		P				C		E		P
	A	B	S	T	E	M	I	O	U	S	L	Y
O		L		O		O		R				E
B	E	E		G	I	V	E	R		P	E	A
V				R		E		I		E		R
I	N	T	R	A	N	S	I	G	E	N	T	
A		H		P				I		N		S
T	E	A	C	H	E	R		B	L	A	M	E
E		W		Y		O		L		N		N
D	U	S	T		O	B	J	E	C	T	E	D

CROSSWORD 139

A	N	C	E	S	T	O	R		T	O	F	U
N		H		L		U		A		W		N
T	R	O	P	E		T	E	N	A	N	T	S
I		R		E		P		N		E		Y
C	L	A	S	P		U		I		D	I	M
L		L		W	A	T	C	H				P
I		E		A				I		S		A
M				L	A	P	E	L		T		T
A	U	K		K		U		A	W	A	S	H
C		N		I		R		T		L		E
T	R	A	I	N	E	E		I	N	E	R	T
I		C		G		L		O		S		I
C	A	K	E		H	Y	P	N	O	T	I	C

CROSSWORD 140

B	A	T	T	L	E		F	A	B	R	I	C
I		A		O		D		T		I		I
C	A	S	C	A	D	E		T		O		R
E		M		C		C	R	E	A	T	O	R
P	O	A	C	H		E		N				U
S		N				I		D	A	M	P	S
		I		B	I	T	E	S		U		
P	E	A	C	E		F				T		P
I				C		U		D	R	I	L	L
P	R	E	V	A	I	L		R		N		U
I		M		U		L	O	I	T	E	R	S
T		I		S		Y		V		E		E
S	E	T	T	E	E		Z	E	B	R	A	S

CROSSWORD 141

	C	L	E	A	R	H	E	A	D	E	D	
C		O		P		I		B		N		D
H		U		R	E	A	C	H		E	V	E
A	U	D	I	O		T		O		M		C
I		E		P		U		R	H	Y	M	E
R	E	S	P	O	N	S	E					I
P		T		S				Y		M		V
E					M	A	C	A	R	O	N	I
R	I	S	E	S		S		R		T		N
S		C		H		S		D	O	I	N	G
O	U	R		A	L	O	H	A		V		L
N		U		K		R		G		E		Y
	A	B	S	E	N	T	E	E	I	S	M	

CROSSWORD 142

M	O	B	S		P	O	S	S	I	B	L	E
A		U		U		R		E		O		A
C	H	R	O	N	I	C		L	O	O	T	S
H		N		F				F		T		T
I	N	T	E	L	L	I	G	I	B	L	Y	
S				A		D		N		E		L
M	R	S		T	W	I	S	T		G	E	E
O		Q		T		O		E				S
	S	U	P	E	R	M	A	R	K	E	T	S
S		A		R				E		X		E
C	O	R	G	I		B	A	S	T	I	O	N
U		E		N		Y		T		L		E
D	I	S	A	G	R	E	E		N	E	E	D

CROSSWORD 143

M	A	R	K	D	O	W	N		O	R	B	S
O		U		E		I				O		U
V	E	E	R	S		D	E	S	K	T	O	P
E		F		I		E				A		E
		U		R		S	W	E	E	T	E	R
V	A	L	I	A	N	T		X		E		I
O				B				C				O
U		E		L		H	O	A	R	D	E	R
C	O	M	P	E	R	E		V		A		
H		P				N		A		R		A
E	M	I	T	T	E	R		T	A	K	E	N
R		R				Y		O		E		E
S	L	E	W		O	V	E	R	D	R	A	W

CROSSWORD 144

	E	G	A	L	I	T	A	R	I	A	N	
I		A		E		W		E		L		C
M	U	M		A	D	I	O	S		M		O
P		U		K		N		C	L	A	I	M
A	P	T	L	Y		G		U		N		M
T					R	E	L	E	G	A	T	E
I		S		O				S		C		M
E	N	T	R	A	I	L	S					O
N		A		R		O		Q	A	T	A	R
T	A	M	E	S		A		U		A		A
L		M		M	I	N	C	E		B	E	T
Y		E		A		E		E		L		E
	F	R	O	N	T	R	U	N	N	E	R	

SOLUTIONS

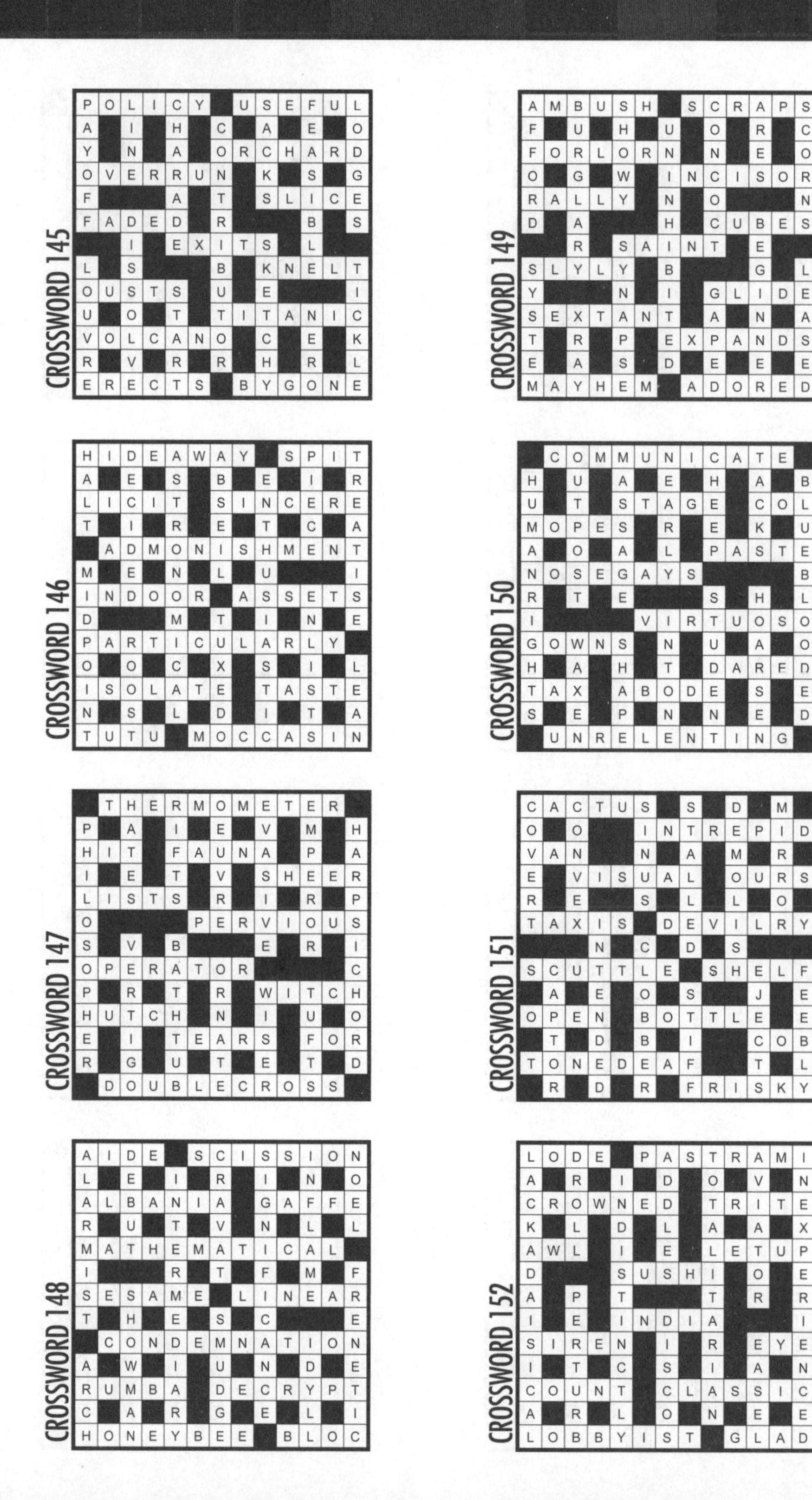

CROSSWORD 145
CROSSWORD 149
CROSSWORD 146
CROSSWORD 150
CROSSWORD 147
CROSSWORD 151
CROSSWORD 148
CROSSWORD 152

SOLUTIONS

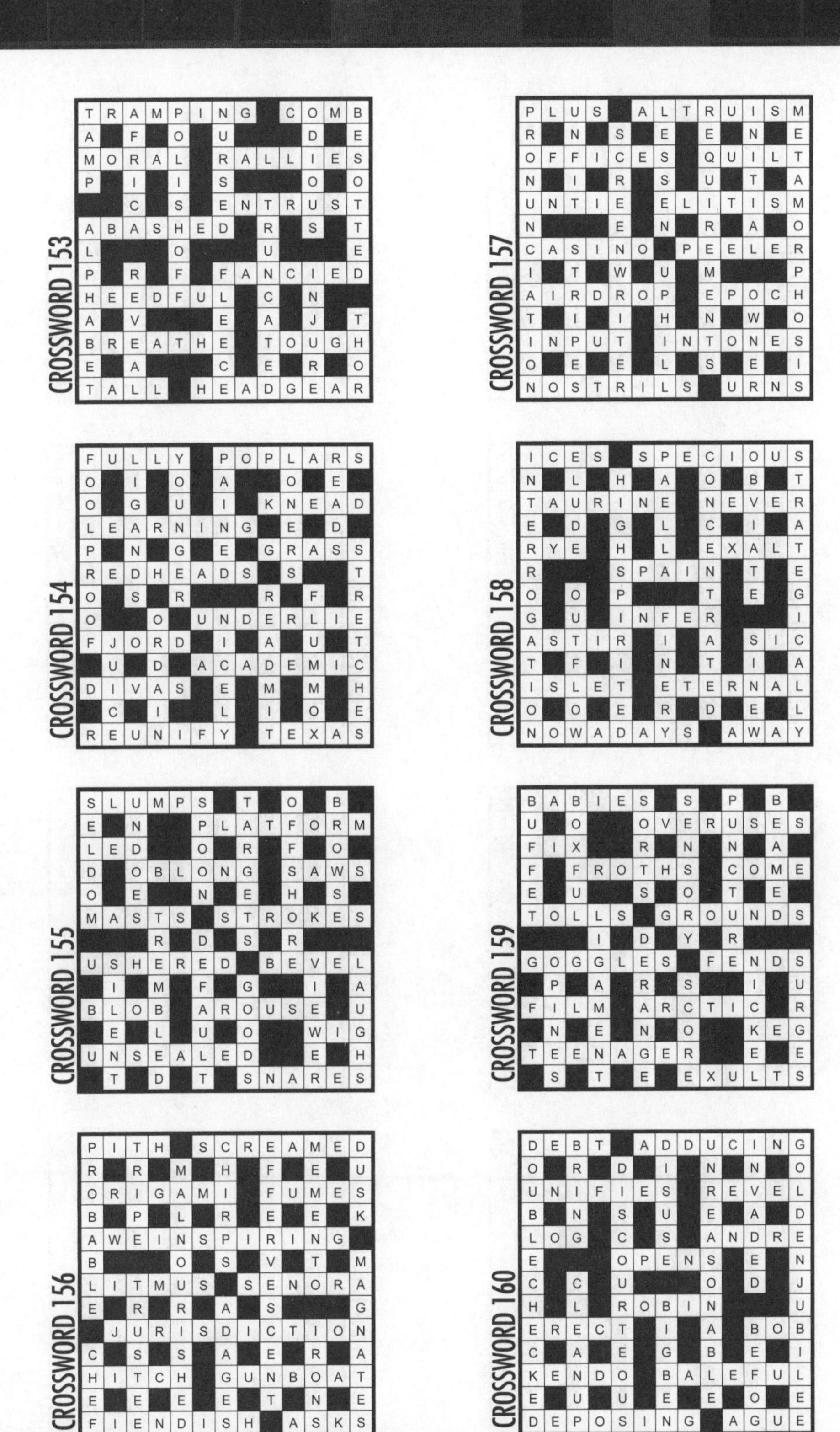

CROSSWORD 153
CROSSWORD 157
CROSSWORD 154
CROSSWORD 158
CROSSWORD 155
CROSSWORD 159
CROSSWORD 156
CROSSWORD 160

SOLUTIONS

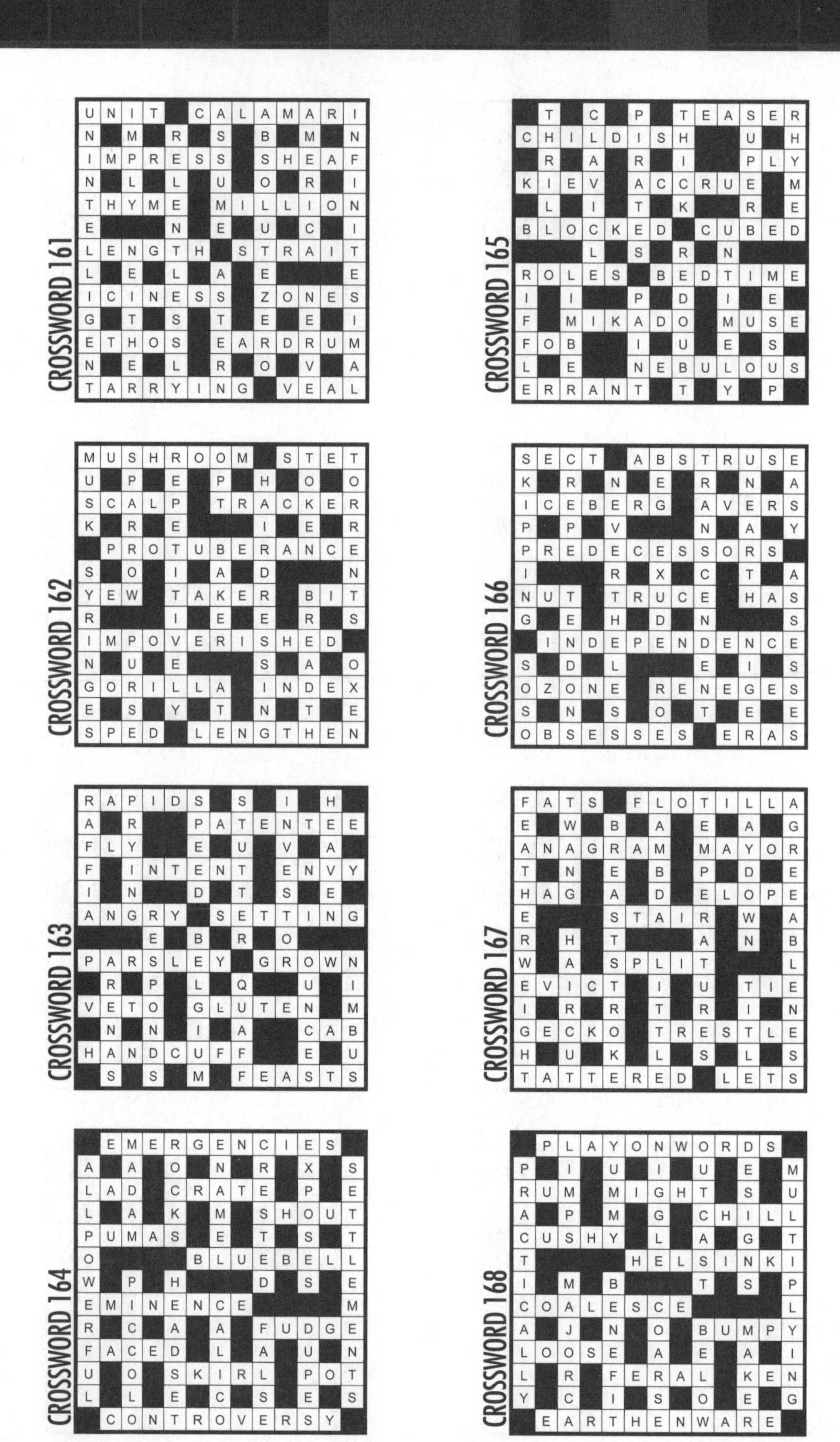
CROSSWORD 161
CROSSWORD 165
CROSSWORD 162
CROSSWORD 166
CROSSWORD 163
CROSSWORD 167
CROSSWORD 164
CROSSWORD 168

SOLUTIONS

CROSSWORD 173

R	E	W	I	N	D		F		K		P	
E		A			I	M	I	T	A	T	O	R
M	A	Y			N		D		N		E	
A		L	A	G	G	E	D		G	A	T	E
R		A			Y		L		A		I	
K	A	Y	A	K		S	E	C	R	E	C	Y
			R		H		R		O			
B	A	C	K	O	U	T		H	O	M	E	S
	M		A		M		V			I		E
L	O	O	N		B	R	O	K	E	N		N
	R		S		L		W			C	O	D
J	A	P	A	N	E	S	E			E		E
	L		S		S		L	E	S	S	E	R

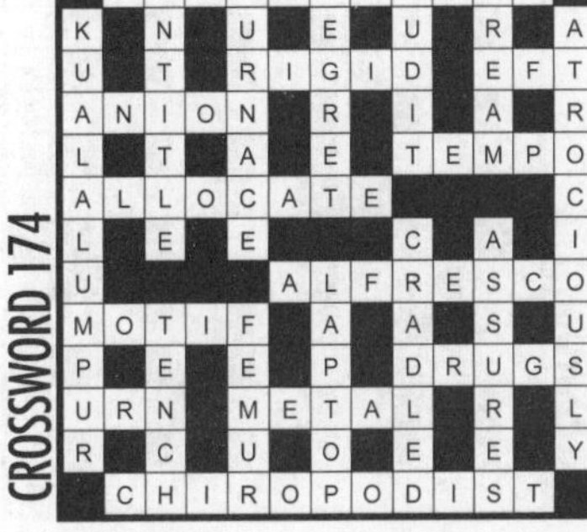

CROSSWORD 175

A	C	R	I	M	O	N	Y		P	L	O	D
L		A		U		I			A		E	
M	A	R	K	S		C	R	Y	P	T	I	C
S		E		H		K				H		I
		F		R		E	N	D	L	E	S	S
P	A	Y	L	O	A	D		I		S		I
A				O				S				V
N		K		M		A	P	P	E	A	S	E
D	R	E	S	S	E	S		E		D		
E		R				T		R		J		W
M	O	N	I	T	O	R		S	P	O	K	E
I		E				A		A		I		I
C	O	L	D		E	Y	E	L	I	N	E	R

CROSSWORD 176

S	A	V	E		G	A	L	A	C	T	I	C
P		E		A		N		B		R		H
L	A	N	O	L	I	N		S	T	O	M	A
E		O		P		U		O		U		R
N	Y	M	P	H		A	T	L	A	N	T	A
D				A		L		U		C		C
I	N	S	A	N	E		A	T	T	E	S	T
F		I		U		S		E				E
E	N	D	E	M	I	C		N	E	W	E	R
R		E		E		R		E		O		L
O	S	C	A	R		O	B	S	C	U	R	E
U		A		I		L		S		N		S
S	T	R	I	C	T	L	Y		A	D	D	S

SOLUTIONS

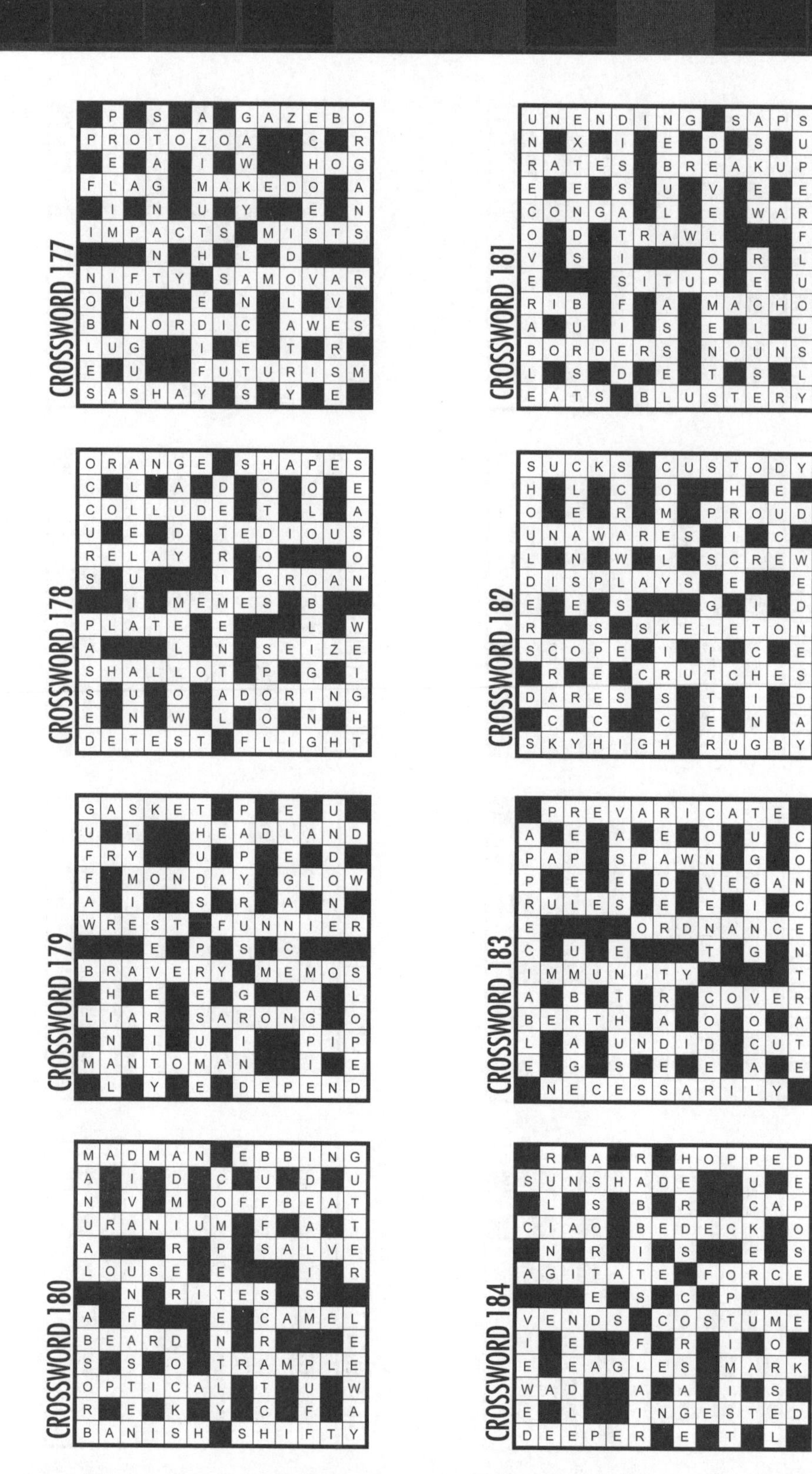
CROSSWORD 177
CROSSWORD 178
CROSSWORD 179
CROSSWORD 180
CROSSWORD 181
CROSSWORD 182
CROSSWORD 183
CROSSWORD 184

SOLUTIONS

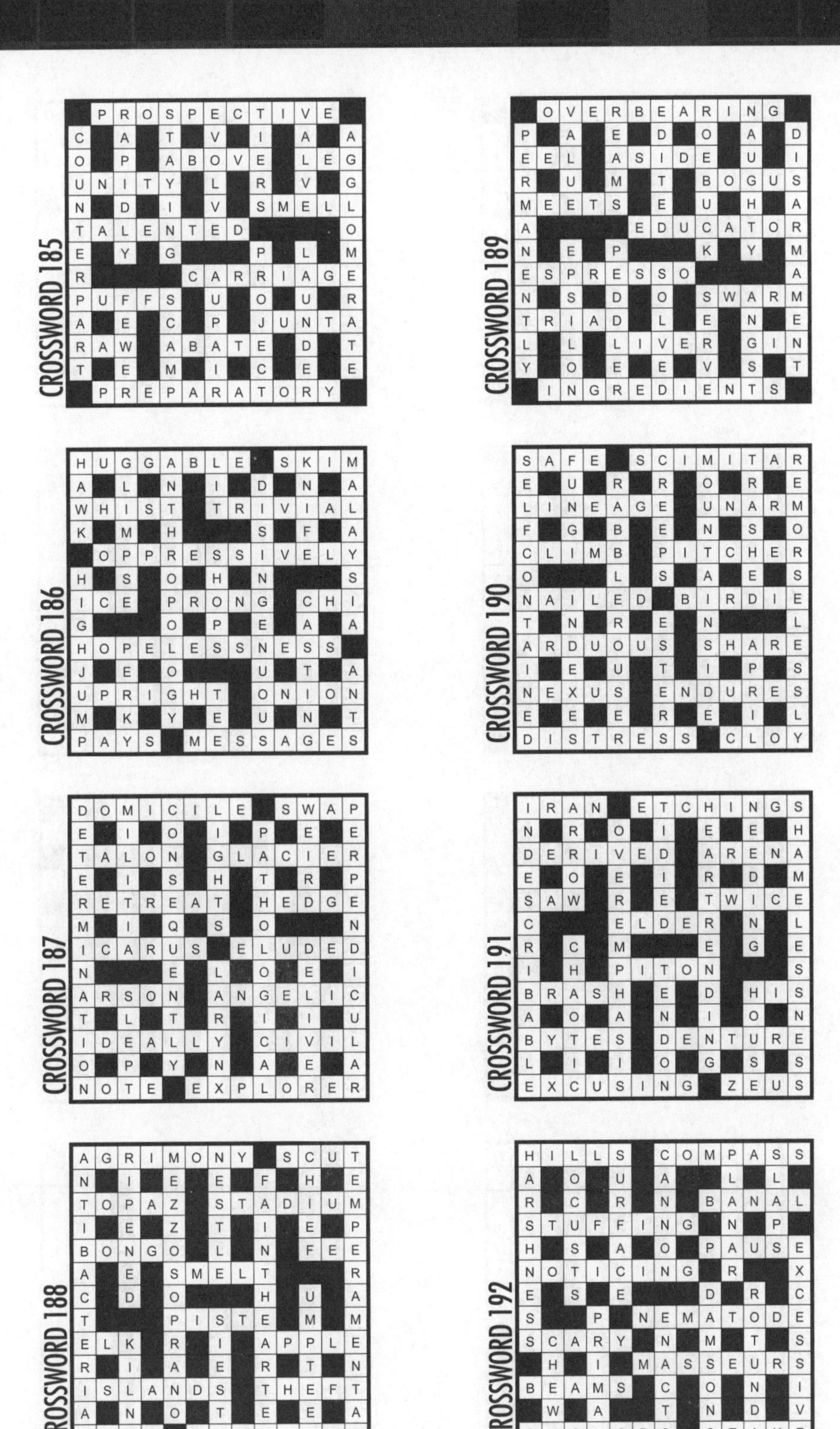

CROSSWORD 185
CROSSWORD 186
CROSSWORD 187
CROSSWORD 188
CROSSWORD 189
CROSSWORD 190
CROSSWORD 191
CROSSWORD 192

SOLUTIONS

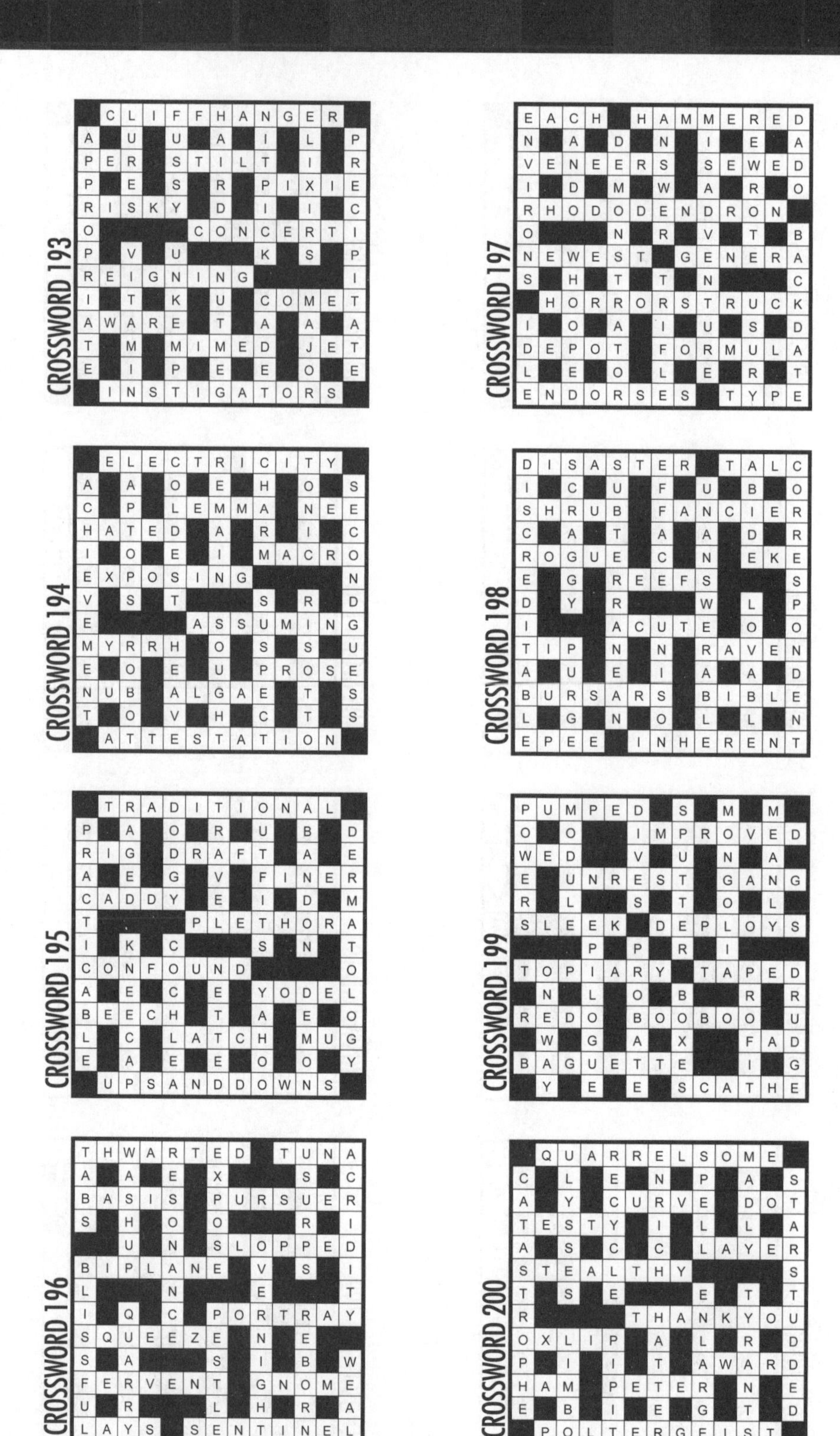
CROSSWORD 193
CROSSWORD 197
CROSSWORD 194
CROSSWORD 198
CROSSWORD 195
CROSSWORD 199
CROSSWORD 196
CROSSWORD 200

SOLUTIONS

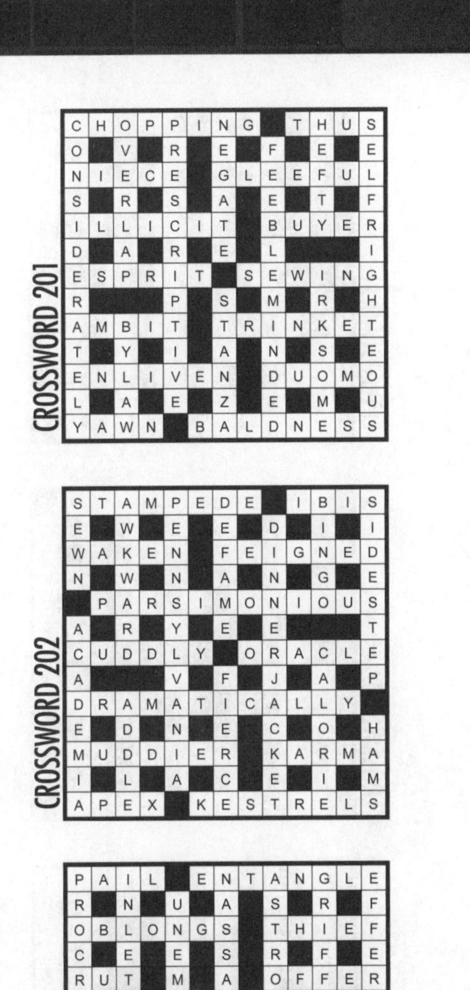

CROSSWORD 204

ALTHOUGH CAMP
R R V O E U A
CHASE SWAGGER
H I R S V U A
INLAW I E RAP
T E HOPES H
E D E D R E
C LEMUR E R
TUB M O ORGAN
U I I U P I A
RATINGS PROWL
A E G S E N I
LURE NEBRASKA

CROSSWORD 205

EMMY TRAITORS
M I B I L U E
IGNORED LITHE
S E E G E W N
SPREADEAGLED
I K S I A L
ODDITY STEREO
N A H S I P
CIRROCUMULUS
H S O H A A I
ADIEU ENTERED
R E G M E C E
MASTHEAD THUD

CROSSWORD 206

REMEMBRANCE
S X X U G E I
U P PANEL DIN
PRUNE K O E A
E N N E WADED
REGISTRY V
L E E A S E
A SPINSTER
TALKS H S E T
I U H R WEAVE
VIM AMAZE M N
E E L S R E T
UNNECESSARY

CROSSWORD 207

PACIFY SPOKEN
L R L H R I U
EPITOME I W G
A T C LEVYING
SNEAK I A E
E R C COURT
I KOOKY N
PLACE P M S
O E T SMOCK
RELAPSE P V A
O O I REALIST
U G N S R N E
STODGY WEDGES

CROSSWORD 208

SENT SCHEDULE
E O B A N N X
LOTIONS TULIP
F C I H R E R
ASHES ELEVATE
W T W P S S
APPLES ARCHES
R R R L E I
EYESORE NACHO
N M U P E O N
EDITS TSUNAMI
S E L O R C S
SPRAYING WHIM

SOLUTIONS

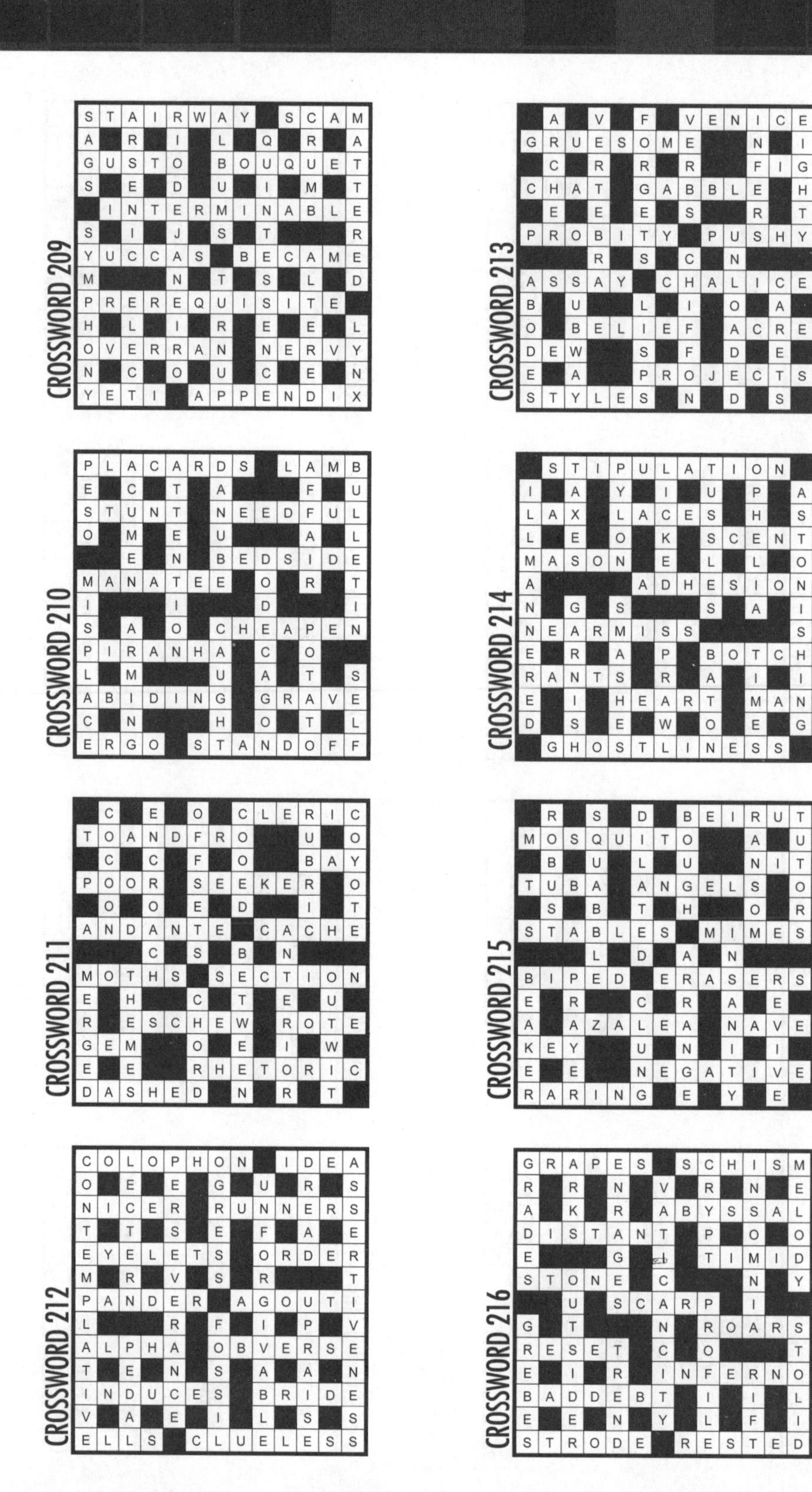

SOLUTIONS

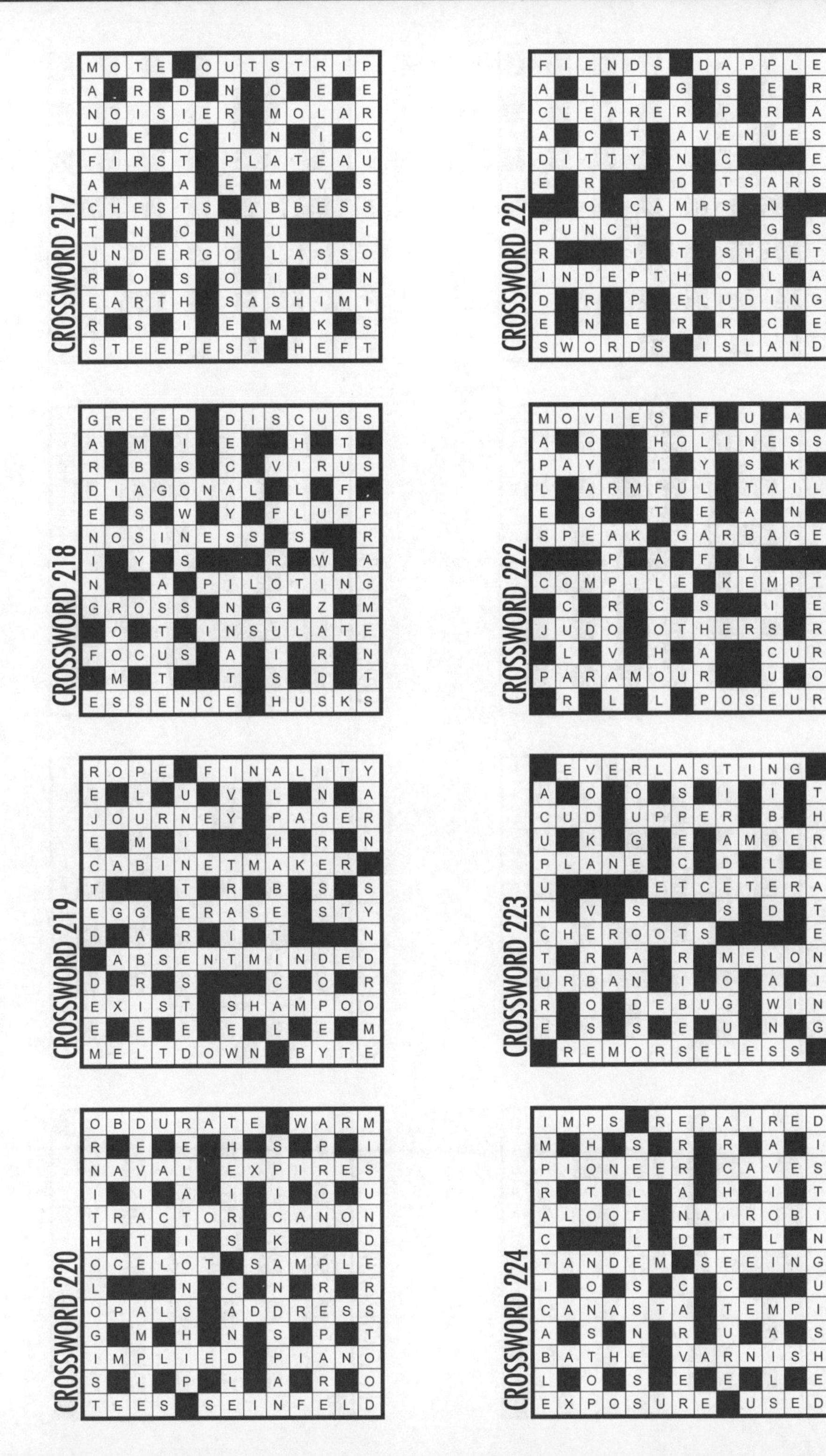
CROSSWORD 217
CROSSWORD 218
CROSSWORD 219
CROSSWORD 220
CROSSWORD 221
CROSSWORD 222
CROSSWORD 223
CROSSWORD 224

SOLUTIONS

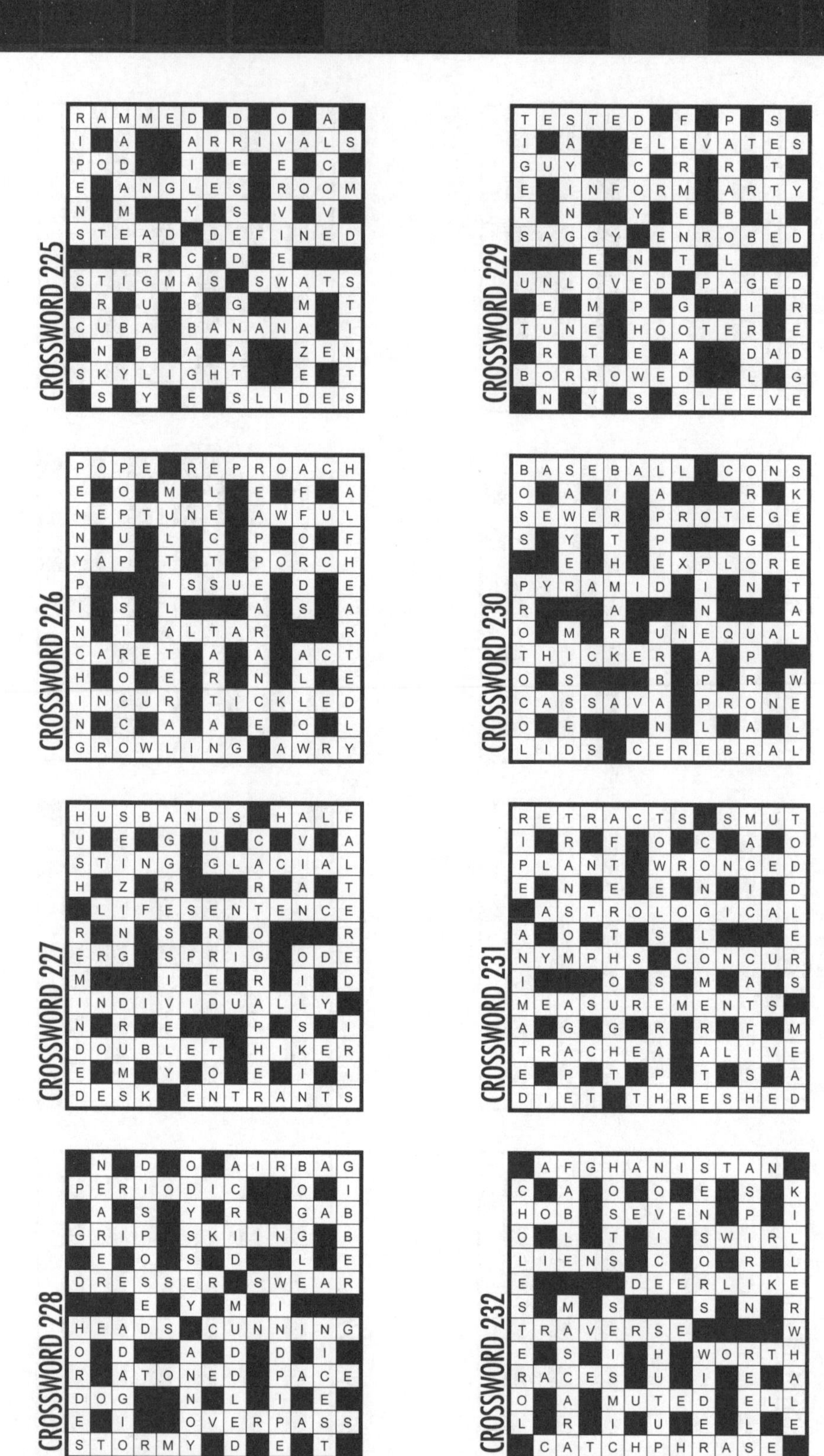
CROSSWORD 225
CROSSWORD 229
CROSSWORD 226
CROSSWORD 230
CROSSWORD 227
CROSSWORD 231
CROSSWORD 228
CROSSWORD 232

SOLUTIONS

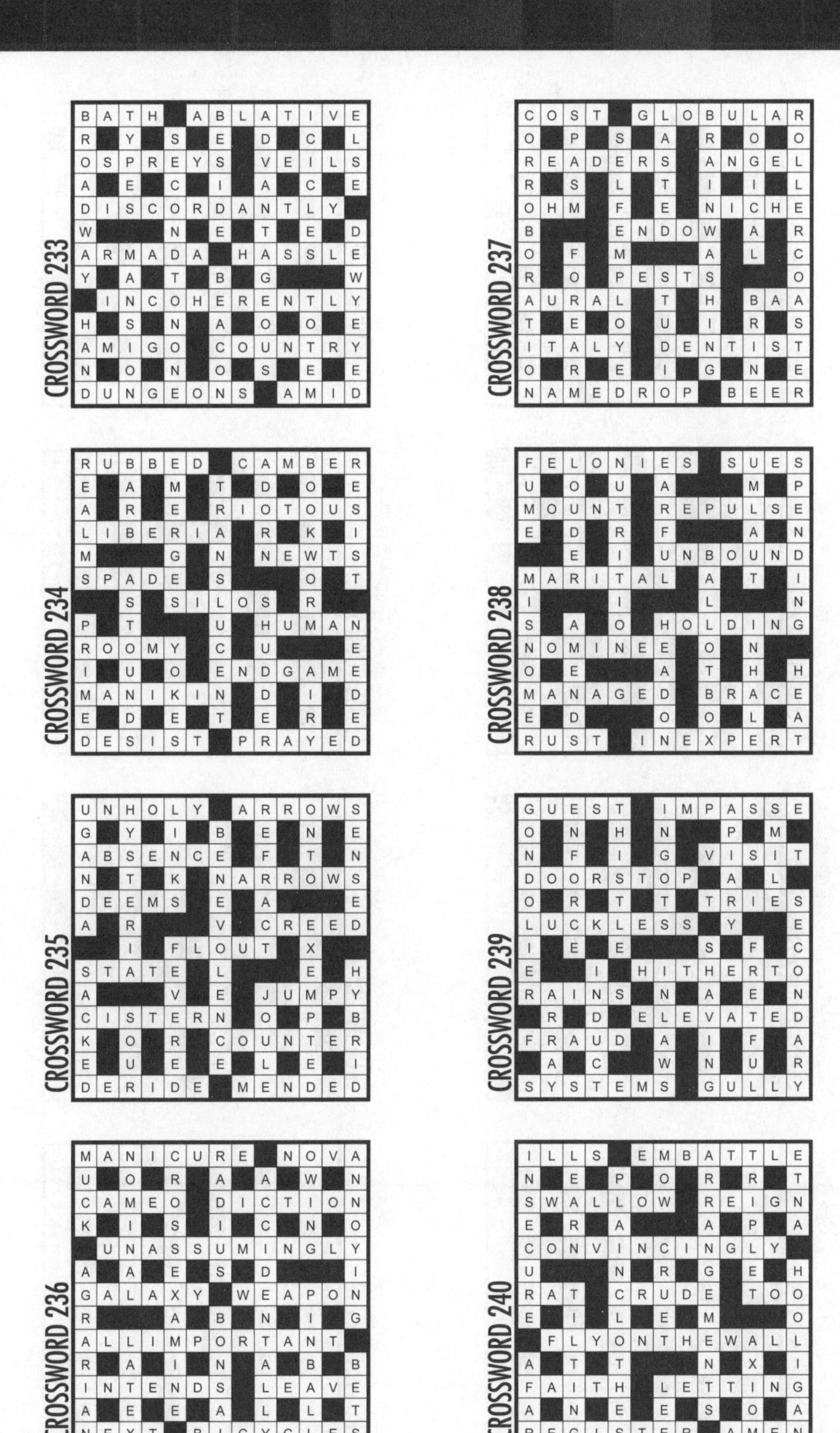

CROSSWORD 233
CROSSWORD 234
CROSSWORD 235
CROSSWORD 236
CROSSWORD 237
CROSSWORD 238
CROSSWORD 239
CROSSWORD 240

SOLUTIONS

CROSSWORD 241

R	A	T	E		M	E	D	I	O	C	R	E
E		H		B		S		N		H		V
P	E	R	F	E	C	T		C	R	I	M	E
U		O		L		H		O		A		N
B	E	W	I	L	D	E	R	M	E	N	T	
L				I		R		P		T		D
I	C	E	A	G	E		G	E	M	I	N	I
C		M		E		S		T				S
	M	I	S	R	E	P	R	E	S	E	N	T
S		N		E		L		N		N		A
T	I	E	I	N		I	N	C	I	T	E	S
A		N		C		C		Y		E		T
G	A	T	H	E	R	E	D		T	R	U	E

CROSSWORD 242

V	I	L	I	F	Y		V		D		U	
O		O			O	R	A	T	I	O	N	S
W	A	G			U		R		A		R	
E		G	L	I	T	Z	Y		L	O	O	T
L		E			H		I		O		L	
S	T	R	A	Y		S	N	U	G	G	L	E
			P		G		G		U			
D	A	S	H	I	N	G		H	E	L	M	S
	G		O		O		C			E		E
P	E	A	R		S	L	A	L	O	M		E
	O		I		T		U			M	O	P
P	L	A	S	T	I	C	S			A		E
	D		M		C		E	R	A	S	E	D

CROSSWORD 243

	I	M	P	R	E	S	S	I	O	N	S	
U		U		O		O		N		A		S
N	O	D		B	R	I	E	F		T		I
C		D		E		R		A	M	I	S	S
A	B	Y	S	S		E		N		V		T
L					A	E	S	T	H	E	T	E
L		Q		P				S		S		R
E	M	U	L	A	T	E	D					I
D		A		T		M		B	R	A	W	N
F	A	R	C	E		I		O		M		L
O		T		L	U	N	G	S		B	O	A
R		E		L		E		O		L		W
	B	R	O	A	D	M	I	N	D	E	D	

CROSSWORD 244

R	E	P	O	S	E		S	C	A	R	A	B
A		O		K		D		O		O		L
R	A	W	H	I	D	E		R		A		A
E		E		M		A	B	R	A	D	E	S
L	A	R	K	S		C		U				T
Y		F				T		P	A	C	K	S
		U		F	A	I	N	T		A		
B	I	L	G	E		V				L		R
U				A		A		P	R	I	M	E
T	Y	P	E	S	E	T		I		G		S
T		I		T		E	X	C	L	U	D	E
E		N		E		D		K		L		N
R	E	S	I	D	E		T	Y	R	A	N	T

CROSSWORD 245

B	L	A	Z	E		C	L	O	S	E	S	T
A		R		N		O			Q		N	
R		M		S		O		H	U	M	I	D
N	O	F	R	I	L	L	S		I		P	
A		U		G		E		F	R	E	E	D
C	U	L	I	N	A	R	Y		M			I
L		S		S				R		C		F
E			D		S	H	R	U	G	O	F	F
S	P	O	O	K		O		I		M		U
	H		M		T	S	U	N	A	M	I	S
S	A	R	I	S		T		O		U		I
	S		N			E		U		N		O
R	E	M	O	D	E	L		S	T	E	R	N

CROSSWORD 246

P	O	T	S		E	N	D	O	R	S	E	D
R		I		P		E		C		C		I
O	U	T	G	R	E	W		C	A	R	D	S
F		H		E				A		E		H
F	I	E	L	D	G	L	A	S	S	E	S	
E				E		Y		I		C		A
R	I	D		T	O	R	S	O		H	U	T
S		E		E		I		N				T
	A	P	P	R	E	C	I	A	T	I	V	E
R		E		M				L		N		N
H	A	N	O	I		A	L	L	E	G	E	D
E		D		N		W		Y		O		E
A	N	S	W	E	R	E	R		S	T	U	D

CROSSWORD 247

I	N	F	I	R	M		E		A		K	
N		I			I	N	C	O	M	I	N	G
J	U	T			X		H		B		A	
U		F	R	E	E	Z	E		R	O	C	K
R		U			D		L		O		K	
Y	E	L	L	S		C	O	N	S	I	S	T
			I		A		N		I			
L	A	T	T	I	C	E		B	A	C	K	S
	P		T		I		P			A		H
T	R	I	O		D	E	A	F	E	N		O
	O		R		I		I			Y	A	W
U	N	L	A	W	F	U	L			O		E
	S		L		Y		S	I	N	N	E	R

CROSSWORD 248

I	S	O	L	A	T	E	S		U	N	D	O
N		P		C		S		S		U		V
D	R	I	N	K		S	E	T	F	R	E	E
E		N		N		A		R		S		R
T	R	I	L	O	G	Y		A	R	E	A	S
E		O		W		S		T				T
R	A	N	K	L	E		S	O	N	A	T	A
M				E		P		S		D		T
I	L	I	A	D		R	E	P	T	I	L	E
N		C		G		E		H		P		M
A	G	I	L	E	L	Y		E	R	O	D	E
C		L		D		E		R		S		N
Y	O	Y	O		A	D	H	E	R	E	N	T

SOLUTIONS

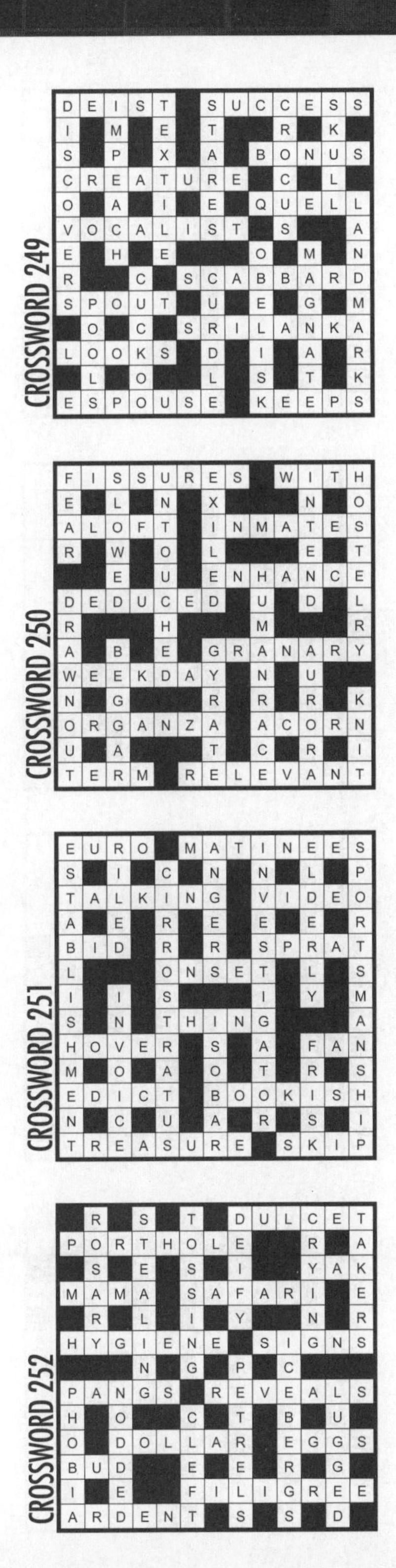

CROSSWORD 253

B	O	W	S		C	A	U	C	U	S	E	S
L		O		W		M		O		E		I
A	I	R	S	H	I	P		U	N	C	U	T
S		S		O				N		U		S
T	I	T	T	L	E	T	A	T	T	L	E	
O				E		E		R		A		A
F	E	N		H	A	N	D	Y		R	U	N
F		U		E		E		W				A
	C	A	T	A	S	T	R	O	P	H	I	C
S		N		R				M		E		O
T	A	C	I	T		T	R	A	D	E	I	N
A		E		E		E		N		D		D
R	E	S	I	D	I	N	G		A	S	I	A

CROSSWORD 254

U	R	D	U		B	O	U	D	O	I	R	S
N		E		B		B		E		M		T
A	I	L	M	E	N	T		M	A	P	L	E
C		F		L		U		O		E		R
C	O	T		L		S		N	U	D	G	E
O				I	T	E	M	S		E		O
U		O		G				T		D		T
N		U		E	I	D	E	R				Y
T	U	T	O	R		E		A		L	A	P
A		C		E		T		T		I		I
B	O	R	O	N		A	C	E	R	B	I	C
L		O		C		I		D		R		A
E	M	P	T	Y	I	N	G		B	A	L	L

CROSSWORD 255

M	O	M	E	N	T		T		J		A	
O		O			U	N	W	I	E	L	D	Y
S	A	D			N		I		T		D	
C		E	M	B	E	R	S		T	W	I	G
O		R			S		T		I		N	
W	I	N	C	E		M	E	S	S	A	G	E
			A		P		D		O			
C	H	I	M	E	R	A		S	N	A	P	S
	O		E		O		P			G		O
D	O	U	R		P	L	A	I	C	E		F
	R		O		H		V			N	E	T
C	A	R	O	T	E	N	E			T		E
	Y		N		T		D	A	M	S	O	N

CROSSWORD 256

O	V	E	R	F	L	O	W		R	O	W	S
A		X		A		B				R		H
K	N	E	E	L		J	A	M	A	I	C	A
S		M		S		E				S		M
		P		E		C	O	N	N	O	T	E
P	O	T	S	H	O	T		A		N		F
A				O				R				U
S		C		O		D	E	C	I	B	E	L
S	O	L	I	D	L	Y		I		E		
W		E				N		S		C		S
O	C	A	R	I	N	A		S	T	A	S	H
R		V				M		U		L		I
D	E	E	P		H	O	R	S	E	M	E	N

SOLUTIONS

CROSSWORD 257

S	E	A	T	S		O	U	T	R	A	G	E
P		R		T		P		E		L		
E		R		A		E		S	C	O	O	T
C	L	E	A	N	I	N	G		I		O	
I		A		D		E		S	T	U	M	P
F	O	R	E	B	O	D	E		E			R
I		S		Y				P		S		O
E			I		A	P	I	A	R	I	S	T
S	P	I	N	E		L		C		L		E
	U		C		C	U	B	I	C	L	E	S
S	T	A	I	D		C		F		I		T
	T		T			K		I		E		E
S	Y	N	E	R	G	Y		C	A	R	E	D

CROSSWORD 258

	C	O	N	S	T	R	U	C	T	E	D	
C		U		C		E		H		L		C
H		T		H	O	S	T	A		A	D	O
R	A	D	I	O		I		F		N		M
O		O		O		N		F	E	D	U	P
N	E	E	D	L	E	S	S					L
O		S		S				C		A		I
G					C	A	T	H	O	L	I	C
R	O	U	G	H		M		I		G		A
A		R		A		U		C	L	E	A	T
P	E	G		V	O	L	G	A		R		E
H		E		O		E		G		I		D
	E	D	U	C	A	T	I	O	N	A	L	

CROSSWORD 259

A	N	T	I	D	O	T	E		M	A	L	I
G		R		O		A		U		L		N
G	R	O	O	M		K	I	N	E	T	I	C
L		W		E		I		D		O		O
O	B	E	Y	S		N		E		S	I	N
M		L		T	I	G	H	T				S
E		S		I				E		T		I
R				C	I	V	I	C		R		D
A	I	L		A		I		T	H	E	R	E
T		I		T		O		A		B		R
I	N	K	W	E	L	L		B	A	L	S	A
O		E		D		E		L		E		T
N	O	D	S		A	T	T	E	N	D	E	E

CROSSWORD 260

	L	I	G	H	T	W	E	I	G	H	T	
A		M		O		A		D		O		G
P		P		T	E	N	S	E		T	W	O
P	A	I	N	S		G		A		E		O
R		E		P		L		S	O	L	I	D
O	U	T	C	O	M	E	S					N
X		Y		T				S		F		A
I					E	L	O	Q	U	E	N	T
M	A	N	I	C		I		U		S		U
A		U		Y		M		E	S	T	E	R
T	U	T		N	E	P	A	L		O		E
E		T		I		E		C		O		D
	E	Y	E	C	A	T	C	H	I	N	G	

CROSSWORD 261

B	A	S	T	I	L	L	E		P	R	O	D
L		M		N		A		C		E		I
A	L	E	R	T		D	O	O	D	L	E	S
C		A		R		D		M		A		A
K	A	R	A	O	K	E		M	I	X	U	P
A		E		V		R		E				P
N	U	D	G	E	S		U	N	T	R	U	E
D				R		P		S		E		A
W	A	G	E	S		E	Q	U	A	T	O	R
H		L		I		D		R		S		A
I	C	E	C	O	L	D		A	L	I	E	N
T		A		N		L		T		N		C
E	L	M	S		S	E	R	E	N	A	D	E

CROSSWORD 262

V	A	C	A	T	E		A	C	I	D	I	C
E		L		H		M		R		W		L
R		E		E		E	R	U	D	I	T	E
B	U	F	F	O	O	N		E		N		V
A				R		T		L	O	D	G	E
L	E	A	S	E		A				L		R
		B		M	E	L	E	E		E		
S		N				B		M	O	D	E	M
P	R	O	X	Y		L		O				O
I		R		E		O	U	T	W	A	R	D
D	E	M	O	T	I	C		I		N		I
E		A		I		K		V		T		F
R	E	L	I	S	H		C	E	L	E	R	Y

CROSSWORD 263

A	L	G	A		E	Y	E	S	I	G	H	T
D		E		U		E		A		I		O
O	U	T	I	N	G	S		T	A	B	B	Y
R		U		D				I		B		S
A	P	P	R	E	H	E	N	S	I	O	N	
B				R		R		F		N		D
L	O	B		A	O	R	T	A		S	H	E
E		O		C		O		C				R
	U	N	C	H	A	R	I	T	A	B	L	E
A		U		I				O		R		L
B	A	S	T	E		T	E	R	M	I	N	I
E		E		V		A		Y		C		C
T	A	S	T	E	F	U	L		S	K	I	T

CROSSWORD 264

R	E	B	E	L	S		P		S		E	
I		O			I	R	R	I	T	A	N	T
B	E	D			N		A		A		G	
B		K	I	N	G	L	Y		R	U	I	N
E		I			S		I		F		N	
D	I	N	K	Y		I	N	S	I	D	E	S
		E		O		G		S				
L	A	W	Y	E	R	S		S	H	O	A	L
	W		B		I		W			U		I
S	H	O	O		F	L	A	U	N	T		F
	I		A		I		I			F	A	T
C	L	E	R	I	C	A	L			I		E
	E		D		E		S	E	A	T	E	D

SOLUTIONS

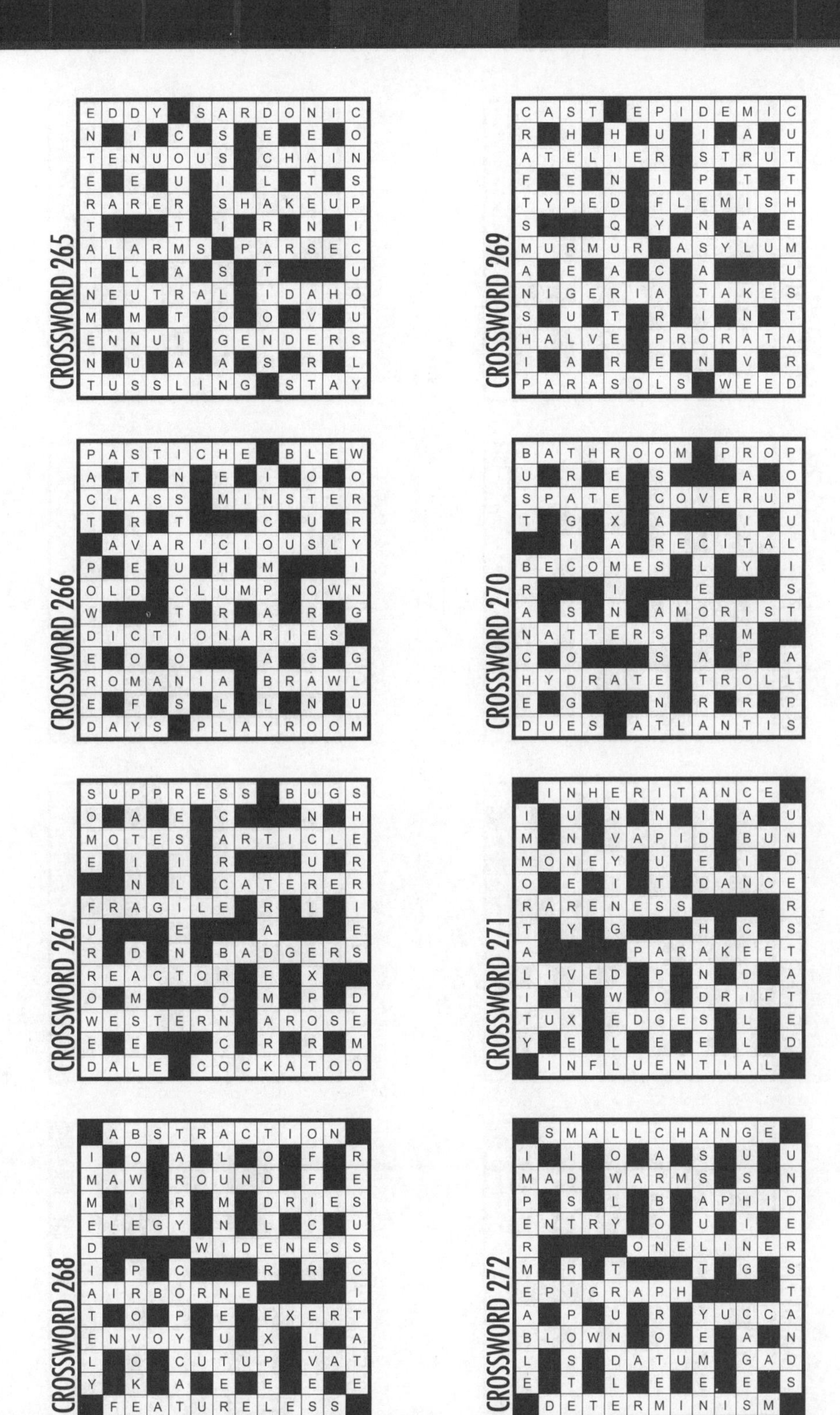

CROSSWORD 265
CROSSWORD 269
CROSSWORD 266
CROSSWORD 270
CROSSWORD 267
CROSSWORD 271
CROSSWORD 268
CROSSWORD 272

SOLUTIONS

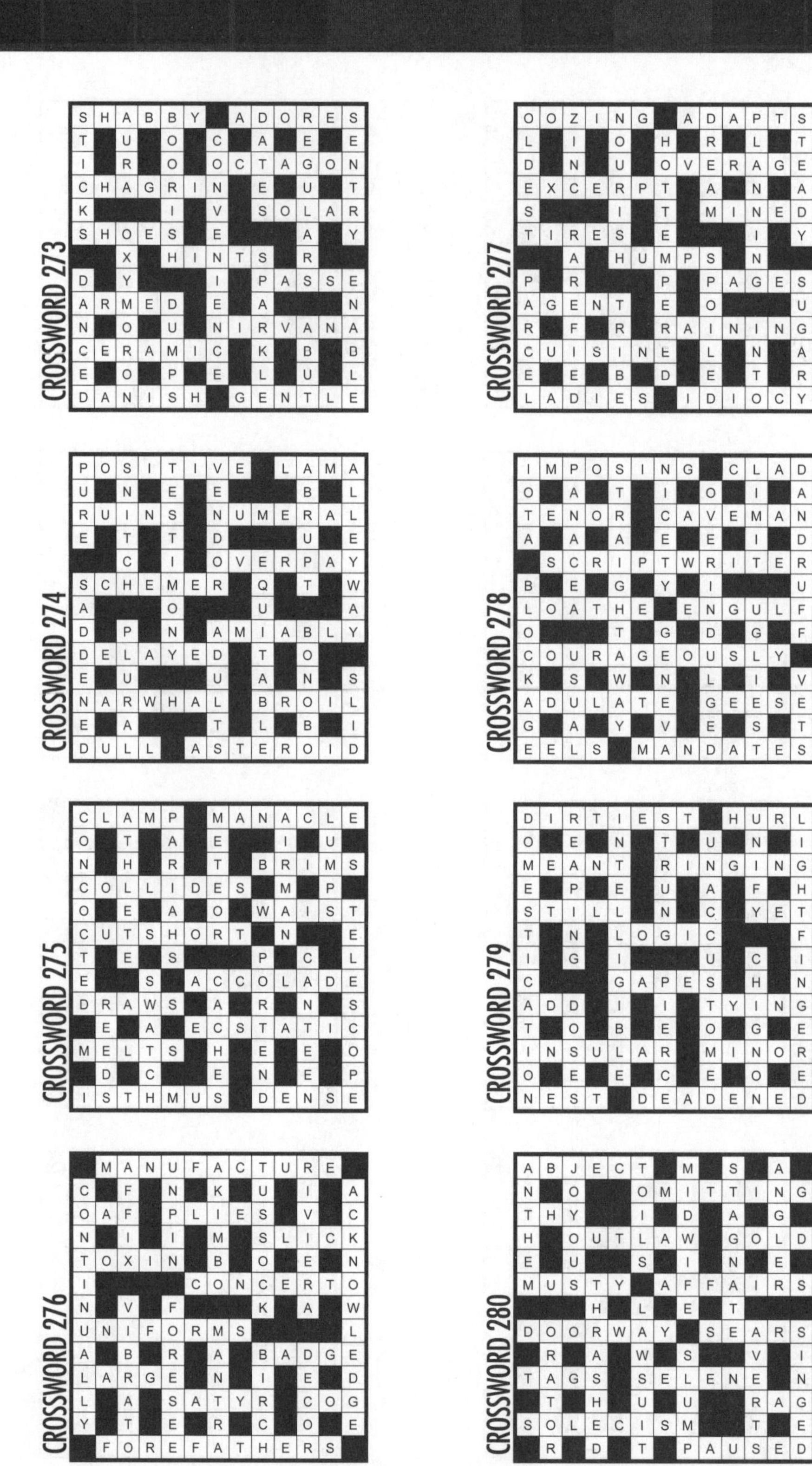

CROSSWORD 273
CROSSWORD 274
CROSSWORD 275
CROSSWORD 276
CROSSWORD 277
CROSSWORD 278
CROSSWORD 279
CROSSWORD 280

SOLUTIONS

CROSSWORD 281

A	C	H	E		M	E	N	I	S	C	U	S
R		A		I		N		N		H		E
A	L	I	G	N	E	D		E	N	A	C	T
C		K		V				X		N		S
H	O	U	S	E	K	E	E	P	I	N	G	
N				R		A		E		E		G
I	L	K		T	I	G	E	R		L	E	A
D		N		E		L		I				R
	D	O	U	B	L	E	D	E	A	L	E	R
A		W		R				N		I		I
C	H	I	N	A		O	C	C	U	L	T	S
I		N		T		W		E		A		O
D	O	G	G	E	D	L	Y		I	C	O	N

CROSSWORD 282

W	R	E	N	C	H		B	R	A	C	E	S
A		V		O		B		O		A		N
S		I		P		E	N	O	U	N	C	E
H	A	L	C	Y	O	N		T		O		E
E				I		E		S	O	N	A	R
D	O	M	E	S		F				L		S
		U		T	R	A	P	S		A		
C		L				C		Y	A	W	N	S
L	U	T	E	S		T		M				E
O		I		P		I	M	P	E	R	I	L
S	O	P	R	A	N	O		T		E		E
E		L		C		N		O		A		C
T	E	E	M	E	D		A	M	I	D	S	T

CROSSWORD 283

D	R	A	Y	S		C	O	L	L	A	G	E
E		T		H		O			A		H	
V		T		A		M		C	R	O	O	K
O	V	E	R	C	A	M	E		G		U	
U		S		K		O		S	E	L	L	S
R	A	T	T	L	I	N	G		R			I
I		S		E				B		S		N
N			L		R	O	M	A	N	T	I	C
G	L	U	E	D		U		B		A		E
	A		T		S	T	R	O	N	G	E	R
K	N	I	T	S		A		O		I		I
	E		E			G		N		N		T
A	S	C	R	I	B	E		S	O	G	G	Y

CROSSWORD 284

D	I	S	P	R	O	V	E		D	H	O	W
I		A		E		O		L		O		O
S	O	N	I	C		T	R	A	W	L	E	R
A		D		O		E		B		D		D
P	A	P	A	L		R		Y		S	I	P
P		I		L	A	S	E	R				R
O		T		E				I		S		O
I				C	R	O	O	N		T		C
N	I	P		T		D		T	R	A	C	E
T		I		I		D		H		R		S
I	M	P	I	O	U	S		I	D	L	E	S
N		E		N		O		N		E		O
G	U	S	H		A	N	T	E	A	T	E	R

CROSSWORD 285

	E		R		L		W	I	D	E	N	S
E	X	T	E	R	I	O	R			N		I
	C		V		B		E			F	E	Z
B	I	K	E		R	O	C	O	C	O		Z
	T		R		A		K			L		L
R	E	V	E	L	R	Y		J	U	D	G	E
			N		Y		S		N			
C	H	U	T	E		A	C	C	L	A	I	M
O		N			P		R		I		N	
R		I	M	P	O	S	E		K	E	L	P
S	I	T			E		E		E		A	
E		E			M	I	D	D	L	I	N	G
T	I	D	I	E	S		S		Y		D	

CROSSWORD 286

S	T	I	T	C	H	E	S		B	A	L	M
I		N		O		X				C		O
G	I	V	E	N		P	L	A	T	T	E	R
H		E		C		I				U		A
		R		L		R	I	T	U	A	L	S
L	E	T	T	U	C	E		R		L		S
A				D				A				E
U		W		E		D	E	V	I	C	E	S
G	R	A	N	D	M	A		E		A		
H		T				W		R		J		B
I	C	E	L	A	N	D		S	P	O	I	L
N		R				L		E		L		O
G	A	S	H		H	E	A	D	R	E	S	T

CROSSWORD 287

P	R	O	T	R	U	D	E		A	P	E	S
A		U		E		I		D		L		O
D	O	T	E	S		S	P	E	C	I	A	L
S		P		E		O		L		E		I
	N	A	R	R	O	W	M	I	N	D	E	D
G		C		V		N		G				I
R	E	E	K	E	D		T	H	E	I	S	T
O				P		S		T		N		Y
U	N	D	E	R	S	T	A	F	F	E	D	
N		E		I		R		U		R		L
D	E	F	A	C	T	O		L	A	T	H	E
E		E		E		L		L		I		A
D	I	R	T		P	L	A	Y	B	A	C	K

CROSSWORD 288

F	I	L	T	H	Y		A	B	I	D	E	D
O		U		E		D		O		R		R
S		L		A		E	M	U	L	A	T	E
T	E	L	A	V	I	V		T		G		S
E				I		A		S	A	G	A	S
R	O	U	T	E		S				I		Y
		N		R	A	T	E	D		N		
M		W				A		R	I	G	H	T
A	T	O	M	S		T		A				E
S		R		H		I	M	P	I	N	G	E
C	U	T	D	O	W	N		E		E		T
O		H		W		G		R		A		E
T	R	Y	I	N	G		U	S	U	R	E	R

SOLUTIONS

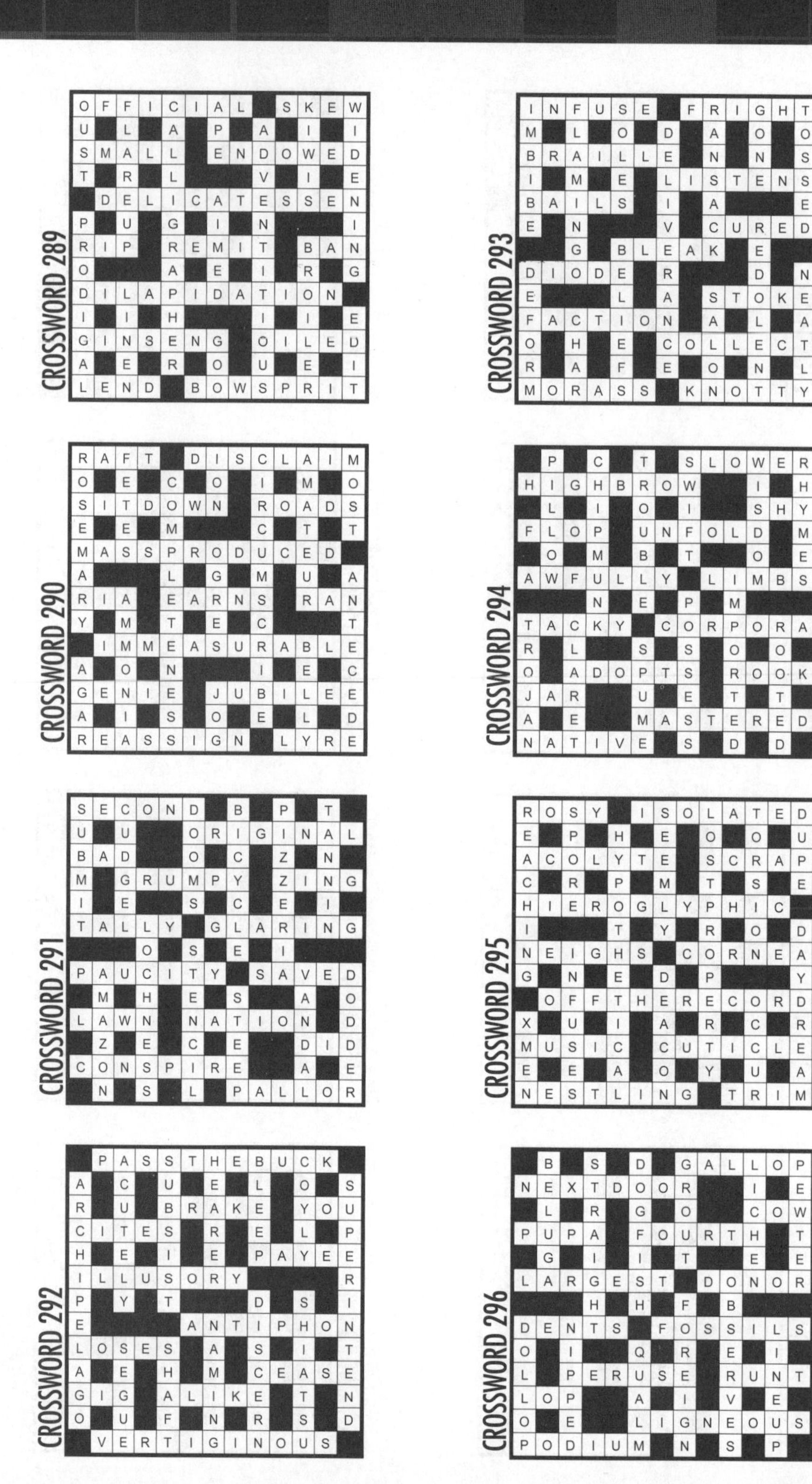

SOLUTIONS

CROSSWORD 297

L	A	D	I	N	G		A		M		P	
A		O			E	U	P	H	O	R	I	C
P	E	W			A		P		N		A	
D		S	T	A	R	V	E		R	A	Z	E
O		E			S		A		O		Z	
G	O	R	E	D		F	L	U	V	I	A	L
			X		L		S		I			
P	R	E	P	L	A	N		P	A	R	E	S
	O		L		G		B			I		T
O	U	Z	O		G	A	L	L	I	C		A
	S		I		A		U			H	A	T
L	E	C	T	U	R	E	R			E		U
	D		S		D		T	U	S	S	L	E

CROSSWORD 298

C	A	S	K		M	I	S	C	H	I	E	F
O		H		R		N		A		K		O
M	A	R	K	E	R	S		T	H	E	I	R
P		U		F		T		E		B		E
A	N	G	E	R		E	A	R	M	A	R	K
N				I		P		P		N		N
I	M	P	U	G	N		V	I	R	A	G	O
O		A		E		A		L				W
N	A	T	U	R	E	S		L	E	G	A	L
S		R		A		T		A		R		E
H	O	I	S	T		H	U	R	R	I	E	D
I		O		O		M		S		L		G
P	A	T	E	R	N	A	L		G	L	E	E

CROSSWORD 299

I	N	C	R	E	A	S	E		Z	E	B	U
N		A		X		I		C		V		N
T	H	U	M	P		C	L	O	S	E	U	P
E		S		E		K		N		R		R
N	A	T	U	R	A	L		S	T	Y	L	E
T		I		I		E		I				T
I	N	C	O	M	E		A	D	V	I	C	E
O				E		P		E		N		N
N	O	W	I	N		A	P	R	I	C	O	T
A		O		T		G		A		E		I
L	U	M	B	A	G	O		B	A	N	J	O
L		E		L		D		L		S		U
Y	A	N	K		L	A	T	E	N	E	S	S

CROSSWORD 300

	H		E		S		P	O	W	D	E	R
V	E	N	D	E	T	T	A			A		A
	R		I		A		R			M	E	N
B	E	E	F		U	P	K	E	E	P		G
	I		Y		N		S			E		E
U	N	H	I	T	C	H		K	A	R	T	S
			N		H		B		T			
B	U	G	G	Y		W	A	R	T	I	M	E
U		A			G		B		A		A	
I		G	U	I	L	T	Y		I	O	N	S
L	A	G			E		I		N		N	
D		E			A	N	S	W	E	R	E	D
S	U	D	D	E	N		H		D		R	

CROSSWORD 301

	S	T	O	M	A	C	H	A	C	H	E	
N		E		E		A		P		E		R
O	W	E		S	I	N	G	E		A		O
N		N		S		A		L	E	V	E	L
S	A	S	S	Y		D		I		I		E
E					B	A	C	K	F	L	I	P
N		F		O				E		Y		L
S	H	R	I	V	E	L	S					A
I		E		E		E		H	O	B	B	Y
C	L	E	A	R		A		E		E		I
A		D		S	A	V	E	R		F	I	N
L		O		E		E		O		I		G
	I	M	P	E	R	S	O	N	A	T	E	

CROSSWORD 302

S	H	R	U	B	S		S	W	E	D	E	N
I		A		E		C		A		R		E
L		P		T		O	R	D	E	A	L	S
V	E	T	E	R	A	N		E		M		T
E				A		S		S	C	A	L	E
R	E	A	D	Y		I				T		D
		R		S	A	G	E	S		I		
C		M				N		C	O	C	K	Y
L	U	C	I	D		M		R				A
I		H		E		E	L	A	S	T	I	C
C	H	A	S	T	E	N		P		O		H
H		I		E		T		P		W		T
E	R	R	O	R	S		H	Y	E	N	A	S

CROSSWORD 303

F	A	R	R	I	E	R	S		A	R	T	S
E		A		N		E		M		O		A
L	A	C	E	D		C	R	E	W	M	A	N
I		C		I		E		T		E		C
C	R	O	S	S	E	D		A	B	O	U	T
I		O		C		E		P				I
T	U	N	D	R	A		R	H	Y	T	H	M
A				E		F		Y		E		O
T	E	M	P	T		I	N	S	U	L	I	N
I		O		I		A		I		L		I
O	B	V	I	O	U	S		C	A	I	R	O
N		E		N		C		A		N		U
S	I	D	E		C	O	L	L	E	G	E	S

CROSSWORD 304

	C	H	O	R	E	O	G	R	A	P	H	
C		E		E		R		E		O		U
E		X		M	E	A	N	S		K	I	N
L	L	A	M	A		L		T		E		S
E		G		R		L		S	T	R	I	P
B	R	O	O	K	L	Y	N					E
R		N		S				B		S		A
A					B	A	L	L	C	O	C	K
T	O	W	E	L		D		A		L		A
I		H		O		J		B	L	U	R	B
O	R	E		S	Q	U	I	B		B		L
N		R		E		S		E		L		E
	S	E	C	R	E	T	A	R	I	E	S	

SOLUTIONS

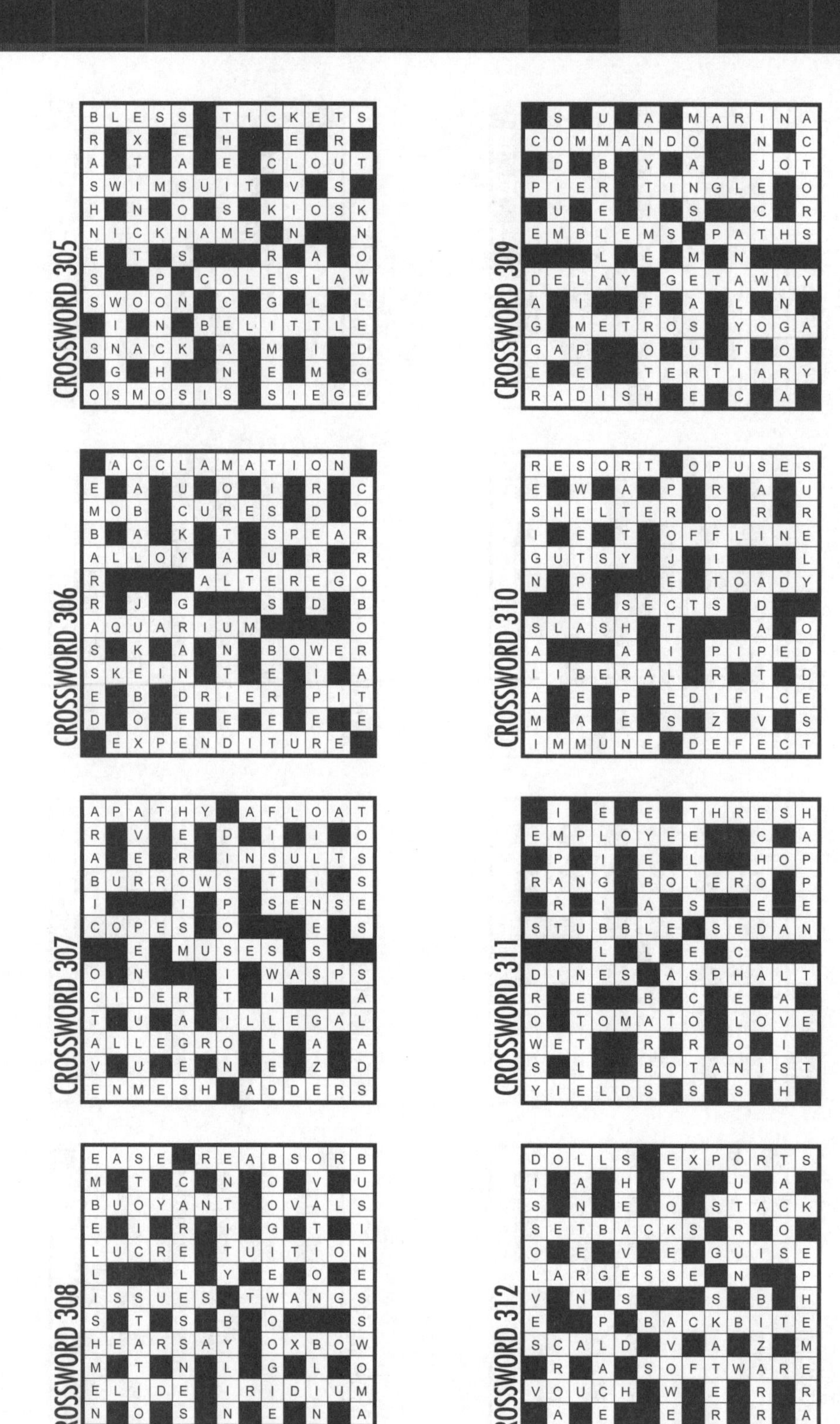
CROSSWORD 305
CROSSWORD 309
CROSSWORD 306
CROSSWORD 310
CROSSWORD 307
CROSSWORD 311
CROSSWORD 308
CROSSWORD 312

SOLUTIONS

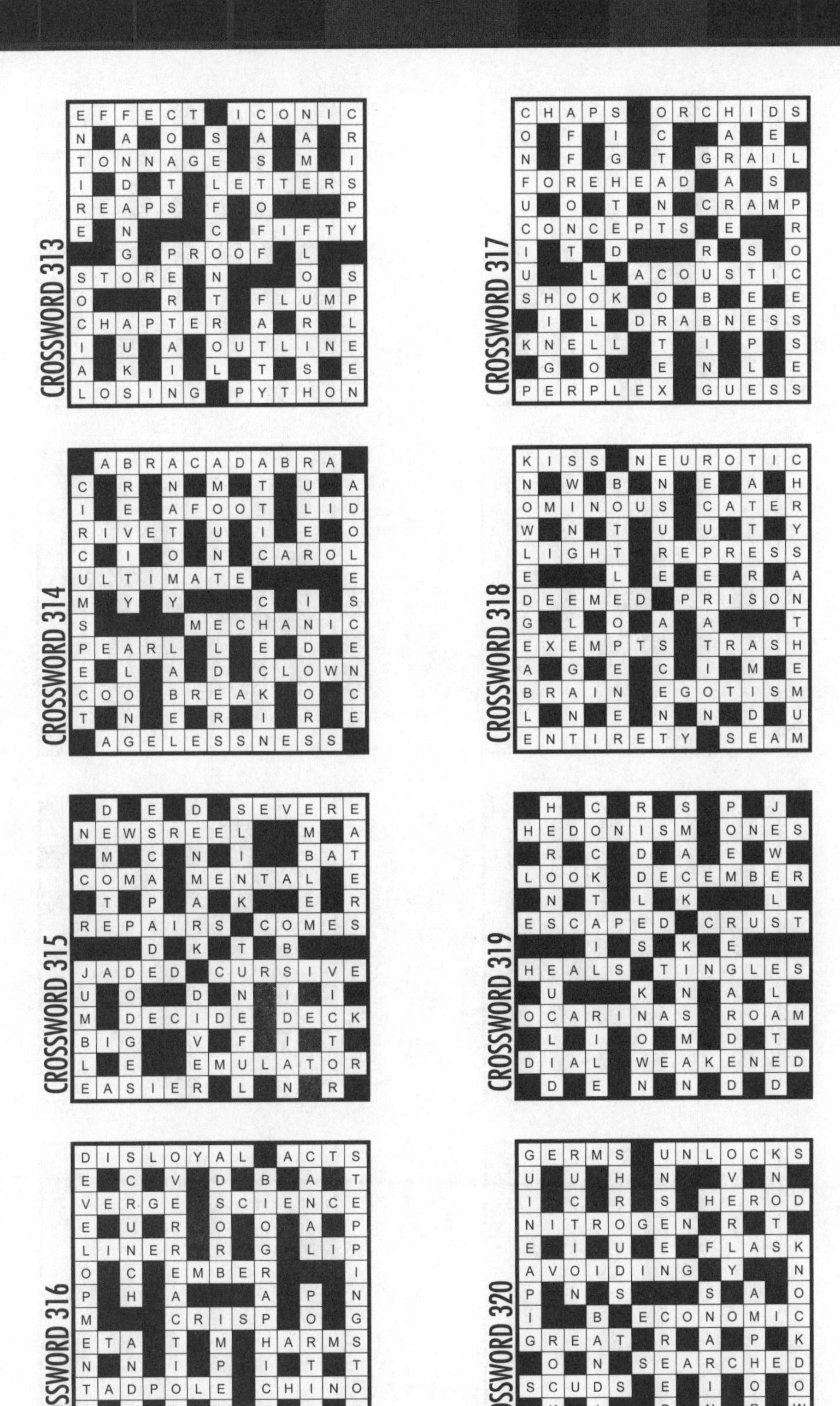

CROSSWORD 313
CROSSWORD 317
CROSSWORD 314
CROSSWORD 318
CROSSWORD 315
CROSSWORD 319
CROSSWORD 316
CROSSWORD 320

SOLUTIONS

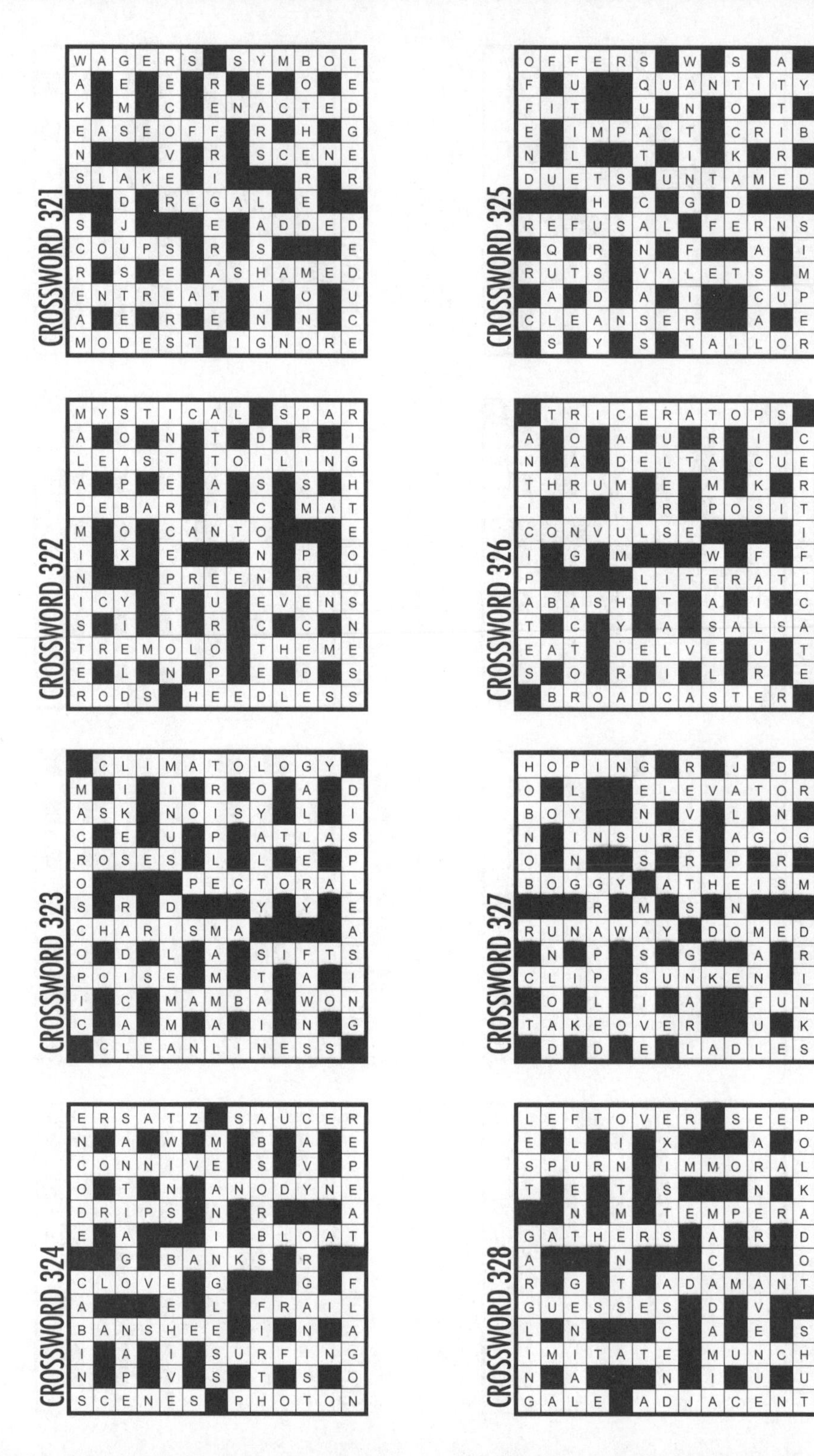
CROSSWORD 321
CROSSWORD 325
CROSSWORD 322
CROSSWORD 326
CROSSWORD 323
CROSSWORD 327
CROSSWORD 324
CROSSWORD 328

SOLUTIONS

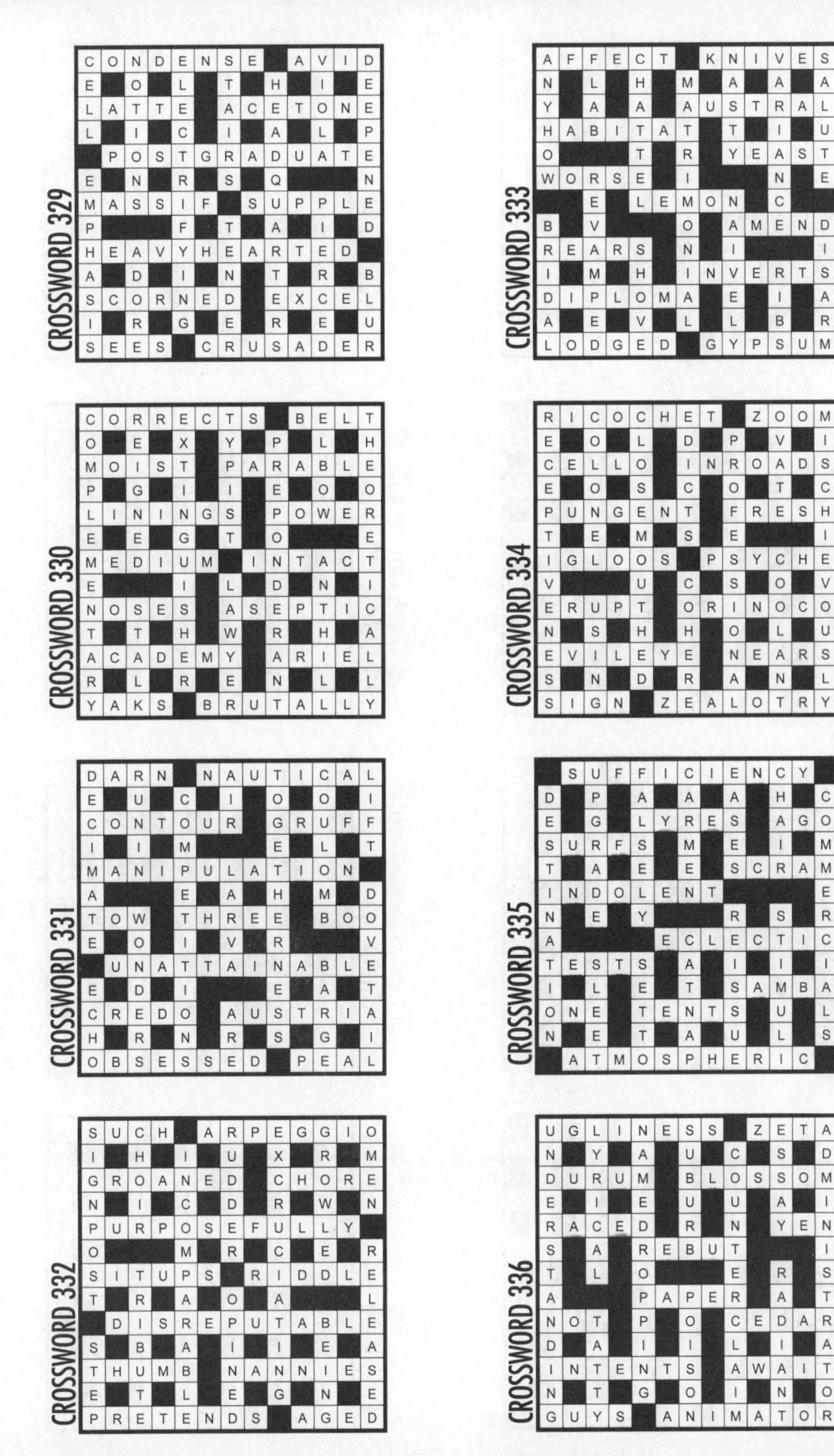
CROSSWORD 329
CROSSWORD 333
CROSSWORD 330
CROSSWORD 334
CROSSWORD 331
CROSSWORD 335
CROSSWORD 332
CROSSWORD 336

SOLUTIONS

CROSSWORD 341

M	A	T	U	R	I	T	Y		A	D	A	M
A		E		E		R		B		O		E
G	R	A	P	H		U	N	A	I	D	E	D
N		C		A		S		N		G		I
I	N	H	I	B	I	T		T	W	E	E	T
F		E		I		Y		A				E
I	T	S	E	L	F		I	M	P	A	I	R
C				I		O		W		S		R
A	D	M	I	T		D	E	E	P	S	E	A
T		A		A		E		I		E		N
I	G	N	I	T	E	S		G	O	R	S	E
O		N		E		S		H		T		A
N	O	A	H		P	A	R	T	I	S	A	N

CROSSWORD 342

D	R	E	N	C	H	E	D		B	E	A	U
E		V		L		A		N		N		N
F	L	O	R	A		S	P	E	E	D	U	P
O		L		I		T		W		E		R
R	O	V	E	R		E		T		D	O	E
E		E		V	E	R	S	E				C
S		S		O				S		H		E
T				Y	A	C	H	T		A		D
A	R	K		A		R		A	M	U	S	E
T		U		N		A		M		T		N
I	N	D	U	C	E	D		E	V	E	N	T
O		O		E		L		N		U		E
N	O	S	Y		F	E	A	T	U	R	E	D

CROSSWORD 343

	B		S		C		H	A	N	G	U	P
B	R	O	C	C	O	L	I			I		I
	O		U		A		R			F	O	X
P	A	L	L		C	R	E	D	I	T		E
	C		P		H		D			E		L
W	H	E	T	H	E	R		T	I	D	E	S
			O		S		B		N			
Z	E	B	R	A		L	A	D	D	E	R	S
A		U			Q		S		E		E	
M		D	E	B	U	N	K		N	U	L	L
B	U	G			I		E		T		I	
I		E			T	O	T	T	E	R	E	D
A	D	D	U	C	E		S		D		F	

CROSSWORD 344

R	I	D	I	C	U	L	E		S	A	G	A
A		R		A		U		A		C		L
S	P	O	O	R		N	O	S	T	R	I	L
H		P		D		G		T		E		A
	V	O	C	I	F	E	R	O	U	S	L	Y
P		F		O		S		N				I
R	U	F	F	L	E		V	I	O	L	I	N
O				O		P		S		E		G
D	E	M	O	G	R	A	P	H	I	C	S	
U		O		I		D		M		T		K
C	O	U	R	S	E	D		E	D	U	C	E
E		S		T		L		N		R		G
S	E	E	K		F	E	A	T	H	E	R	S

SOLUTIONS

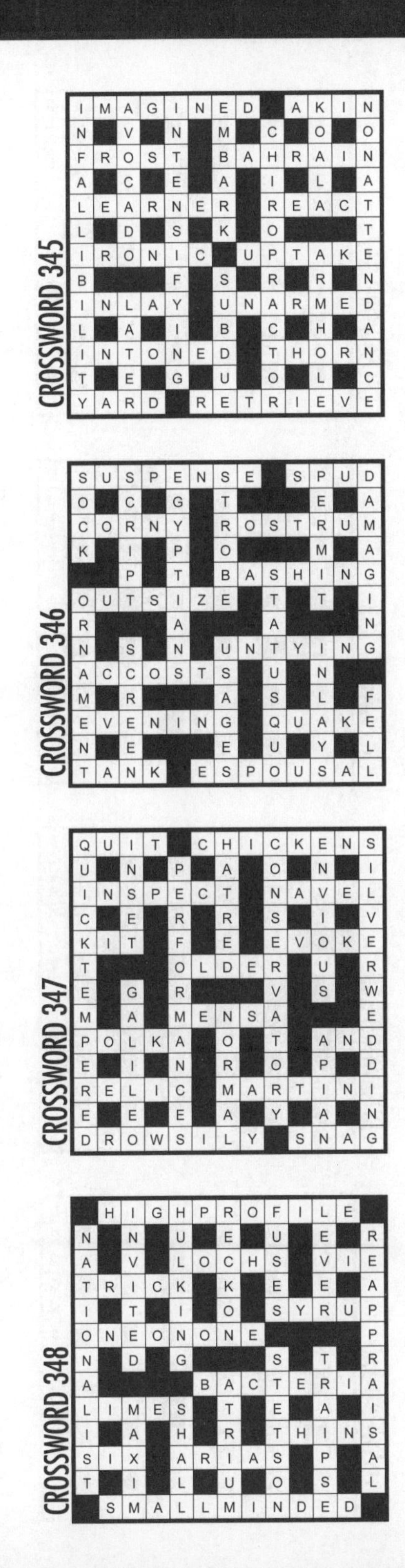

CROSSWORD 349

C	U	R	T		A	D	V	A	N	C	E	S
O		O		P		A		M		H		H
M	O	N	A	R	C	H		B	R	A	V	O
M		D		I		L		I		M		R
E	G	O		D		I		D	E	B	I	T
N				E	V	A	D	E		E		T
S		R		O				X		R		E
U		E		F	I	G	H	T				M
R	E	C	A	P		E		R		T	A	P
A		O		L		R		O		O		E
B	U	R	M	A		B	L	U	S	T	E	R
L		D		C		I		S		A		E
E	A	S	T	E	R	L	Y		C	L	O	D

CROSSWORD 350

E	W	E	S		H	A	R	D	S	H	I	P
X		A		D		C		R		E		R
T	U	R	B	I	N	E		E	E	R	I	E
R		L		S		T		S		B		T
A	E	S	O	P		I	N	S	T	A	T	E
O				L		C		I		G		N
R	I	T	U	A	L		I	N	S	E	R	T
D		R		C		C		G				I
I	N	A	N	E	L	Y		D	I	T	T	O
N		V		M		C		O		R		U
A	B	A	S	E		L	A	W	L	E	S	S
R		I		N		E		N		S		L
Y	U	L	E	T	I	D	E		E	S	P	Y

CROSSWORD 351

V	I	B	R	A	T	E	S		V	A	M	P
E		R		S		A				L		L
R	E	E	K	S		T	E	Q	U	I	L	A
B		A		O		E				B		T
		K		C		R	E	C	T	I	F	Y
J	U	S	T	I	F	Y		R		S		P
E				A				A				U
A		C		T		A	F	F	E	C	T	S
L	E	A	V	E	N	S		T		U		
O		N				T		S		P		C
U	N	C	O	V	E	R		M	O	O	S	E
S		E				A		E		L		D
Y	O	L	K		E	L	O	N	G	A	T	E

CROSSWORD 352

G	O	D	S		N	E	U	T	R	A	L	S
O		I		O		Y		R		M		T
O	C	C	L	U	D	E		I	M	A	G	E
D		E		T		L		G		L		A
N	O	D	E	S		E	N	G	A	G	E	D
A				T		T		E		A		F
T	H	E	O	R	Y		C	R	I	M	E	A
U		S		E		A		H				S
R	E	C	I	T	E	S		A	D	O	P	T
E		A		C		S		P		B		N
D	E	P	T	H		I	M	P	R	O	V	E
L		E		E		G		Y		E		S
Y	I	E	L	D	I	N	G		U	S	E	S

SOLUTIONS

CROSSWORD 353

D	A	B	S		B	I	G	A	P	P	L	E
I		E		B		R		L		E		V
D	I	S	L	I	K	E		L	A	N	C	E
A		O		B				E		G		S
C	U	M	U	L	O	N	I	M	B	U	S	
T				I		O		B		I		G
I	L	L		O	U	T	E	R		N	O	R
C		I		G		E		A				E
	I	N	T	R	O	D	U	C	T	I	O	N
A		G		A				I		N		A
T	R	U	M	P		T	A	N	K	A	R	D
O		A		H		E		G		N		E
M	I	L	K	Y	W	A	Y		L	E	N	S

CROSSWORD 354

C	H	I	R	P		S	U	B	U	R	B	S
O		N		H		P			N		L	
N		F		A		A		S	C	R	E	E
S	W	A	L	L	O	W	S		L		A	
E		N		A		N		M	O	N	T	H
N	I	C	E	N	E	S	S		G			A
S		Y		X				M		E		R
U			F		A	D	V	A	N	C	E	D
S	P	I	R	E		A		R		H		S
	R		O		T	I	C	K	L	I	S	H
F	I	E	L	D		N		E		D		I
	D		I		T		T		N		P	
M	E	R	C	U	R	Y		S	P	A	R	S

CROSSWORD 355

A	C	I	D	R	A	I	N		A	N	N	A
P		N		E		M		N		A		I
P	O	S	E	S		B	R	O	W	S	E	R
R		I		U		U		N		A		W
E	N	G	O	R	G	E		F	O	L	I	O
H		H		R		D		L				R
E	S	T	E	E	M		C	A	R	P	E	T
N				C		T		M		E		H
S	L	A	N	T		S	A	M	U	R	A	I
I		T		I		E		A		S		N
B	L	O	W	O	U	T		B	R	O	K	E
L		N		N		S		L		N		S
E	V	E	R		V	E	T	E	R	A	N	S

CROSSWORD 356

	C	O	U	N	T	R	Y	S	I	D	E	
P		P		E		E		I		O		N
E		U		E	M	B	E	D		W	O	O
R	U	L	E	D		A		E		S		N
S		E		L		T		S	W	E	E	P
P	O	N	D	E	R	E	R					A
I		T		D				K		V		R
C					A	C	T	I	V	I	S	T
U	N	L	I	T		R		N		N		I
I		U		O		A		G	A	T	E	S
T	O	R		W	A	V	E	D		N		A
Y		K		E		E		O		E		N
	A	S	T	R	O	N	O	M	E	R	S	

CROSSWORD 357

S	H	A	M	P	O	O	S		A	G	E	S
I		N		R		A		H		U		U
F	E	N	C	E		K	E	Y	P	A	D	S
T		E		P				P		V		P
	E	X	T	O	R	T	I	O	N	A	T	E
T		E		S		O		C				N
W	A	S		T	O	U	C	H		G	O	D
I				E		T		O		A		S
S	U	R	P	R	I	S	I	N	G	L	Y	
T		O		O				D		L		B
I	M	P	O	U	N	D		R	A	I	S	E
N		E		S		E		I		U		A
G	I	S	T		U	N	H	A	R	M	E	D

CROSSWORD 358

L	Y	R	I	C	I	S	T		C	R	A	M
A		A		O		T		M		E		U
V	I	T	A	L		R	H	O	M	B	U	S
A		I		L		U		T		E		I
	N	O	N	A	L	C	O	H	O	L	I	C
A		N		B		K		E				I
C	O	S	M	O	S		T	R	I	V	I	A
C				R		C		T		I		N
O	L	D	F	A	S	H	I	O	N	E	D	
R		R		T		I		N		W		R
D	R	A	G	O	N	S		G	R	I	P	E
E		P		R		E		U		N		I
D	O	E	R		A	L	L	E	R	G	E	N

CROSSWORD 359

O	U	T	L	O	O	K	S		B	E	T	A
A		R		R		N				E		C
T	H	I	R	D		I	N	S	U	R	E	R
S		C		I		G				I		O
		K		N		H	A	S	T	E	N	S
U	P	S	T	A	R	T		W		R		T
N				N				A				I
A		G		C		P	O	L	E	M	I	C
B	A	R	B	E	L	L		L		A		
A		I				A		O		R		G
T	R	E	L	L	I	S		W	A	V	E	R
E		V				M		E		E		I
D	E	E	R		M	A	N	D	O	L	I	N

CROSSWORD 360

U	T	A	H		R	E	C	A	L	L	E	D
N		N		C		C		E		E		E
A	X	O	L	O	T	L		R	E	A	L	M
N		D		M		A		O		F		O
T	H	E	R	M		I	N	D	R	A	W	N
I				E		R		Y		G		S
C	O	S	I	N	E		I	N	F	E	S	T
I		H		C		L		A				R
P	L	A	C	E	B	O		M	E	D	I	A
A		L		M		G		I		A		T
T	I	L	D	E		J	A	C	U	Z	Z	I
E		O		N		A		S		E		V
D	O	W	N	T	I	M	E		E	D	G	E

SOLUTIONS

CROSSWORD 361

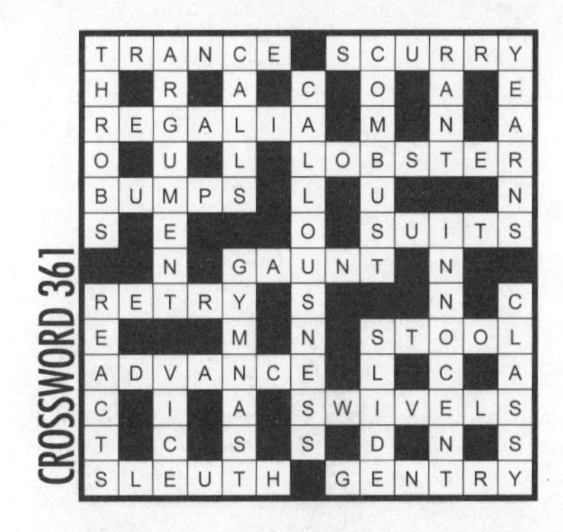

T	R	A	N	C	E		S	C	U	R	R	Y
H		R		A		C		O		A		E
R	E	G	A	L	I	A		M		N		A
O		U		L		L	O	B	S	T	E	R
B	U	M	P	S		L		U				N
S		E				O		S	U	I	T	S
		N		G	A	U	N	T		N		
R	E	T	R	Y		S				N		C
E				M		N		S	T	O	O	L
A	D	V	A	N	C	E		L		C		A
C		I		A		S	W	I	V	E	L	S
T		C		S		S		D		N		S
S	L	E	U	T	H		G	E	N	T	R	Y

CROSSWORD 365

	D	E	V	A	L	U	A	T	I	O	N	
C		M		R		P		E		T		E
A		A		C	I	R	C	A		H	U	M
N	I	N	T	H		E		C		E		B
D		A		E		A		H	I	R	E	R
L	I	T	E	R	A	R	Y					O
E		E		Y				T		F		I
L					I	N	C	U	R	R	E	D
I	N	E	P	T		U		N		O		E
G		A		I		C		I	N	N	E	R
H	E	R		B	E	L	T	S		T		E
T		L		I		E		I		A		R
	D	Y	N	A	M	I	C	A	L	L	Y	

CROSSWORD 362

T	A	I	N	T	S		A	R	R	I	V	E
E		N		A		D		E		N		N
M		F		K		I	G	N	I	T	E	D
P	R	O	W	E	S	S		E		A		U
T				O		R		W	A	G	E	R
S	T	A	F	F		E				L		E
		B		F	I	S	H	Y		I		
S		R				P		E	P	O	X	Y
H	O	O	K	S		E		L				O
O		G		M		C	O	L	L	O	I	D
C	H	A	R	I	O	T		O		V		E
K		T		T		S		W		E		L
S	E	E	T	H	E		O	S	I	R	I	S

CROSSWORD 363

M	O	C	K		U	N	L	O	C	K	E	D
I		O		S		I		B		N		I
S	U	C	C	U	M	B		S	N	O	O	P
S		O		B				E		W		S
P	R	A	I	S	E	W	O	R	T	H	Y	
E				T		H		V		O		N
N	U	N		A	R	O	M	A		W	H	O
D		O		N		L		T				R
	P	O	S	T	M	E	R	I	D	I	E	M
A		D		I				O		D		A
V	I	L	L	A		G	E	N	T	E	E	L
O		E		T		N		S		A		L
W	A	S	T	E	F	U	L		C	L	A	Y

CROSSWORD 364

E	X	H	A	L	E		S	T	A	T	I	C
S		I		A		D		R		O		E
T	A	G	L	I	N	E		E		O		A
A		H		R		M	U	M	B	L	E	S
T	I	L	E	S		O		O				E
E		A				N		R	A	I	D	S
		N		D	U	S	T	S		N		
W	A	D	E	R		T				A		U
E				Y		R		D	E	C	K	S
A	N	T	E	N	N	A		I		T		H
V		R		E		T	E	R	R	I	N	E
E		A		S		E		G		V		R
R	E	P	A	S	T		S	E	V	E	R	S